INTERNATIONAL SERIES OF MONOGRAPHS ON·
PURE AND APPLIED BIOLOGY

Division: **BOTANY**

GENERAL EDITORS: R. C. ROLLINS AND G. TAYLOR

VOLUME 8

OTHER TITLES IN THE BOTANY DIVISION

General Editors: R. C. ROLLINS AND G. TAYLOR

Vol. 1. BOR — *The Grasses of Burma, Ceylon, India and Pakistan*

Vol. 2. TURRILL (Ed.) — *Vistas in Botany, Vol. 1*

Vol. 3. SCHULTES — *Native Orchids of Trinidad and Tobago*

Vol. 4. COOKE — *Cork and the Cork Tree*

Vol. 5. TURRILL (Ed.) — *Vistas in Botany, Vol. 2*

Vol. 6. TURRILL (Ed.) — *Vistas in Botany, Vol. 3*

Vol. 7. TURRILL (Ed.) — *Vistas in Botany, Vol. 4*

OTHER DIVISIONS IN THE SERIES ON PURE AND APPLIED BIOLOGY

BIOCHEMISTRY

ZOOLOGY

MODERN TRENDS
IN PHYSIOLOGICAL SCIENCES

PLANT PHYSIOLOGY

SHORT GUIDE TO
GEO-BOTANICAL SURVEYING

КРАТКОЕ РУКОВОДСТВО
ПО ГЕОБОТАНИЧЕСКИМ СЪЕМКАМ

С. В. ВИКТОРОВ, Е. А. ВОСТОКОВА,
Д. Д. ВЫШИВКИН

SHORT GUIDE
TO GEO-BOTANICAL
SURVEYING

by

S. V. VIKTOROV, Ye. A. VOSTOKOVA,
D. D. VYSHIVKIN

Translated by

J. M. MACLENNAN

Translation edited by

M. C. F. PROCTOR

DEPARTMENT OF BOTANY
UNIVERSITY OF EXETER

PERGAMON PRESS
OXFORD · LONDON · NEW YORK · PARIS
1964

PERGAMON PRESS LTD.
Headington Hill Hall, Oxford.
4 and 5 Fitzroy Square, London W 1

PERGAMON PRESS INC.
122 East 55th Street, New York 22, N. Y.

GAUTHIER-VILLARS ED.
55 Quai des Grands-Augustins, Paris 6ᵉ

PERGAMON PRESS G.m.b.H.
Kaiserstrasse 75, Frankfurt am Main

Distributed in the Western Hemisphere by
THE MACMILLAN COMPANY · NEW YORK
pursuant to a special arrangement with
Pergamon Press Limited

Library of Congress Catalog Card Number 63-10080

This book is a translation of the original Russian
Kratkoye rukovodstvo po geobotanicheskim s"emkam,
published in 1959 by the Publishing House of the
University of Moscow

MADE IN GREAT BRITAIN

CONTENTS

INTRODUCTION

THE development of the national economy of our country, and especially agricultural development, call for thorough study of the natural resources of the Soviet Union. One of the most important features of that study is the compilation of geo-botanical maps, i.e. maps showing plant cover.

The compilation of geo-botanical maps has become a matter of special urgency because of the reclamation of virgin and waste lands in Kazakhstan and Western Siberia, and in work on the utilization of the natural resources of Siberia and the Far East. The study of forests, peat resources, pastures and arable lands must be carried out to a considerable extent on the foundation of geo-botanical maps of the above areas.

In spite of the fact that work on the compilation of geo-botanical maps on various scales has been very extensively developed, especially since the October Revolution, insufficient attention has been given to methods of geo-botanical cartography. Published works in this field have been few. In existing text-books on methods of geo-botanical investigation and on geo-botany in general, only brief sections are devoted to cartography (see, for example, "Programmes for geo-botanical investigations", written by an authors' collective in 1932; "Short guide to geo-botanical investigations in connection with windbreak-planting and the creation of a permanent food base in the south of the European part of the U.S.S.R.", 1952; and a number of other instructions, programmes, and text-books).

Therefore the production of a short guide to geo-botanical surveying methods is expedient. The present work is an attempt to draw up a suitable short guide.

We should draw attention to a few of its features:

(1) In preparing the guide the authors did not set themselves the task of creating any new, original method. They have tried, as far as possible, to collect and consolidate what is known, published, and in some measure already tested in geo-botanical survey practice.

(2) In this guide information is presented on geo-botanical survey methods, i.e. on the collection of data for compiling geo-botanical maps and on the maps themselves. Questions dealing with methods of geo-botanical investigation are treated only to the extent that they are connected with geo-botanical cartography. Therefore a large number of methodological questions (symbols for plant communities, means of recording such symbols, the order of description of areas, methods of phenological observation, questions relating to methods of studying the food value of plants, botanical collecting, and several others) have intentionally not been touched by the authors, as all these questions have already been covered in detail in many text-books, instructions, and programmes.

Thus this guide is directed to specialists already familiar with the basic principles of geo-botanical investigation methods and of topography and geodesy.

(3) There is no single standard system of instruction and there are no uniform norms for geo-botanical surveying, and it is doubtful whether such can be instituted, in view of the variety of problems faced by geo-botanical cartography. All possible instructions and norms within the field are subject to constant change. Therefore the authors have tried not to overload the guide with tables of norms, or to make rigid assertions to the effect that the fulfilment of any specific norms is necessary. As far as possible they have tried only to explain how to carry out various types of surveys (being guided by material published in the literature), leaving to the investigator who uses the guide full freedom either to follow a path already established or to seek out new methods.

(4) The basic task of geo-botanical maps is to fulfil the requirements of the national economy. Therefore it did not appear possible for us to set forth a method of cartography going beyond its links with those tasks for which it was designed. For that reason, after giving in the first chapters the most general information on geo-botanical maps and surveys, the authors have arranged the greater part of the guide under the headings of those branches of the national economy in which geo-botanical cartography is most widely used (forestry, peat industry, pastoral industry, etc.).

The short course on geo-botanical cartography held in the biogeography section of the geography faculty of Moscow University is based on this guide. Therefore, clearly, the guide can serve as a textbook for study of the course.

The greater part of the text of the guide was written by the senior scientific assistant in the biogeography section, S. V. Viktorov (chapters II, III, IV, and parts of chapters I, V, and VII). Chapter VI was written by Ye. A. Vostokova and D. D. Vyshivkin. Vostokova also wrote parts of chapters I and VII, and Vyshivkin part of chapter V.

In conclusion we must remark that in compiling the present guide we have made extensive use of many works on the methods of geo-botanical, forestry, pasture and other investigations by V. V. Alekhin, V. N. Andreyev, N. P. Anukhin, Ye. A. Galkina, G. I. Dokhman, I. V. Larin, M. P. Petrov, V. B. Sochava, V. N. Sukachev, S. N. Tyuremnov, and A. V. Tyurin, in which are given a great number of hints regarding geo-botanical cartography.

The authors express warm gratitude to N. V. Dylis, N. N. Pel't and L. A. Shaposhnikova, who made many useful suggestions on reading different chapters of the present guide, and also to Prof. A. G. Voronov, occupant of the chair of biogeography in the geography faculty of Moscow State University.

CHAPTER I

GEO-BOTANICAL MAPS AND PLANS

1. GENERAL FEATURES OF GEO-BOTANICAL MAPS AND PLANS

ONE should apply the term geo-botanical maps, in the widest sense of the word, to maps showing the distribution of plant communities or various groups of them. In that connection the total number of taxonomic entities shown on a map has no decisive significance: both a map of vegetation types and a map of the most detailed items of the plant cover (as, for instance a map of associations or synusiae) may equally be classified as geo-botanical maps.

We must distinguish between geo-botanical maps and geo-botanical plans. The difference between them is of the same kind as that between maps and plans in general. A representation of the plant cover over a considerable part of the earth's surface, on a topographical background designed with allowance for the curvature of the earth, should be called a geo-botanical map. If the plant cover is shown on a representation of part of the earth's surface on a horizontal plane on orthogonal projection, such a picture of the vegetation is called a geo-botanical plan. In addition, plans are distinguished from maps by the fact that they usually cover only very limited areas (separate plots of land, marshes, sandy plains, etc.) on a fairly large scale.

The chief task of geo-botanical cartography is to depict the distribution of communities forming the plant cover, in connexion with environmental conditions. That results from all the most important theoretical premises of modern geography, which is essentially built upon representation of the profound interrelations among all elements of nature. Such representations, developed mainly in the works of V. V. Dokuchayev, constitute also the most important theoretical foundation of geo-botanical cartography.

Therefore one must admit the correctness of Sochava's definition of a geo-botanical map: "A geo-botanical map on any scale is a map of plant communities, so designed as to show simultaneously not only the location of the communities in the narrow sense of the word, but also the relations between the vegetation and the geographical environment."*

The necessity of showing on a geo-botanical map the relations between the vegetation and all other components of the landscape is pointed out also in works by foreign scientists. That proposition is set out especially clearly in the work of Scharfetter (1928).

At the same time the geo-botanical cartographer is very often faced with the task of not only showing the relations between the plant cover and environmental conditions but also describing the plant cover from the point of view of some specific branch of the national economy. That is the reason for a number of features of such maps, which are discussed below. From the point of view of the accepted definition, many maps and plans that show the distribution of particular plant species or groups of species are not in the strict sense geo-botanical. They may rather be called floristic or botanical in a narrow sense of the word, as they deal not with plant communities but with species. They are, however, closely related to geo-botanical maps and plans, and are of great importance in geo-botanical investigations.

One may classify geo-botanical maps by their scales into small-scale (less than 1:1,000,000), medium-scale (from 1:25,000 to 1:1,000,000), and large-scale (more than 1:25,000).

The above divisions between groups of maps on different scales, however, are arbitrary, and different investigators group them in different ways.

According to the scale of the maps, different units of the plant cover—from types of vegetation to communities—may be represented on them.

Sochava (1954) proposes to classify small-scale maps into: (1) maps of geo-botanical zones and belts, and (2) maps of the most important plant formations and their combinations and complexes. Maps of the first type should, in Sochava's opinion, be drawn on a scale of less than 1:5,000,000, and those of the second on a scale between 1:2,500,000 and 1:5,000,000.

* V. B. Sochava. Principles and tasks of geo-botanical cartography. Sborn. "Vo-prosy botaniki" (Collection "Botanical problems"). Akad. Nauk SSSR, Moscow—Leningrad, 1954, p. 259.

For small-scale and medium-scale maps the "Programme for geo-botanical investigations" of the Botanical Institute of the Academy of Sciences proposes that one should be guided by the relation set out below. (Table 1.)

TABLE 1. RELATION BETWEEN THE DEGREE OF DEFINITION OF THE PLANT COVER AND THE SCALE OF A GEO-BOTANICAL MAP.

Unit of plant cover	Corresponding scale
Principal communities	not less than 1:25,000
Groups of communities	1:50,000 to 1:100,000
Principal groups of communities	not less than 1:250,000
Subtypes and types of vegetation	less than 1:250,000

The methods of representing vegetation in relation to environmental conditions on a geo-botanical map are of very different kinds. On small-scale maps it is done, on the one hand, by depicting the plant cover in close dependence on the division into zones and vertical belts, and on the other hand by using terms that simultaneously define both a certain type of vegetation and its corresponding type of landscape (for instance, *Stipa* steppe or *Artemisia* semi-desert). On medium-scale and large-scale maps and plans it is generally necessary to extend the legend considerably, introducing into it symbols for conditions in which various communities are linked together. Sometimes it is necessary to add to the legend a form of table in which one column shows plant communities and another shows conditions corresponding to them.

The depicting of the relations between the plant cover and environmental conditions must be considered the most important feature of a geo-botanical map. Neglect of this fact seriously diminishes the scientific and practical value of the map, in some cases depriving it of any claim to be called a proper geo-botanical map.

From the point of view of this basic requirement of geo-botanical maps there are two opposite but quite widespread errors made in constructing them.

One often-repeated fault is inadequate characterization of the conditions with which communities are linked. The compiler in this case is trying to show a large number of communities on the map, giving only their names and saying nothing about their conditions of existence.

Another and not less frequent type of error is at the opposite extreme, namely, showing on the map types of terrain without any in-

dication of the character of their vegetation. Here one must include
cases where the compiler marks on the map "sand vegetation" or
"chalk vegetation", i.e. he takes away any concrete geo-botanical
significance from the items that he shows on the map. These errors
should be avoided in compiling a map.

It happens quite often that one finds inserted in geo-botanical maps
(maps of plant communities) elements not pertaining, in the strict
sense of the word, to its geo-botanical content. Most often these are
floristic features, such as the limits of distribution of selected representative or physiognomically important species. Scharfetter (1928)
actually recommends insertion of such boundaries in a map, and
also indication on the map of some climatic isometric lines and of
soil boundaries that are important in understanding community
boundaries.

Although the introduction of such data into a geo-botanical map
is frequent and increases its content it cannot be recommended, as
it complicates the map and destroys the unity and logicality of its
structure. When necessary, such data are better presented in a diagram appended to the map (inset), instead of encumbering the map
with accessory material.

2. CLASSIFICATION OF GEO-BOTANICAL MAPS

There is no generally-accepted classification of geo-botanical maps
and plans.

Geo-botanical maps are classified in different ways by different
investigators according to their content.

A rather full classification of geo-botanical maps has been proposed by Prozorovskii (1940). His classification embraces not only
geo-botanical maps but also all other kinds of botanical maps. He
divides all botanical maps into two large groups: (1) floristic maps,
and (2) geo-botanical maps. He divides each of these groups in turn
into contemporary or "factual" maps and reconstruction or "theoretical" maps.

Further, within each of the above four types (geo-botanical contemporary, geo-botanical reconstruction, and the corresponding
types of floristic maps) Prozorovskii sets up three smaller subdivisions: (1) location maps, (2) range maps, and (3) regional maps.

A geo-botanical location map presents the separate localities of occurrence of a single plant community or group of communities (or some other phytocenological unit). If the map shows the locations of all the communities in a given territory, the map is a vegetation map or a map of the phytocenoses of that territory.

A geo-botanical range map shows the ranges of one or more phytocenological units.

A geo-botanical regional map is a map on which the territory is divided into regions of dissimilar vegetation. The basis of definition of a region, according to Prozorovskii, may be predominance of a specific type of vegetation (a forest region, a steppe region) and also the age of the plant cover; the author stresses the fact that in compiling a regional map one should take advantage of data from different disciplines—geology and geomorphology.

For floristic maps, both factual and theoretical, Prozorovskii gives similar subdivisions; in that case one is concerned with locations and ranges of one or several species, and not with communities; a floristic regional map divides the territory into regions of dissimilar flora (the characteristics by which regions are defined may vary widely—they may make use of the number of entities in the flora, its richness in endemic forms, etc.). Prozorovskii's classification of botanical maps and the interrelations of botanical maps and geographical maps are illustrated in Fig. 1.

In the above classification of geo-botanical maps no attempt has been made to divide geo-botanical maps into groups from the point of view of the functions to be fulfilled by the maps or the problems that they solve.

It appears, however, that these very points—thefunctions and intended uses of a map—are its most important characteristics. From that point of view geo-botanical maps and plans should be primarily divided into two main types: (1) present plant cover, and (2) reconstruction plant cover. The first type serve a variety of purposes related to utilization of the existing plant cover, and the second is mainly for the solution of various palaeogeographical problems. Since reconstruction maps are not as yet in mass production by geo-botanical cartography and their number is small, further classification of them is at present difficult, and therefore no finer subdivision of that type is offered.

The first type can be divided into two subtypes: (1) general geo-botanical maps and plans, and (2) special geo-botanical maps and plans.

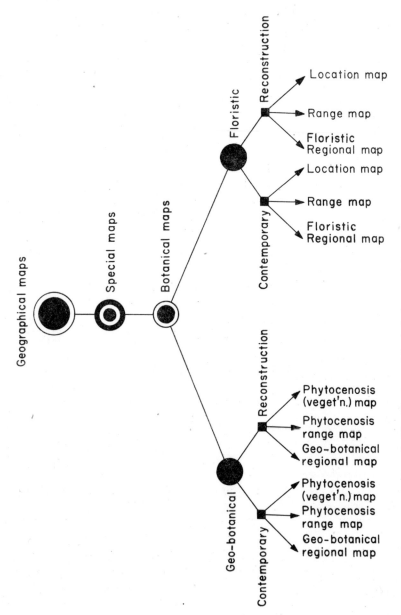

Fɪɢ. 1. Classification of botanical maps (after N. A. Prozorovskii)

The first subtype includes maps and plans that provide a general outline of the plant cover, without making it the basis for solution of any specific economic problems. The second subtype includes maps and plans compiled with the aim of serving the needs of some specific branches of the national economy (forestry, peat industry, etc.)

The first subtype includes all small-scale maps of plant cover and those medium-scale maps and plans that have no specialized economic significance. Within that subtype we have to distinguish three groups of maps:

(a) maps of zones and altitudinal belts,

(b) maps of dominant plant communities,

(c) maps of geo-botanical regions.

Maps of zones and altitudinal belts give information on the most general basic characteristics of the plant cover. They give a picture of the distribution of the main well-known types of vegetation linked with zones and belts, and not of specific communities. They are small-scale maps.

Maps and plans of dominant plant communities present a considerably more complete picture of plant distribution, and not one related only to zone and belt characteristics. Here one includes the majority of widely-distributed geo-botanical maps on the most varied scales. These maps show the distribution of habitats of dominant plant communities, i.e. those that occupy an area capable of being shown on the scale of the map.

A number of communities, although very marked in character and of considerable productive or scientific interest, either are not shown at all on such a map or are indicated by symbols not drawn to scale. In compiling such maps and plans the investigator tries, as far as possible, to observe the common features of stands of vegetation in different areas by which he can refer them to one and the same community: thus he looks for repetitive features and in many cases omits secondary individual differences between areas.

On the whole such an approach to the plant cover may be described as typological, i.e. as being primarily directed to the differentiation of certain typological units, the distribution of which is later shown on the map.

General characteristics of such maps are as follows:

(1) They give exactly equal representation of the whole vegetation cover, not offering any economic interpretation of it or emphasizing any features of specific communities from an economic point of view.

(2) They give a very generalized picture of the distribution of the vegetation cover, but only from its geo-botanical aspect and not from its economic aspect.

(3) They give us a picture of community distribution, irrespective of the fact that different habitats of the same community, located in different parts of a territory, have a number of individual local peculiarities (these local peculiarities of different habitats of the same community are to a great extent lost on such maps).

(4) They give us a picture of the distribution of dominant communities, but tell us nothing of how different communities combine with each other in different parts of the territory.

Unlike maps of dominant communities, maps of geo-botanical regions divide a territory into areas (regions) characterized by unique combinations of plant communities peculiar to each region, i.e. by a definite ecological grouping. This uniqueness of its ecological grouping is considered by some geo-botanists (Sokolov, 1938) to be the most important characteristic of a region. Other investigators suggest that, besides having a unique ecological grouping, a region may be characterized by other varied features, not only strictly geo-botanical, but partly also ecological and floristic (dominance of certain life-forms, wide distribution of certain physiognomically important plant species—Shennikov, 1938) and even geological and geomorphological (Prozorovskii, 1940). In the discussion of the region concept by the majority of investigators, however, apart from dependence on the features that they consider it expedient to use, there clearly emerges the idea of the individuality, the uniqueness of each region. Sokolov (1938), for instance, states that each community habitat (phytocenosis), taken together with the area that it occupies is an elementary region—a micro-region. This becomes fully comprehensible if one takes into account that each habitat (phytocenosis) possesses its individual specific features. "A region may be named geo-botanically after the appearance of specific ("regional") features of its vegetation."*

Thus in compiling a regional map we travel a path opposite to that of the compiler of a map of dominant plant communities. Whereas before compiling the latter map one has to give the typology

---

* A. P. Shennikov. Report in the discussion by Komarov Botanical Institute of the U.S.S.R. Academy of Sciences (stenographic report). Trud. BIN Akad. Nauk SSSR, ser. III, 1938, p. 29.

of the plant cover, to specify its repetitive elements and then to show their distribution, in the former case, on the other hand, we try to divide the territory into sections possessing peculiarities that make these sections substantially different. Whereas typology is the foundation of the dominant-community map, the geo-botanical regional map is based on maximum individualization.

That manifests itself particularly in the fact that different regions receive their own geographic names (Komarov, 1938; Grossgeim, 1936; *et al.*).

The other subtype under our consideration—special geo-botanical maps and plans, compiled to solve problems in specific branches of the national economy—contains a large number of different groups. These groups are distinguished one from another by the aims and functions for which the maps are compiled. Features that they have in common are:

(1) Generalization in the maps is done more from an economic than from a geo-botanical standpoint (i.e. communities of equal economic value may be combined); and

(2) A map may show, in addition to its geo-botanical content, a number of supplementary economic elements, not directly related to the plant cover (e.g. stock-pens, cheese factories, veterinary stations, harvesting bases, and stock-driving routes on maps of pasture types; leskhozy*, saw-mills, access-roads for timber transport on forestry maps and plans; etc.).

Groups within that subtype are quite numerous. We list only the principal ones below:

(1) Maps of pasture types.

(2) Maps and plans prepared for forestry needs (survey charts prepared for evaluation, plans of plantations and leskhozy*, special forest maps).

(3) Plans and diagrammatic maps prepared for the peat industry and for agricultural reclamation of marshes.

(4) Maps prepared for geological, geo-chemical, and hydro-geological investigations, on the basis of use of plant communities as indicators (indicational maps). This extensive group contains hydro-indicational maps, lithological maps and maps of salt-content of soils, compiled from geo-botanical data, and maps of geo-botanical indi-

---

* Forest industry establishments.

cators of certain useful minerals (boron, polymetallic ores, petroleum, uranium, etc.).

(5) Maps and plans prepared for predicting from geo-botanical indicators the quality of soils for road-making and hydrotechnical investigations.

(6) Maps and plans made for evaluation of the prospects of agricultural development of a territory (Vysotskii, 1904, 1909 ; Ramenskii, 1938).

In the above list (which is far from complete, as all methods of practical application of geo-botanical cartography are as yet far from having been investigated) different groups of maps have been arranged in the approximate order of their relative prevalence and economic value. Naturally it is in the pastoral, forestry and bog industries that geo-botanical cartography has found its widest application over the years.

In recent years geo-botanical cartography has been fairly widely applied to the so-called geo-indicative and hydro-indicative investigations, when vegetation occupies the role of indicator of geological and hydro-geological conditions and of useful minerals. To some extent the practical applications of geo-botanical cartography are being realized in all other directions.

A special group, not directly referable to special geo-botanical maps but close to them, consists of maps made for investigation of raw plant materials. On these maps primary attention is given not so much to plant communities as to individual species. Usually, however, the distribution of raw-material species of economic value is linked with that of specific communities. Therefore the compilation of maps of their distribution is impossible without elements of geo-botanical cartography.

There are no standard symbols and colours for geo-botanical maps and plans. Different investigators use different systems of symbols. Therefore in regard to the choice of symbols we have to restrict ourselves to general statements. For instance, we must remark that in selecting a colour to represent a particular community one must preserve some relationship between the natural appearance of the community and its colour-symbol.

Thus, for example, in depicting on a large-scale map in the semi-desert zone a combination of greenish-brown *Anabasis salsa* communities with bluish-grey *Artemisia*, one should keep these characteristic colours for them on the map. On the whole the more moisture-

loving communities are usually designated by shades of blue, meso-
phytes by shades of green, xerophytes by shades of yellow and brown,
bare-rock vegetation by the colour of the corresponding rocks (chalk
—white, granite—pink or red), and so on.

Very often colour symbols are supplemented by symbols inscribed
on a coloured area. Such symbols are especially widely used on forestry maps and plans, where by combinations of such supplementary
symbols one may specify precisely the composition of a plantation.

Extremely detailed systems of symbols used in various geo-botanical
maps may be found in special works dealing with various kinds of
maps (Tsvetkov, 1950; Shaposhnikova, 1954; Borodina, 1953).

In "Method of field geo-botanical investigations" (published by Bot.
Inst. of Acad. of Sc., 1938) the colours and symbols listed in Table 2
are proposed for the main types of vegetation and for some of the
most widespread groups of communities.

TABLE 2. COLOURS FOR DESIGNING SOME OF THE CHIEF TYPES OF VEGETATION
ON GEO-BOTANICAL MAPS

Basic type of vegetation	Colour
Tundra and alpine belt on mountains	Pink
Conifer forest of fir, spruce, *Pinus sibirica*	Violet-brown, brown
Conifer forest of pine, juniper	Reddish-yellowish-brown
Broad-leaved forest (oak, hornbeam, etc)	Green
Small-leaved forest (birch, etc.)	Yellowish-green
Aquatic and marsh vegetation	Blue
Meadow steppe	Pale yellow
Mixed herbage-grass steppe	Bright yellow
Grass and grass-*Artemisia* steppe	Yellowish-grey
Semi-desert and desert	Various shades of light violet
Saline soil vegetation (Solonchak)	Various shades of light violet with dark violet hatching
Alkali soil vegetation (Solonetz)	Brownish-grey or violet-grey
Sand vegetation	Yellow background with yellowish-red dots
Chalk vegetation	White
Granite vegetation	Red
Meadow vegetation	Bluish-green

V. I. Baranov (1933) proposed a system for indicating various items
of the plant cover only by conventional signs, without the use of co
lours (Baranov proposed to indicate soils by means of colours, thus
combining soil maps and geo-botanical maps) for maps on a scale
of 1:500,000.

Baranov distinguishes between primary and supplementary symbols. A primary symbol represents a type of plant cover in the widest sense of the word (forest, tundra, steppe, etc.). Baranov does not propose definite primary symbols, so enabling different investigators to design their own symbols for different types of vegetation (only for forest formations does he propose a small circle). Baranov suggests that primary symbols may be made precise by introducing supplementary details into them. Thus if a small circle represents a forest in the widest sense of the word, a circle with a dot inside it may represent a forest with one dominant species (e.g. *Pinus*) and a circle with a horizontal dash inside it a forest with another dominant species (e.g. spruce).

A supplementary symbol is placed beside the primary and should indicate either understory vegetation (in forests) or secondary components intermingled with the mass of the main community (in steppes, deserts, etc.).

For instance, a single dot placed beside a small circle denoting a forest indicates the presence in it of sparse lichen beds; two dots indicate great density of lichens; a single horizontal dash indicates light development of moss cover, and two denser development; a single vertical dash scattered herbage, and two such dashes more continuous herbage in a forest; and so on.

We give the following example of community symbols in Baranov's system (Fig. 2).

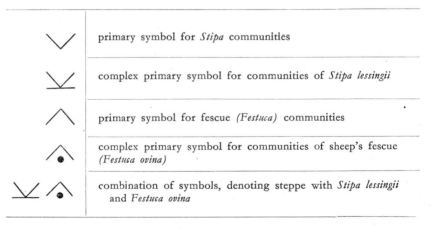

$\vee$	primary symbol for *Stipa* communities
$\underline{\vee}$	complex primary symbol for communities of *Stipa lessingii*
$\wedge$	primary symbol for fescue *(Festuca)* communities
$\overset{\wedge}{\bullet}$	complex primary symbol for communities of sheep's fescue *(Festuca ovina)*
$\underline{\vee}\ \overset{\wedge}{\bullet}$	combination of symbols, denoting steppe with *Stipa lessingii* and *Festuca ovina*

FIG. 2. Examples of conventional symbols for plant communities, according to V. I. Baranov

Baranov set forth only the principles of drawing a geo-botanical map with the aid of symbols, and suggested definite symbols only for a few communities. Baranov's suggestions have been well received by geo-botanical cartographers (Shiffers, 1934).

Such a method of employing symbols, although not widely used, is worthy of attention, because a map so designed is suitable for reproduction, as the reproduced copies do not require colouring.

CHAPTER II

GEO-BOTANICAL SURVEYS

1. GENERAL INFORMATION ON GEO-BOTANICAL SURVEYS

A GEO-BOTANICAL survey is the name given to a system of work on the collection of field material and on the compilation of a geo-botanical map on any scale.*

In the narrow sense of the word "survey" implies only a combination of tasks directed to the collection of field material necessary to compile a map. The compilation work itself, which is not carried out in field conditions, is called office work.

In the widest sense, however, the whole complex of tasks—field and office—performed in order to create a geo-botanical map may be called a survey.

The chief types of geo-botanical surveys are:

(a) transect surveys,
(b) grid surveys,
(c) continuous outline surveys,
(d) aero-geo-botanical surveys.

The term "transect surveys" means surveys conducted by ground travel (on foot, on horseback, or by automobile or other transport) by a geo-botanist along definite previously-marked transect lines; the distribution of plant communities along the transect is marked on the map directly from observations, and their distribution in the areas between the transects is estimated either by interpolation or by analysis of aerial photographs (if such exist). In some text-books

---

* This definition of the term "survey" was devised by Aprodov (1952) for geological surveys; in our opinion, it quite fully defines other kinds of surveys also—geobotanical, soil, etc.

(e.g. "Short guide to geo-botanical investigations in connection with windbreak-planting..."—U.S.S.R. Acad. of Sc., Moscow, 1952) transect surveys are called profile surveys.

Transect ground surveys are often supplemented by examination of the area from an aeroplane. Such vegetation surveys from the air are called aerovisual geo-botanical observations. These observations are not an independent type of survey, but only serve to supplement transect surveys—therefore they should not be confused with aero-geo-botanical surveys (for detailed description of aerovisual observations see below).

Grid surveys are very close in nature to transect surveys, but differ from them in that the lines (transects) along which the geo-botanist travels are laid out in a dense network of straight paths and are broken up into equal sections, the boundaries of which are marked with pegs or stakes; the density of the transect network is such that the geo-botanist, moving along one of the transects (paths), can see the markers of the adjoining transect, and he sketches the areas of vegetation both along the transect and between the transects on the basis of direct observation of their boundaries.

Continuous outline surveys are made not by laying out transects but by direct visits of the geo-botanist to all habitats of the various plant communities observed by him, with sketching of their contours by eye, either with a survey of them with the aid of a plane-table (with the assistance of a topographer) or with partial tracing of their boundaries on aerial photographs.

Aero-geo-botanical surveys are those made from an aeroplane both by visual sketching of observed boundaries (aerovisual surveys) and by a combination of preliminary and field analysis of aerial photographs. These surveys must be supplemented by selective ground observations.

2. TRANSECT SURVEYS

Transect surveys are to-day the most widespread form of geo-botanical surveys. They are widely used in surveys of pastures, marshes and forests, and also in geo-botanical investigations for geological and hydro-geological purposes. Therefore the greatest attention is given in this guide to problems of organization and technique in carrying out transect surveys.

There are two kinds of transect surveys:

(a) surveys made without the use of aerial photographs, or transect-visual surveys, and

(b) surveys made with the use of aerial photographs.*

(i) *Transect-visual Surveys*

The first step in a transect-visual survey is designing the transect network. The transect network is laid out with careful attention to (a) the natural peculiarities of the territory and especially its relief, and (b) the purposes of the work.

A general rule is to lay out the transects across the relief features. Very much information is obtained for geo-botanical cartography from transects laid out in the form of ecological series or profiles from watersheds across river valleys or from the crest of a mountain range to its foot, and also transects crossing landlocked depressions through their centres, along their greatest diameters.

Transects may be very different in their configuration, since in designing a transect network one must take account of the possibilities of travel in the locality (especially if the transect is made by automobile). In some cases (e.g. surveys in extensive sands) it is recommended that transects be designed in the form of parallel sightings, laid out across the macrorelief and the mesorelief of the sands (see "Programme for geo-botanical investigations", 1932).

The laying-out of the transect network is a highly responsible task in a survey. It should be done on the basis of a detailed study of the map, since the network originally designed must be varied and corrected in accordance with data obtained in the course of the survey. After the transect network is laid out, one advances to the transect survey.

Before setting out on a transect survey the investigator should transfer his proposed route to the map (in dotted lines, with a pencil) so that during the transect his actual route can be marked with a solid line. He should also mark on the map with dotted lines adjacent transects that have already been laid out and the results of surveys along them.

On a transect-visual survey the investigator sets out on the transect having at his disposal only a topographical map. He identifies the commencing-point of the transect by using local landmarks (it

* Some investigators, e.g. Bykov (1953), designate "parallel-path surveys" as a special kind of surveys.

is very convenient to begin a transect from some clearly-visible and unmistakable landmark), determines by compass the direction of his route, and sets off in the chosen direction. On his way he must note on the map the boundaries of plant community habitats crossed by him, also inserting on it the sections of the transect covered by him; each change in transect direction must also be determined with the compass and noted on the map, so that at the end of the transect the geo-botanist will have on the map, as far as possible, an exact reflection of the path travelled with a record of the boundaries of communities traversed.

Since an uninterrupted count of an investigator's steps or of the revolutions of a wheel of the vehicle in which he travels along the transect (Kunitsyn, 1934) would be extremely fatiguing and would distract the investigator from necessary observations of the plant cover (and, if the transect is very long, such calculations would be practically impossible), the geo-botanist must enter on his map the community boundaries crossed by him either by eye, making a visual estimate of the distance of a recorded boundary from some landmark (a hill, a bridge, a characteristic bend in a river, etc.) shown on the map, or else being guided by the time elapsed since the beginning of his travel along the transect. In order to use the second method the investigator should know the average speed of his movement. The latter may be determined experimentally. For that purpose one should note the time taken by the investigator to cover the path between two successive landmarks, measure the distance between them on the map, and divide it by the number of minutes taken to move from one landmark to the other. Such determinations of speed should be made two or three times and the average taken. It is recommended that such determinations be made for each transect, as the geo-botanist's speed of movement depends both on the relief along the transect and on the weather on the day of travel.

The problem of orientation is much simplified if the survey is carried out by automobile (this type of survey is described in detail by Tsatsenkin, 1949). In this case the transect survey is usually made by two workers. The responsible participant sits in the body of the vehicle, where a suitable seat is arranged for him. He makes observations on the plant cover and takes notes as he goes on the plant communities that are traversed. On crossing the boundary of a community he informs (by word of mouth or by some agreed sign) the junior participant, who is a geo-botanical technician or a collector, sitting in the driving cab; the latter notes the speedometer reading at the moment of crossing the boundary. Having such notes, and knowing the speedometer reading at the beginning of the transect, it is easy to determine both the location of any point on the transect with relation to the beginning of the transect and the length of sections of the transect occupied by the various communities.

In some survey parties there is a practice of making direct measurements along the transect by measuring-chain (for instance, in land management work in the tundra). In such cases two workers, carrying the unrolled chain, accompany the surveyor. The first of them has a certain number of surveyors' pins. Going to the length of the chain away from the second worker, the first worker drives in a pin at the end of the chain and then walks on. The second worker, arriving at that pin, stops and waits until the chain is again stretched. When the chain is stretched and the position of its end marked with another pin, the worker coming from behind takes out of the ground the pin at which he stood and walks to the next one.

In that way the geo-botanist can tell at any moment, by the number of pins transferred from the first worker to the second, how many times the chain has been moved.

When all the pins have been transferred from the first worker to the second, the geo-botanist marks the spot on the map or plan, the pins are again transferred to the first worker, and the count of the movements of the chain begins afresh.

The geo-botanist notes in his journal each community that is traversed, with more or less detail according to the purpose of the investigation (see below).

In moving along the transect one must note the time (in automobile surveys, the speedometer reading) of passing all landmarks shown on the map, even when no geo-botanical boundary is associated with these landmarks. Such constant fixing of all landmarks greatly helps the correct tracing of the transect on the map.

During movement along the transect the investigator halts from time to time to make detailed geo-botanical notes: (a) when he encounters a new community, not previously described, in which sample quadrats should be laid out; (b) when he comes upon habitats that are particularly typical and therefore worthy of detailed description; (c) when he traverses habitats that in some way are particularly interesting for the purposes of the investigation; (d) to take specimens; (e) for botanizing of the vegetation.

Some departmental instructions call for detailed notes at more or less definite intervals in order to attain a definite necessary density of points where descriptions are made.

Having marked on the map the points where the transect crosses various geo-botanical boundaries, the geo-botanist must trace, within the limits of visibility, the direction and configuration of that boundary to left and right of the transect line and transfer them by eye to the map, linking them closely to the relief shown on the map. In addition he must constantly observe the terrain through which the transect passes, and if to the side of the transect line there is visible the boundary of any community, he must mark it also on the map by eye.

The investigator may make side trips from the main line of the transect. If he does so, however, he must carefully fix on the map the direction and length of these trips, in order to avoid errors in recording the transect on the map.

As noted above, it is necessary that the nearest adjacent transects and the results of surveys along them should be entered on the map used by the geo-botanist. This considerably simplifies the work. Going along a transect and observing changes in the plant cover, the geo-botanist in that case tries primarily to find on his transect the continuations of the plant community habitats already discovered on adjacent transects.

If he observes any new community that is absent from an adjacent transect, then he may make a side trip from his transect in order to determine the boundary of that community in the area between the transects.

Fig. 3 illustrates the above point. The geo-botanist went out on the transect CD, having on his map the previously-travelled transect AB, along which are marked the boundaries of three communities (communities I, II, III). Going out from point C the geo-botanist crossed the area occupied by community I, fixed its boundary and joined it up with the boundary of that community marked on transect AB. But farther along on transect CD the geo-botanist encountered part of community IV, which was not marked on transect AB; to establish the boundary of that community the geo-botanist made a side trip from the transect along the line *a b c*. Later the geo-botanist observed on transect CD the boundaries of communities II and III and joined them up to the corresponding boundaries marked on transect AB.

It must be remarked that side trips to discover the boundaries of communities between transects are not always possible. In the great majority of cases the geo-botanist has to complete the outlines of communities on a transect-visual survey by means of more-or-less-probable interpolation.

The determination of boundaries in the areas between transects is one of the most important links in a transect-visual survey and calls for use of all the knowledge and experience of the geo-botanist.

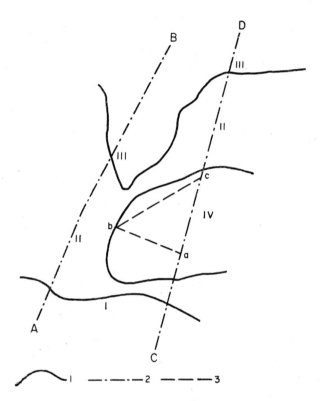

Fig. 3. Diagram of a side trip on a mapping transect:
1 — boundaries and indexes of geo-botanical divisions;
2 — lines of main transects; 3 — line of side trip.

It is impossible to recommend standard rules for such interpolations. We may, however, offer some suggestions, application of which may, in our opinion, be useful.

(1) One should examine in detail the relief along the transects and between them, and discover whether the areas of communities coincide with any elements of the relief or are bounded by definite contours.

(2) One should examine whether the community boundaries coincide with divisions already marked on the topographical map (saline oil, marshes, meadows, scrub, etc.). A warning is necessary, however, against too free use in a geo-botanical survey of divisions shown on a topographical map without adequate verification of the latter. Very often the contents shown on the map do not tally completely with the real state of affairs: thus we have frequently observed that areas shown on a map as saline soil proved in reality to be desert soil, meadow areas to be saline soil, scrub areas to be marshes, etc. The reasons may be found both in the natural evolution of the territory and in defects in the geographical work of the topographer.

(3) One should carefully analyse the adaptations of the plant communities on the transect to various local conditions and take that into account in showing the boundaries of communities lying between transects.

(4) The drawing of boundaries in the area between transects should be done either during the work on a transect or at the end of the working day, when all impressions received on the transect are still fresh and clear, and this task should not be long deferred. Subsequently these boundaries may be changed on the basis of any additional observations, if necessary.

To sum up, we may specify the following basic stages in a transect-visual survey:

(1) Laying out the transect network.

(2) Traversing the area by the selected transects, at the same time making notes in field journals, botanizing, intersecting the boundaries of habitats of various communities and entering them on the map or plan;

(3) Joining up boundaries observed while following different transects.

(ii) *Transect Surveys with Use of Aerial Photographs*

A transect survey with use of aerial photographs presupposes the existence, for each district of the work, of material from aerial photographic surveys—contact prints, uncontrolled and semi-controlled mosaics and reproductions of them on different scales.

Generally aerial photographs obtained without any special preparatory work are used. For some types of survey, however, such as forest-evaluation by means of aerial photographs, special preparatory measures are carried out on the territory where the work is to be done, consisting in laying out or renewing a network of transects and in establishing on the areas traversed by them some clearly-defined landmarks (piles of cut logs, broken rock, etc. — see Kolosova and Rayzer, 1953).

A transect survey with use of aerial photographs begins with examination of existing aerial photographs and preliminary analysis of them. This consists in going over with black indian ink outlines that are distinguishable from each other on the print, indexing them, and from the results of the preliminary analysis drawing up a legend in which each index is given a definite geo-botanical significance.

The following scheme of work is a very suitable method for the preliminary analysis. First, on the basis of examination of all work known and published in the literature and basic material for the district, a table of all communities ever previously found there is drawn up. In the table, against each community the conditions to which that community is adapted are shown in a special column (data on that point are also taken from the literature). Each of the communities is given its own index. Guided by this table, the investigator examines the mosaics or contact prints, trying to identify each of the listed communities, to go over its outlines with indian ink and to make a corresponding index entry. While doing so he enters in the table, in a special column, the features by which he has preliminarily identified a given community (features of preliminary analysis).

As a result he obtains a table of the following type (Table 3).

TABLE 3. SUMMARY OF PRELIMINARY ANALYSIS OF AERIAL PHOTOGRAPHS

Index	Name of Community	Ecological Conditions	Features of Preliminary Analysis

If the investigator finds difficulty in referring any area to one of the known communities, he enters on that area some conventional sign (e.g. "?") showing that that area is not defined.

In some types of survey work, e.g. in forest-evaluation by means of aerial photographs (Kolosova and Rayzer, 1953) each of the outlines defined by preliminary analysis, or group for these, is described in the journal; after the entry space is left for the description of the same area in the field.

After the preliminary analysis the laying-out of the transect network may be commenced. That is done on the basis of examination of aerial mosaics or reproductions of them. When he examines the aerial mosaics, the investigator sees a large number of outlined areas, differing in shade and in the nature of the surface. These outlined areas may be of considerable extent or may be an aggregation of small areas, forming a rather chequered mosaic pattern. The transect network should be designed so that the investigator will traverse areas whose surface is shown on the map with different types of hatching, and thus elucidate what community corresponds to each kind of hatching—this is one of the principal conditions for successful interpretation and simultaneous checking of the correctness of the preliminary analysis. On areas where a large number of small patches of different communities are combined, the transects should be close together; on areas uniform in hatching, they may be more widely separated. It is essential to check areas whose nature remained undefined in the preliminary analysis.

The next stage of the survey is field analysis on the transects. The most important condition of successful work on a transect is constant use of aerial photographs during the transect in which the field analysis of them is made. Naturally for this purpose the surveyor must take aerial photographs with him on every transect. If the transect is made by automobile, it is convenient to have with him aerial mosaics on "flight scale*" and reproductions of them on a scale of 1 : 50,000, mounted on cardboard or plywood; use of contact prints on auto-mobile transects is technically difficult.

On transects made on foot, contact prints are most suitable; they should be carried in a special container (e.g. of plywood).

During movement along a transect the surveyor carries out a number of tasks:

(1) He continually checks the aerial photographs and the terrain, and at any moment on the transect he should have a clear idea of his location.

(2) He identifies on the terrain all geo-botanical boundaries visible on the aerial photographs.

(3) He traces these boundaries on the aerial photographs with a pencil (so that in camp he can go over them with indian ink), indexes the community habitats recognised and describes them; in the descrip-

---

* "Flight scale" is the original scale on which the aerial photographic survey was made.

tion he must assign space to the symbols used to define communities on the photographs, recording them in the notes.*

(4) On coming upon the location of a boundary not shown in the photograph (which would occur in cases where two adjoining habitats of different communities are the same in physiognomy he inserts that boundary on the photograph by eye, using local landmarks, but denotes it with a dotted line to distinguish it from boundaries that are clearly visible on the aerial photographs.

(5) He notes the degree of correctness of the preliminary analysis of each outlined area that he crosses.

He must also keep in mind certain rules, observance of which may be useful:

1. Boundaries on the aerial photographs not only are drawn, as far as possible, at the place where they cross a transect, but are followed as far as possible on each side of it; the drawing of the boundaries on the aerial photographs is very conveniently done if the locality is viewed from some elevated point from which a considerable area is visible.

2. In descriptions accompanying the transect, the specific aerial photograph on which the described habitat appears should be stated; generally that is stated in brackets after the number of the description. If on the transect the investigator works from mosaics and not from aerial photographs, then he should state on which quarter of which sheet the described habitat is shown.

3. On returning to camp he should go over in indian ink all boundaries noted during the transect.

As a result of field analysis on the transects the surveyor possesses aerial photographs on which there are, on more or less wide belts along the transects, habitats analysed in the field. In order to obtain continuous coverage of the territory by outlines of different communities, it is necessary to analyse habitats lying between the transects (inter-transect analysis). That analysis is best done in camp, but before going away from the area, so that it will be possible to check on the spot the correctness of analysis of particularly complex habitats. Generally one can commence inter-transect analysis when some portion of the territory has been covered by several transects, the results of which can be compared.

---

* It must be noted that so far there is no standard and properly-designed terminology for describing drawings of vegetation on aerial photographs, and each investigator uses his own terminology.

At the beginning of the inter-transect analysis it is useful to draw up a table of features whereby the various communities can be identified. For that purpose one makes a list of communities found on transects crossing the territory, and against each community one writes the features identifying it (the latter are taken from field descriptions, where these features, as stated above, should be noted); in a special column it is stated whether that community was correctly identified in the preliminary analysis.

The table so compiled serves as the chief guide to the inter-transect analysis. The easiest and most trustworthy identifications in the inter-transect analysis are those of communities that were correctly identified in the preliminary analysis. They, of course, need no change in description, and their preliminary outlines thus correspond with the actual ones. The outlines of communities whose preliminary analysis proved to be incorrect require radical revision and should be checked again on the basis of features recorded during the field work on the transects.

In field-investigation practice, inter-transect analysis is often done without compiling analytical tables, on the basis of the personal experience of the surveyor. In that case many subjective evaluations are introduced into the analysis, and the quality of the analysis is almost impossible to check objectively and depends entirely on the surveyor's experience. Therefore the compiling of some kind of auxiliary analytical tables is desirable. It is important also because it combines the experience of several investigators in a single table.

After inter-transect analysis has been carried out for a specific part of the territory and continuous coverage of its plant-community outlines has been obtained, the results of the analysis should be transferred to the map, which is most conveniently done by pantograph; most often, however, the transfer is made semi-visually and not with instruments, with the use of various local landmarks or by copying the outlines on a grid.

The above methods of transferring outlines from aerial photographs to a map can be used only for districts of smooth relief. For hilly areas and especially for mountainous districts these methods cannot be used. The differences in scale of different parts of an aerial photograph will be so large that there will be no similarity of representation on the photograph and on the map. Therefore one must resort to special photographic methods for cartography in districts of very uneven relief.

Thus one may list the following basic steps in transect surveys with use of aerial photographs:

(1) preliminary analysis of the aerial photographs;

(2) laying out a transect network;

(3) traversing the area by the selected transects, together with field analysis of aerial photographs, notes in field journals, plant collecting, etc.;

(4) inter-transect analysis;

(5) transfer to the map of the plant-community outlines obtained.

3. AERO-GEO-BOTANICAL SURVEYS

Aero-geo-botanical surveys are made from an aeroplane, but are necessarily accompanied by selective ground-survey tasks.

Two types of aero-geo-botanical surveys are distinguished:

(1) aerovisual surveys, carried out by making drawings by eye on millimetre-squared paper or on the map, and

(2) aero-geo-botanical surveys with use of aerial photographs, carried out by means of a combination of preliminary desk analysis and subsequent final analysis made from an aeroplane.

An aero-geo-botanical survey is distinguished from aerovisual observations by the fact that the latter is merely supplementary to ground work and covers only a certain part (sometimes comparatively small) of the territory under study, whereas in aero-geo-botanical surveys the transects (flights) of the aeroplane cover the whole survey territory uniformly, and the data collected in observations from the aeroplane are not supplementary but basic survey material. Ground investigations in aero-geo-botanical surveys, although necessary, are made on a very small part of the territory and are selective in character.

Aero-geo-botanical surveys are the youngest and most progressive type of geo-botanical surveys, with a very great future in front of them. In some branches of the national economy (in studies of tundras, forest districts and deserts) this type of survey finds wide application, as it permits survey coverage in the shortest time of enormous areas, difficult to traverse and sparsely populated. Unfortunately the methods of aero-geo-botanical surveys have not as yet been adequately worked out, and to perfect them intensive scientific research work is needed.

(i) *Aerovisual Surveys*

An aerovisual survey is a combination of, first, aerovisual transects (i.e. transects by aeroplane) during which the geo-botanist prepares an outline (a draft) of the geo-botanical, and partly of the topographical, situation in the locality; and, secondly, ground work, consisting in detailed study of selected typical habitats (étalons), collection of data relating to a number of economic indexes (amount of forage in pastures, etc.), elaboration of the aerovisual drafts, and in some cases also geodesic confirmation of the map compiled.

Aerovisual surveys are used mainly in districts poorly provided with topographic material, i.e. where topographic maps either are lacking or are on a very small scale (little-studied territories). They are used pre-eminently in cases where it is necessary to photograph large areas. Aerovisual surveys are particularly widely used in compiling maps of types of reindeer range in the tundras and forest-tundras. The development of this method of surveying in the U.S.S.R. is mainly linked with this type of industry, and also with forestry work. The principal work on the method of aerovisual surveys has been done by the eminent investigator of tundra pastures, V. N. Andreyev (1938, 1940).

Aerovisual surveys can be carried out both in districts provided with terrestrial geodesic maps and districts without these. In the latter case, however, material obtained through the surveys should be regarded as sketches and in no way as maps.

For the geodesic foundation of an aerovisual survey a network of astronomical points is required; it is desirable, in order that these points may be linked with linear landmarks (rivers, lakes, sea-coasts), that the landmarks themselves should be photographed on the ground all along their length. Near the astronomical points it is necessary either to erect artificial landmarks or to use natural landmarks (characteristic river bends, isolated peaks, etc.). Therefore aerovisual surveys must be preceded by terrestrial geodesic work. That work, however, need be carried out only in territories for which there are no sufficiently precise topographical maps. Within the U.S.S.R. the necessity for special ground work for the compiling of basic maps is passing away; the basic maps are compiled from the most detailed large-scale maps.

The first step in an aerovisual survey is, in the first case, compilation of a basic map (preferably on a scale of about 1 : 500,000), on which are entered all the astronomical points obtained in the process of carrying out the geodesic basis of the work, and also all data regarding the hydrographical network, roads, settlements, etc., existing on the various cartographic material relating to the district as a whole or to separate parts of it. The map is reproduced in the necessary number of copies.

After the basic map is compiled one may begin designing the aero-visual transect grid. The transect grid is laid out in such a way that:

(a) the interval between transects is constant (on a scale of 1 : 500,000 it should be of the order of 7–9 km);

(b) the beginning and the end of a transect are linked to well-marked geodesically-fixed points;

(c) the transect length is not too great (not more than 60–70 km);

(d) the transects should be parallel to each other (within a single group of transects, covering a specific part of a district).

The transect grid diagram is provisional in nature and may be corrected after aerial reconnaissances have been made.

Simultaneously with the laying out of the transects a number of other preparatory tasks are performed. In the course of this work a number of strips of millimetre-squared paper are prepared. The width of each strip is 12 cm. Each such strip is designed for the outline (i.e. a combination of sketches of geo-botanical outlines) of a single transect to be drawn upon it. Therefore the length of the strip is calculated so that on the given scale of the survey one transect can be drawn on one strip (e.g. with a transect about 100 km long, on a scale of 1 : 500,000, the length of a single strip should be not less than 20 cm). The centre of the strip (6 cm from each of its long sides) is marked with a line representing the line of flight: it is divided into transverse sections, the length of each of which corresponds, on the selected scale, to the distance covered by the aeroplane in one minute. The line of flight in the minute-sections is entered in drawing-ink of different colours; the minutes are shown by successive numbers at the side of each section, counting the starting-point as zero.

Additional strips are prepared for training flights, and also notebooks with numbered pages and a special journal for recording photographs taken from the aeroplane (photojournal).

The aeroplane for aerovisual surveys must also be specially prepared.

This preparation consists of, first, deciding on a location for the observer's seat that will give the best view of the territory; second, painting bright coloured marks on the edges of the wings of the aeroplane, enabling the observer to estimate the distance of objects lying to the sides of the transect; third, placing in a convenient location in the aeroplane cabin a cylindrical "aeroplanshetka" (i.e. special apparatus designed for continuous rolling-up of the paper strip as the aeroplane travels along the transect), and also other working equipment.

When the preparatory work is finished, air training of specialists and reconnaissance flights must be commenced. Air training consists in flights above areas for which geo-botanical maps or plans have already been compiled by terrestrial methods, by means of ordinary transect surveys. Such areas, called "étalons", may be selected not necessarily in the district of the work, but near it in territory covered by surveys in previous years. If such étalons cannot be located near by, preliminary transect-visual surveys are made of them. It is desirable that an étalon should have an area of 10,000–20,000 hectares and an elongated rectangular shape (if an étalon is smaller and of different shape observations on it from the air become difficult).

The training of a surveyor consists in flying over an étalon, having with him a map of its plant cover, and learning to identify correctly from the air communities shown on the map, their economic valuation being given. It is desirable to repeat such flights several times and to make landings in places where the picture of the vegetation is particularly complex. During the flights over the étalons, and also during other preparatory tasks, the surveyors must be trained in drawing the outlines of the vegetation and of the general geographical situation on the transect strips.

When the surveyors are adequately trained, reconnaissance flights begin.* The aim of these flights is to find out how the basic map corresponds with the actual situation and to familiarize the geo-botanist with the principal types of vegetation and the most general laws of their distribution. As the result of the reconnaissances the basic map is corrected and consequent changes are made in the transect grid. Andreyev (1940) recommends that not more than 10 per cent of the flying time planned for the whole survey should be spent on reconnaissance transects.

After the reconnaissance flights, survey work in the narrow sense of the word takes place. When the surveyor sets out on a transect, he must prepare the aeroplanshetka and the map of the flight, possess a field journal and photojournal, and check the condition of his working

---

* It should be noted that Andreyev (1940) includes flights over étalons among reconnaissance flights. It seems to us, however, more correct to include them among training flights.

place and his supply of pencils and other working equipment. A strip
with the first transect is placed in the aeroplanshetka; the number of the
transect is entered on the margin of the strip, the chief landmarks are
inserted, and data of the flight and the surveyor's name are recorded.

During the flight the geo-botanist-surveyor draws on the transect-
strip the outlines of geo-botanical objects lying in the surveyed
area (types of pasture, plant communities or complexes of these, etc.)
and also elements of the hydrographic network* and he marks on the
strip within each outline drawn by him conventional symbols for its
geo-botanical or economic content. This is the chief task of the geo-
botanist, and the greatest attention should be given to uninterrupted
recording and correct use of conventional symbols.

The making of brief notes in the journal, aerial photography, and
also the changing of the strips in the aeroplanshetka is done in the
intervals of time when the aeroplane is passing from one transect
to another. The drawing is done in pencil.

It is important that all special equipment should be in the right place,
since, because of the speed of the aeroplane, the surveyor must spend
a minimum of time on each operation.

At the end of the flight, preliminary work on the transect strip is
done on the same day (pencil lines are traced over with indian ink,
conventional symbols placed within the outlines are improved and corrected) and a brief description of the transect is drawn up, for which
both the sketch obtained and the short rough notes made in the aeroplane are used. Photographic plates and films are packed in boxes with
labels showing the transect number and the date of the survey.

Later on, in field conditions, before the field party leaves for its office
base, data obtained from separate transects are combined and transferred to the basic map. In this way a preliminary geo-botanical map is
compiled. This map is usually drawn up on the basis of aerovisual
observations only, and insertion of data and corrections obtained
from ground surveys is deferred to the office-work period.

In some cases—especially in aerovisual surveys of forests (Samoilovich,
1953)—when fairly precise topographical maps exist, showing the distribution of various types of natural landscape (forests, meadows,
scrub, etc.), the geo-botanist may embark on an aerovisual survey
directly with the map. During the flight he should identify the types
of landscape shown on the map, verify and sketch their boundaries

---

* For orientation purposes.

(and sometimes also draw in additional boundaries inside those shown on the map) and note on the map the geo-botanical content of the outlined areas. Use of topographical maps for aerovisual surveys considerably simplifies the preparatory work.

At the same time as the aerovisual work ground investigations are made, as a result of which maps of certain selected areas étalons, or "keys") are compiled by the transect-visual survey method. Andreyev (1940) recommends that the area of a ground survey in the tundra should be not less than 3–5 per cent of the entire surveyed area. For more precise determination of the relation of étalon area to survey area he (1938) proposes the following formula:

$$x = \frac{100}{\sqrt{\dfrac{a}{b}}},$$

where x = required area of étalons (keys) as a percentage of the total area, a = average size of outlines on the final map, b = average size of outlines in the étalon.

Étalons are selected with the aim of discovering the precise composition of the plant cover in the principal, most widely-distributed geo-botanical entities (the most important types of pasture and of plant formations, etc.). Data from ground surveys serve as supplementary material, giving precise information on each group of communities identified during the survey.

(ii) *Aero-geo-botanical Surveys with Use of Aerial Photograps*

This type of aero-geo-botanical survey is at present not widely used. Its most widespread use is in aero-valuation of forests, i.e. in carrying out valuation of forests from the air (Samoilovich, 1953).

Naturally this type of survey presupposes the existence of aerial photographs of the entire territory to be surveyed. Their scale may vary: the largest scale of contact prints is not required here, as a survey from an aeroplane, because of its tempo (due to the speed of the aeroplane) makes it impossible for the surveyor to dwell upon the smallest details of the plant cover. In the practice of geo-botanical aero-valuation work prints on a scale of 1 : 50,000 are widely used.

The first stage of the work is preliminary analysis of aerial photographs. This is done as carefully as possible with the aid of a stereoscope or stereoscopic spectacles. At the same time it is expedient to use the methods given in the description of the preliminary analysis made at the beginning of transect surveys with use of aerial photographs (see above).

The results of the analysis are entered on the contact print in black indian ink. Each defined outline is indexed in accordance with the results of the preliminary analysis.

The analysed contact prints are arranged in the order of the projected survey-transect, i.e. in the order in which they succeed each other, and in that order they are affixed to a long strip of paper. Between the attached prints narrow intervals should be left so that the whole strip can easily be folded up concertina-fashion.

If it is intended to lay out the transects so close together that on one transect one can look over several series of adjoining aerial photographic prints, these series of prints should be attached side by side on the same strip.

In other cases one can prepare mosaics from the analysed contact prints, on which, in this way, all the outlines obtained as a result of the preliminary analysis are kept.

Both the mosaics with outlines shown on them and the mounted analysed prints are important documents in aero-geo-botanical surveys. Therefore the preliminary analysis should be given the most careful attention.

At the same time a warning must be given against analysis that is too detailed or that is open to question, being inadequately based. Outlined areas determined as a result of the preliminary analysis should be clearly-defined, indubitably different, and definitely separated from one another, as the surveyor has to identify each of the determined areas from the air. Therefore here it is particularly harmful to make the error of separating areas that are not clearly distinguished from each other.

At the same time as the preliminary analysis, the transect grid is designed. The transects are laid out in the form of parallel flights of the aeroplane, with strictly-defined intervals between them. The transects should be laid out at such a density that the surveyor will be able to view the whole strip between two transects. To that end it is necessary that the strip in which the geo-botanist makes observations from one side of the aeroplane should be contiguous with the strip in which he will make observations from the other side in moving along the neighbouring transect on the return journey. Therefore the width of the interval between transects should be twice the width of a strip in which the geo-botanist can make observations from one side of an aeroplane.

Samoilovich (1955) states that the limiting distance for geo-botanical observations (in aero-valuation of forests) is three times the altitude of the flight. In view of the fact that the altitude of a flight usually fluctuates between 200 m and 300 m (Ageyenko, 1954; Samoilovich, 1955), it may be concluded that aero-geo-botanical surveys are possible over a strip 2 km in width (i.e. 1 km on each side of the aeroplane). Then the distance between transects should also equal 2 km, as strips 1 km wide, seen from the aeroplane along two adjacent transects, will be contiguous with each other.

Practical experience, however, shows that a rather wider separation of transects is possible—up to 6 km from each other (Ageyenko, 1954).

The next stage of the work is aerial training. In its basic outlines it is similar to training for aerovisual surveys. For the training one must have an area for which a geo-botanical map has been compiled by terrestrial transect surveys. The surveyor makes a flight over that area, having with him mosaics or strips with mounted photographs showing the results of geo-botanical analysis, but not being familiar with the results of the terrestrial mapping. During the flight he should write down on all the areas that are outlined on the mosaic brief formulas defining the geo-botanical content of the areas. After the flight he compares the results so obtained with the results of the ground survey, and notes weak spots in his work (inability to identify from the air a certain community, etc.). It is desirable that the training should be carried out over not fewer than three test areas.

During training it is very useful to make several reconnaissance flights.

After the laying out of the transect grid, the training and the reconnaissances, the survey work proper begins. A survey group consists of a pilot, a pilot-navigator and a geo-botanist. The navigator attends to the correct orientation of the aeroplane and observance of the plotted course, and also carries out photography in areas previously noted on the mosaics, in order to obtain typical oblique photographs of the most important plant communities; it is desirable to have stereoscopic pairs of such photographs.

The chief task of the geo-botanist on the flight is to determine from the air the geo-botanical content of each of the outlined areas on the mosaic in his possession. The geo-botanical content of these areas is written down in brief formulas. The character and content of these formulas may vary considerably, depending on the aim of the survey. The formulas may have either a geo-botanical character (e.g. the initials of the names of dominants in various communities) or a partly economic significance (valuation formulas in aero-valuation, or conventional symbols for types of pastures in mapping the latter).

During the survey the geo-botanist may also make some changes in the boundaries of areas shown on the mosaic. Such changes are mainly as follows:

(1) making the existing boundaries more precise,

(2) removing boundaries between areas that on survey from the air prove to be similar in their geo-botanical content (the superfluous boundary in such cases is struck out with a cross-line),

(3) drawing new boundaries noted from the air (this work is done on the spot, in the aeroplane).

If the plant cover of any outlined area has a complex character clearly visible from the air, each community must be recorded by means of a conventional formula, and the percentage of it in the composition of the complex should be stated.

A very important technical condition for a successful transect is suitable placing of the mosaics. They should be arranged in the order in which the transect will cross them, and they should be so placed that they can easily be picked up, changed, etc. To each mosaic there should be attached a compact, clearly-visible tally with its designation.

The next stage of the work is the post-flight analysis of the material. It consists of examination of all the mosaics covered by the survey, and tracing in indian ink all additional boundaries discovered during the transect; checking the correctness and the accuracy of writing of formulas; sometimes (if required) compiling a description of each transect (on the basis of data on the mosaics); and delivery for processing of all oblique photographs that were taken.

In the office all outlines are transferred from the mosaics to the map, using all available locations and landmarks. From a methodological viewpoint, when the final report on the work is made it is of great importance to construct a comparative table in which one shows how many of the outlined areas of each community were correctly identified in the preliminary analysis and in how many areas the preliminary analysis proved to be incorrect. Opinions as to the reasons for incorrectness of the preliminary analysis should be expressed in notes. Such a table is very important for perfecting the method of aero-geo-botanical surveys.

It is essential that ground survey work should be carried out on a part of the territory during the survey. Part of it should be done before the beginning of the survey, in order to obtain étalons for training purposes. Part may be done simultaneously with the aero-geo-botanical work. The aim of ground work is, as already stated in the description of aerovisual surveys, to add precision to the geo-botanical picture and to collect a range of economic indicators from the vegetation cover (samples, etc.).

Thus an aero-geo-botanical survey with use of aerial photographs consists of the following main stages: (1) preliminary analysis; (2) training and reconnaissance flights; (3) laying out a transect grid; (4) survey transects; (5) post-flight analysis of material; (6) office work.

4. OTHER TYPES OF GEO-BOTANICAL SURVEYS

(i) *Grid Surveys**

Grid surveys constitute a form of geo-botanical surveys considerably less widely used than transect surveys. They are used exclusively for compiling large-scale maps, and more often plans. Thus, for instance, they are widely used in surveying small "keys" (Larin, Schiffers, Byeidyeman, 1952) and for making plans of sample plots in grasslands (Kolosova, 1928a, 1928b).

The first step in a grid survey is the choice of the area to be surveyed. It is desirable to lay out the area in the form of a rectangle. In that connection one should give special attention to the orientation of the area, and it should be so located that it includes habitats of all the communities whose distribution with respect to each other it is desired to show on the plan. Therefore one should first note in what direction the communities succeed each other in the field, and then lay out the area in that direction. Very often it is necessary for that purpose to lay out the area across the relief of the terrain.

The dimensions of the area may vary considerably, but usually its sides do not exceed a few hundred metres, as a grid survey of an area of too large size is extremely difficult. Fairly often the area occupies only a few tens of square metres (in studying the features of the micro-

* Literally "piquetage surveys"; but there seems to be no English term in common use which is a close translation of this. (Editor's note).

complex in semi-desert, in experimental work in meadows and steppes, etc.).

The next step in the work is the setting-up of conventional markers whereby the area is divided into smaller areas within which, strictly speaking, the survey is made. One goes about the placing of markers in the following way: one side of the area (usually one of the long sides, if the area is shaped like an elongated rectangle) is taken as the so-called base line. That line is measured with a measuring-chain,

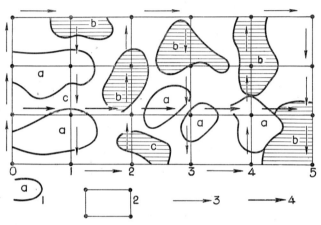

FIG. 4. Diagram of transects on an area being mapped by grid survey (after I. V. Larin, Ye. V. Shiffers and I. N. Byeidyeman): 1 — boundaries and index-letters of geo-botanical divisions; 2 — diagram of lay-out of marker stakes in the area; 3 — direction of main transect; 4 — direction of supplementary longitudinal transect.

and markers are set up on it at intervals of definite length. The distance between the markers depends on the scale of the survey; in a survey on a scale of 1:5000 the distance between markers is generally fixed at 50 m, on a scale of 1:2500 at 25 m, and so on (Fig.4).

From each of the markers on the base line a path is marked out (a sight is taken) at right angles to the line and is divided into sections of the same length as the sections of the base line, and the limits of these sections are marked with stakes.

Larin, Shiffers and Byeidyeman (1952) recommend that at first two paths should be marked with stakes or pegs, perpendicular to the base line at the first and last markers (obtaining thus the short lateral sides of the surveyed area), and then a second base line should be measured (i.e. a second long side of the area) and should be divided into sections in the same way, and markers should be set up on it; the other paths are marked out by joining the corresponding markers on the first and second base lines. Thus by this method of laying out the network of paths, all the outer boundaries are first marked in succession, and then the inner paths.

After the paths are laid out and the markers set up, one may start to draw the outlines of the communities. To do that the surveyor goes over the area by the transverse paths (i.e. the paths perpendicular to the base line), beginning at any corner of the area, going along one of its lateral sides, traversing it by the first path from the end, then by the second, and so on. On the way he counts the number of paces taken to cross each community, and sketches by eye the outlines of the community habitats lying between the path he is taking at the time and the nearest adjoining path. The sketching is done on millimetre-squared paper. The sheet of millimetre-squared paper on which the drawing is to be made should be fixed to a firm backing (cardboard or plywood). Before the traverses begin, the boundaries of the area and all the cross-paths should be indicated on the paper, and also the points where the stakes are set up. All these items should be drawn on the scale on which it is proposed to conduct the survey. On the margin of the sheet of paper the orientation of the area should be shown by an arrow.

To increase the precision of the sketches, some longitudinal paths may be laid out as well as the cross-paths, i.e. traversing the area in a direction parallel to the base line. In surveys on the largest scale additional stakes should be set up in the centre of each of the rectangles bounded by two pairs of stakes on adjacent paths (Kolosova, 1928a, 1928b).

When the areas are of very small size (below 10 m², i.e. when the area is in fact a sample plot) only its corners are marked with stakes; a measuring-chain is laid along one side, and the sketching is done by eye, without counting paces.

In grid surveys of very small areas ready-made nets of cord are also used. These nets have sides of definite length (20–50 m). From each side of the net, at fixed intervals, strings are stretched so that, crossing each other, they form rectangular cells. The net is laid out on the area designated for the survey, its corners are fixed with posts, and the net is stretched and straightened out so that all the cells have rectangular outlines, after which the outlines of the communities are sketched cell by cell.

4

(ii) *Continuous Outline Surveys*

A continuous outline survey is one of the most difficult kinds of geo-botanical survey, and therefore is used only for compiling large-scale plans and maps of small areas. Thus, for instance, Prozorovskii (1940) considers that such surveys can be used on scales of 1:5000—1:25,000. A continuous outline survey consists in direct coverage by a geo-botanist of all parts of the habitats of plant communities, with scale drawing of them on millimetre-squared paper.

The first step in the survey is the selection of an area and the delimitation of its boundaries. In doing this one generally uses all the rules for selecting an area listed in the description of grid surveys (location of the area across the relief, so that it will include the greatest possible number of different phytocenoses, etc.). It is desirable to make the corners of the area and its boundaries coincide with some local landmarks, or if the latter are absent to mark them artificially (with cairns, pegs or heaps of broken rock).

After the above preparatory work one may begin the survey. The survey is made by going round the boundaries of each phytocenosis, drawing the boundaries on millimetre-squared paper (fixed to a stiff backing); all the sinuosities of the boundary are drawn with the greatest possible care, and changes in direction of the boundary (breaks in the outline) are determined with a compass. The length of sections of the boundary between the breaks is measured by pacing. Each outline of a plant community habitat drawn is numbered, and is described under that number in the field journal.

A special variation of the continuous outline survey is "appraisal by perambulation" (Prozorovskii, 1940), as a particular method of survey of small areas (not larger than 1500 m²). In a survey of such a very small area there is no need to walk round every outline; the surveyor goes round the boundaries of the whole area, drawing the location of the community boundaries within it; from one side of it he makes a preliminary complete sketch of the whole area, and on going along the other sides he merely corrects the various outlines and makes them precise.

If, however, the geo-botanist sketches the outlines on millimetre-squared paper, he can obtain only a plan. To obtain a map he must either have a prepared topographical base of corresponding scale or make a topographical survey of the area, linking the area to the topographical grid of the map. In that case the topographical work precedes the geo-botanical.

A continuous outline survey may be made considerably more precise if it is combined with an instrumental survey made by a topographer. For that purpose it is necessary that each point where the boundary of a given community habitat makes a sharp turn should be marked with a rod and entered on the plan by the topographer. The work is generally organized as follows: the geo-botanist, walking round the outline of the community, is accompanied by workers with a rod and measuring-tape; at all breaks in the outline the rod is successively erected, and these points are entered on the plan by the topographer according to the usual instrumental-survey methods; the distance between the points is measured with the tape. The plan so obtained is much more accurate than one obtained by visual survey.

5. SOME AUXILIARY METHODS OF INVESTIGATION IN GEO-BOTANICAL SURVEYS

(aerovisual observations, descriptions of "keys", profile-surveying, line-transect estimation)

Many kinds of geo-botanical surveys are supplemented by some auxiliary methods of investigation. The most widely-used of these are aerovisual investigations (i.e. viewing the plant cover from the air), survey of "keys" and survey of geo-botanical profiles.

(i) *Aerovisual Observations*

Both transect-visual surveys and transect surveys with use of aerial photographs may be supplemented by aerovisual observations, i.e. observations made from an aeroplane (if the expedition has one at its disposal). The following are differentiated among aerovisual observations: (a) aerovisual reconnaissance, (b) aerovisual survey transects, and (c) final aerovisual transects (Kas'yanova, 1955).

Aerovisual reconnaissance is done at the beginning of field work. It is desirable to do it before laying out the transect grid, and to use data from aerovisual observations in laying out the transects. Kas'ya-

4*

nova (1955) considers that the aim of aerovisual reconnaissance is general familiarization with the landscape of the district and also with the appearance and distribution of the principal plant communities. In reconnaissance it is recommended that one should have mosaics with him, and note how the various communities look on them.

During the reconnaissance the surveyor familiarizes himself with the road network of the district and with the possibilities of traversing it, and also notes camp sites in sparsely-settled areas.

In view of the impossibility of making notes during a flight, the surveyor makes summaries of his rapid observations as rough notes either in his journal or on the mosaic or map.

It is expedient to lay out aerovisual survey transects over areas where, according to aerovisual reconnaissance, the plant cover is more or less uniform and is not characterized by frequent changes in the communities. In such conditions the carrying-out of aerovisual survey transects over a given territory makes it possible for the network of ground transects to be more open there. It is best for two surveyors to take part in making an aerovisual survey transect; one of them constantly keeps an eye on the orientation of the transect and on its location, and notes by conventional symbols on the mosaic the geo-botanical content of outlined areas visible to him (if the flight is made with only a map, he enters on it by eye also the outlines of communities), and the other surveyor briefly (with rough notes) describes the features of the plant cover in each of the outlined areas.

Accuracy in orientation is the most important condition of a successful survey. To that end it is expedient to make previous preparation for the flight. The day before the flight (the best hours for aerovisual observations are the morning hours) the geo-botanist, together with the pilot, marks out the transect and, working from the average speed of the aeroplane, calculates the duration of its flight from one landmark to another; these data, and also the course to be taken by the aeroplane from one landmark to another, are noted by the surveyor in his working aerovisual journal.

The transect is entered on the map by both the geo-botanist and the pilot. It is useful to divide the transect into sections corresponding to the distance covered by the aeroplane in one minute, and to number these sections in the same way as is done in an aerovisual survey (see above). This makes orientation considerably easier.

Experience shows that an aerovisual transect should not be given too complex a configuration, with numerous turns, as each turn increases the probability of error in the course of the transect.

In addition, it is expedient to have changes in the course of the aeroplane (turns) related to some landmarks that are well and clearly defined.

During the transect it is necessary to watch the time closely, noting in the working aerovisual journal the time the aeroplane takes off, the times of changing course, the times of passing over clearly-identified landmarks, and also the beginning and end of landings made during the transect.

It is difficult to make detailed notes on the transect. Therefore the surveyor should make notes in condensed form, either denoting communities by the initials of their names or using some system of conventional symbols, worked out beforehand. After the end of the flight all working notes should be expanded and a fair copy written up in the form of detailed and connected text without any contractions.

Data obtained on aerovisual survey transects are used equally with other transect data in compiling a map.

Final aerovisual transects are most often designed either to consolidate the whole chequered and complex picture of plant cover in the district under study, or to survey a locality that is particularly complex and difficult of access, and that remains as an isolated "blank spot" on the background of a compiled map. Particularly important are transects designed to synthesize the geo-botanical data of a district. In the words of Kas'yanova (1955), the observer on such a flight, as it were, sketches a vast profile, in which all communities are combined into a single ecological series: naturally such a synthetic survey of a locality calls for high qualifications in the surveyor.

Final aerovisual transects are a good method of checking the results of previous work. The senior specialist, when inspecting the work, flies over the territory covered by the survey, having with him the map compiled by junior specialists, and verifies its correspondence with the actual geo-botanical situation.

If aerovisual observations do not have an auxiliary character but are looked upon as one of the principal bases of a survey, they should be organized according to the instructions in the section on aero-geo-botanical surveys (see above).

(ii) *Survey of "Keys"*

Like transect surveys, other kinds of surveys—and particularly aero-geo-botanical surveys—are supplemented by the survey of "keys" or selected typical areas. "Key" is the name given to a habitat characterized by a typical combination, constantly repeated in a given district, of several plant communities, and also by typical conditions of relief, soils, etc. Survey of a "key" is made on a larger scale than survey of the district as a whole, and the map of a "key" is, as it were, a supplementary illustration, more thoroughly revealing the content of separate elements of the legend of a small-scale geo-botanical map. The dimensions of "key" areas and the amount of detail in surveys of them vary in accordance with the natural conditions of the zone in which the work is done, and also on the tasks to be fulfilled by the work. Therefore the question of the dimensions of "keys" will be considered more than once again in discussion of methods of surveys undertaken for various national-economic purposes (see below).

We may remark that "key" surveys are most widely used in zones distinguished by the complexity and patchiness of the plant cover, namely, in tundras, in semi-deserts, and especially in deserts.

The compiling of plans and maps of "keys" may be done by the transect-visual survey method; often grid surveys are also used.

The selection of "keys" is a very responsible element of the work. It is necessary, before selecting "keys", to become thoroughly familiar with the district of the work, to ensure that the selected area is typical.

(iii) *Constructing a Geo-botanical Profile*

One of the most important auxiliary processes in a transect survey is the construction of a geo-botanical profile. A geo-botanical profile is the name given to a special type of drawing of the plant distribution along a transect, with simultaneous showing on the same drawing of changes in relief and sometimes also other factors (soils, hydrogeological conditions, principal rock strata, etc.). To construct a profile in a typical area, where the dependence of plant community distribution on ecological conditions is expressed most fully, a transect is laid out. Along that transect the relief is sketched (by eye, or drawn from levelling data) and also the changes in plant cover over different elements of the relief. In as many as possible of the community habitats crossed by the profile, the soils and underlying strata are described (for which purpose sample pits are dug: it is desirable to collect samples of soil and ground-water for chemical analysis). All communities found in the profile are described in detail. The extent of each community along the profile is measured with a tape or by pacing, and the whole drawing of the profile is made on a strictly-defined scale selected by the investigator. The plant communities are designated by conventional symbols.

If the investigator has at his disposal several concrete profiles constructed in different habitats, which, however, are characterized by the same regularity of plant distribution, he may construct an abstract "generalized profile" by selecting from the concrete profiles data on typical combinations of phytocenoses. Such a profile does not apply to any definite area and only illustrates the general picture of plant distribution, which the geo-botanist approaches on the basis of study of the concrete profiles. Therefore, introducing the "generalized profile" into the account of the material, he must, even so, introduce part of the concrete profiles from which it was constructed. In the contrary case the reader, familiarizing himself with the recorded material, is deprived of the possibility of subjecting the generalized profile to critical examination.

Profiles are a very graphic and effective means of illustrating the recorded material in a geo-botanical survey, and present in the best way typical ecological series characteristic of any part of the territory.

The length of a profile may vary greatly—from several metres to several kilometres.

The drawing of geo-botanical profiles is most often used in compiling maps of the vegetation of river valleys, lake basins, marshes, mountain slopes, and especially of the complex vegetation of semi-deserts. Geo-botanical profiles are widely used as supplements to geo-botanical indicational maps (see below). As an illustration we present Fig. 5.

(iv) *Line-transect Estimation*

Line-transect estimation is a method of recording the ratios of the areas of plant communities, applied when there is considerable complexity of plant cover (in marshes, tundras, semi-deserts).

Line-transect estimation consists of measuring (by pacing or tape)

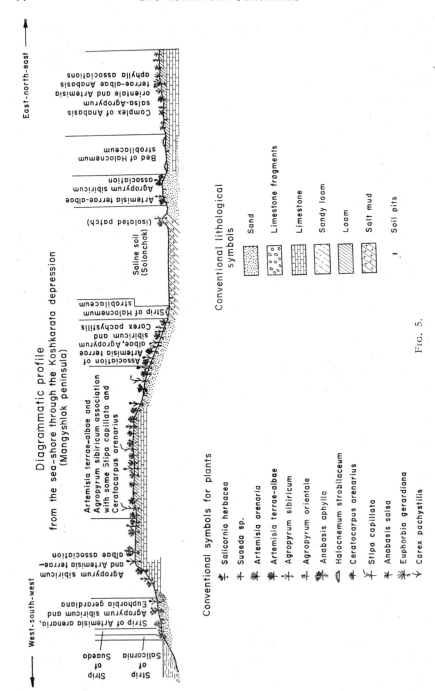

Diagrammatic profile
from the sea-shore through the Koshkarata depression
(Mangyshlak peninsula)

Conventional symbols for plants

⚹ Salicornia herbacea
✳ Suaeda sp.
❋ Artemisia arenaria
❉ Artemisia terrae-albae
⊥ Agropyrum sibiricum
⚘ Agropyrum orientale
✿ Anabasis aphylla
❦ Halocnemum strobilaceum
⊥ Ceratocarpus arenarius
⅄ Stipa capillata
✳ Anabasis salsa
❋ Euphorbia gerardiana
⅄ Carex pachystilis

Conventional lithological
symbols

▦ Sand
◦◦◦ Limestone fragments
▥ Limestone
⫽ Sandy loam
╱ Loam
▨ Salt mud
⏐ Soil pits

FIG. 5.

the length of the intercepts of separate habitats of plant communities combined in a complex, with subsequent calculation, on the basis of the figures obtained, of the percentage ratios of the areas of these communities in the complex. Linear valuation is done as follows: the geo-botanist first examines the area of the complex and selects a direction for the transect line so that all members of the complex occur successively more than once in it. Then he lays out a line, counting his paces (or measuring with a tape) and recording the length of the intercepts for each community passed through.

Later the material obtained may be analysed in two ways. The simplest way is to calculate the ratios of different communities in the complex directly from the ratios of the sums of the lengths of their intercepts. Thus let us suppose that in a complex consisting of communities a and b the following results were obtained: community a was encountered twice, in intercepts 12.5 m and 5 m long; community b three times, in intercepts 1, 3, and 3.5 m long. The sum of the intercepts of community a is 17.5 m, and of b 7.5 m; the whole length of the valuation path is 25 m. Then community a forms 70 per cent of the complex and community b 30 per cent.

Shiffers (1938) states that one may replace the ratio of the sums of the intercepts by the ratio of the totalled squares of the lengths of these intercepts. He presents the following example of such a "calculation".*

Community a occurs twice over lengths of 5 and 10 m, b once over a length of 7 m, and c three times with intercepts of 5, 7 and 10 m. Then the ratio of the areas of these communities is calculated as follows:

$$
\begin{aligned}
a &= 5 \times 5 + 10 \times 10 = & 125 \\
b &= 7 \times 7 = & 49 \\
c &= 5 \times 5 + 7 \times 7 + 10 \times 10 = & 174 \\
\hline
& & 348
\end{aligned}
$$

Calculating the percentage of each community, we get a 36 per cent, b 14 per cent, and c 50 per cent.

The greater the area of the complex that it is proposed to evaluate, the greater should be the length of the valuation path.

* Percentage cover is in fact *linearly* related to the length of the intercepts on the line transect, as assumed in the previous paragraph: see e.g. G. A. McIntyre (1953), *J. Ecol.* 41, 319—330.

The lengths of valuation paths for the study of different types of complexes (in marshes, semi-deserts, etc.) should be different (see below on this point).

If the area under study in which linear valuation is made is almost a square or a rectangle, the valuation paths are better laid out either perpendicular to the sides of the area or along the two diagonals. According to Kunitsyn (1933), data obtained by measurements along the two diagonals of an area are closer to the true ratios of the communities in a complex than data taken from measurements along paths perpendicular to the sides of the area.* The best method of calculation, in Kunitsyn's opinion, is to use four paths—two diagonal and two perpendicular to the sides of the area. In that case the average value obtained from all four paths is very close to the true ratio of the communities obtained by means of a continuous outline survey of the area and calculation of the respective areas with a planimeter.

---

* This procedure results in over-representation of the central parts of the sample area; see P. Greig-Smith (1957), *Quantitative Plant Ecology*, London. p. 22.

CHAPTER III

GEO-BOTANICAL SURVEYS
FOR FORESTRY NEEDS

1. GENERAL INFORMATION ON GEO-BOTANICAL
SURVEYS IN FORESTS

FORESTS occupy about two-fifths of the surface of the U.S.S.R. They
are of colossal economic value from the points of view of their industrial utilization and water-conserving importance, and also in
many other respects.

The compilation of forest maps and plans of various kinds is one
of the important elements in making an inventory of forest resources,
without which proper organization of the economy of the U.S.S.R.
would be impossible.

All geo-botanical survey work in forests can be divided into two
large groups:

(1) forest-typological surveys, i.e. compilation of plans and maps
of types of forest, and

(2) surveys connected with forest management and valuation,
i.e. dividing a forest into sections uniform from a forestry point of
view.

These two types of work are to a considerable extent overlapping
but have, however, certain differences. The latter mainly consist in
the fact that forest-typological surveys have as their aim the revealing
of more varied geo-botanical and geographical characteristics of forest
communities. A forest-typological survey, as is clear from the name
itself, is a survey of types of forest. Since the type of a forest has the
closest connection with definite local growing conditions, a map of
forest types becomes to a certain extent also a map of different ecological conditions. Such a map is of great interest for the forest man-
ager and the forest surveyor when determining the possibility of
exploiting a given area for the needs of the forest industry; for the

forester when deciding the questions of the regeneration or rehabilitation of a forest stand; and also for the forest improver, the soil
officer and the geographer, when studying methods for the comprehensive reclamation of a given territory.

Of somewhat less wide practical significance are plans and maps
compiled during forest valuation and regional forest maps obtained
by generalization of these plans. Here the primary questions are a
matter of showing on the plan the boundaries of defined areas, similar
in the valuation features that determine the economic value of a
given area.

Plans compiled for valuation, however, are of great value for
forest-typological surveys, just as the latter are of great use in valuation work.

The most widespread kind of geo-botanical surveys in forests is
survey work connected with valuation of forests. Less widely used
are forest-typological surveys, which have a more general geo-botanical character. Accordingly forest-valuation work is discussed first
below, and forest-typological investigations later.

2. SURVEY WORK IN FOREST VALUATION

In the process of valuation work the forest area must be divided
into "forest parcels" ("valuation parcels", "valuation sectors").
A "forest parcel" is a forestry, and not purely a geo-botanical, term.
In one forest parcel several territorially-adjacent stands are included
if the differences between them are not very marked, if they have the
same average forestry characteristics and if the same forestry measures can be carried out in them (Tyurin, 1945).

Valuation survey work is done by the following principal methods:
(a) ground transect-visual survey, (b) ground continuous-outline
survey, (c) ground visual survey with use of aerial photographs, (d)
aero-geo-botanical survey (both aerovisual and with aerial photographs).

The majority of these surveys, however, are preceded by preparatory forest-management tasks. These preparatory tasks are carried
out in the case of all kinds of valuation surveys (except certain kinds
of aerovisual surveys).

The preparatory tasks consist of laying out rides, i.e. wide cut-
out strips dividing the forest into rectangular blocks (compartments),

and sightings (narrower cut-out strips within the blocks); these strips serve for travel through the blocks during the survey.

Both the rides and the sightings have (in addition to their forestry functions) the role of roads by which a surveyor travels during a ground transect-survey; thus they are, as it were, permanent fixed transects. In addition, they are an important element in orientation—especially in aero-geo-botanical methods of survey.

The rides are laid out north-and-south and east-and-west; the sightings are cut perpendicular to the rides. On the sightings marking-posts are set up every 250–500 m. Trees along the sightings are blazed on three sides to make it easier to recognize the sighting (since, because of the small width of the sighting—the least permissible width of which is 0.25 m—it is not always easily observed).

The density of the rides depends only on the category of the work, but the density of the sightings depends both on the category of the valuation work and on whether aerial photographs are to be used in the survey or not.

There are five categories of valuation work. Category I, which presupposes the most detailed forest management, includes forests in districts where all kinds of wood from all cuttings are fully marketed. Category II includes forests where only wood from the main cutting and improvement cutting is fully marketed. In category III valuations are made in districts where only 75 per cent of the wood from the main cutting is marketed. Category IV includes areas with

TABLE 4. DENSITY OF GRID OF RIDES AND SIGHTINGS FOR VARIOUS CATEGORIES OF VALUATION

Category of work	Length and width of block (km)	Distance between sightings (in metres)	
		in work with aerial photographs	in work without aerial photographs
I	1 × 0,5	—	125
	1 × 1	—	250
II	1 × 1	—	250
	2 × 1	—	250
III	2 × 2	400	500
	4 × 2	800	500
IV	4 × 4	2000	1000
	8 × 2	2000	1000
V	8 × 4	4000	2000
	16 × 4	4000	2000

marketing of from 25 to 75 per cent of the wood from the main cutting, and category V areas with marketing of less than 25 per cent of the wood from the main cutting.

The density of rides (expressed in the size of the blocks) and the density of sightings may be determined from the table given above (Table 4).

After the preparatory work has been done, the survey work in the strict sense of the word is begun.

During the survey it is necessary to divide the forest into "forest parcels". That division is made according to a number of characteristics. These characteristics are briefly listed below (a more detailed list of the characteristics and the content of each characteristic and the method cf determining it may be found in the forest-valuation text-books of Anuchin (1952) and Tyurin (1945).

Characteristics for Division of Forest into Parcels

1. *Structure of the stands*. Stands are divided by their structure into simple and complex. When simple the stand forms a single high canopy; when complex, several. Stands that may be close in other characteristics but differ in structure are placed in separate parcels.

2. *Composition of the stands*. Stands are divided by their composition into pure and mixed. The composition of a stand is expressed in a formula composed of the initial letters of the Russian names of the tree species and of the coefficients of composition, describing the proportion of each species in the stand. The coefficients are expressed in whole numbers from 1 to 10 and their sum should be equal to 10.

In the stands a distinction is made between a "dominant" species, i.e. a species having the greatest coefficient of composition, and a "principal" species, i.e. that which best serves forestry needs in a given forest area, although its coefficient of composition may be very small.

If in two mixed stands, with other characteristics similar, the coefficients of the dominant species differ by more than 2, these stands are placed in separate parcels.

3. *Age*. Stands may be referred to different age classes. Age classes for conifers and mature hard-leaved species are measured by 20-year intervals, for soft-leaved species and all growing stands by 10-year intervals, and for shrubs by 5-year intervals.

Stands differing by only one age class are put in separate parcels.

4. *Habitat conditions.* They are characterized by the quality class of the stand. The quality class is determined by the ratio between age and average height of the stand. To determine the quality class special tables are used (either a general table of quality classes or tables of growth of separate species). Stands are placed in separate parcels with a difference of one class in their quality classes.

5. *Density of stocking.* That is determined by the ratio of the total area of cross-section (basal area) of the given stand to the basal area of a full stand of the same species in the same growing conditions. To determine the latter one uses tables of the course of growth of the species. Stands differing from each other in density of stocking by 0.2 are placed in separate parcels.

6. *Soundness.* This term is not clearly defined and is variously interpreted. Tyurin (1945) proposes four classes of soundness: I— stands with up to 10 per cent deadwood, II—10 to 30 per cent, III—33 to 50 per cent, IV—over 50 per cent. Stands differing in class of soundness are put in separate parcels.

7. *Marketability.* This is determined by the output of workable wood and is calculated by a number of special methods (see Tyurin, 1945; Anuchin, 1952). Classes of marketability may be determined from the following table (Table 5). Stands referred to different classes of marketability are placed in separate parcels.

TABLE 5. DETERMINATION OF CLASS OF MARKETABILITY FROM THE OUTPUT OF WORKABLE WOOD

Class of marketabliity	Output of workable wood (per cent)	
	for coniferous spp.	for broad-leaved spp.
I	over 70	over 45
II	51—70	31—45
III	31—50	10—30
IV	under 30	under 10

As may be seen from the list of characteristics, some of them may to a considerable degree be used for the geo-botanical characteristics of a forest, whereas others have a purely forestry significance.

It must be remarked that in the process of valuation work the characteristics of geo-botanical and ecological nature—structure, composition, age, quality class—are of the greatest physiognomical importance for establishing the boundaries between different parcels.

Valuation survey work may be divided into a number of kinds, depending on the means whereby it is carried out. Each of these kinds of work has its own special name. Actually, however, each of these kinds can be referred to one or another type of geo-botanical survey (see above). A comparison of kinds of valuation work with kinds of geo-botanical survey work is given in the following table:

TABLE 6. CLASSIFICATION OF VALUATION WORK BY TYPES OF GEO-BOTANICAL
SURVEYS

Kind of valuation work	Type of geo-botanical survey to which the given work can be referred
1. Ground visual valuation (reconnaissance valuation)	Transect-visual survey
2. Ground instrumental evaluation	Continuous outline survey
3. Ground valuation with aerial photographs	Transect survey with use of aerial photographs
4. Aerovisual forest investigation	Aerovisual aero-geo-botanical survey
5. Aero-valuation (forest valuation from the air with aerial photographs)	Aero-geo-botanical survey with use of aerial photographs

We give below methods of carrying out investigations with different kinds of valuation survey work.

(a) *Ground Visual Valuation*

This kind of valuation is a transect-visual survey. It is also called "reconnaissance valuation" (Anuchin, 1952). It consists in the traversing of the forest area by the forest surveyors along rides and sightings: in that connection the points where the boundaries of different forest parcels cut a ride or a sighting are determined. All parcels abutting on the route of the forest surveyor are briefly described by him and their limiting points are entered on a sketch showing the grid of rides and sightings. In order to obtain the boundaries of parcels between the sightings, the points of intersection of the boundaries of a specific parcel with adjacent rides or sightings are joined by straight lines, ignoring all bends or breaks in the boundary between sightings. If any parcel is broken between sightings and is not traced on the adjacent sighting, the inter-sighting area in that locality is divided exactly in half, and one half of it is referred to the parcel cut across by one sighting and the other half to the parcel cut across by the next sighting (method of I. N. Bernatskii; Anuchin, 1952). Naturally in reconnaissance valuation parcels lying entirely in the inter-sighting area and touching neither a ride nor a sighting are not drawn on the sketch and their very existence remains unknown to the forest surveyor.

All parcels entered on the sketch are numbered. They are described under these numbers in the valuation journal.

(b) *Ground Instrumental Valuation*

This type of valuation is essentially a continuous-outline survey. It is used for defining, within a forest massif, unforested patches, i.e. areas either devoid of forest or where the forest has been radically destroyed (it should be noted that burned areas and cut-over areas without regrowth, where forest is only temporarily absent, are from the forestry point of view included in forest). In addition, this method is used for valuation of particularly valuable stands of trees (rare species, etc.).

In this method, sightings—following all the curves and breaks in the boundary—are cut along the boundaries of each parcel that is to be given instrumental valuation (the sightings are not cut out if a survey of the boundaries of an unforested area is being made). The sections of the sightings between breaks and bends in the boundary are measured, and the angles of the bends themselves are measured with instruments (compass, goniometer, theodolite). In this way the geo-botanist and the geographer make a full circuit of the surveyed parcel.

(c) *Ground Valuation with Aerial Photographs*

This type of valuation corresponds to transect surveys with aerial photographs.

In valuation with aerial photographs we have to distinguish two cases:

(1) when the valuation is being done for the first time in previously-unsurveyed territory;

(2) when the valuation is being done for the second time in territory previously under forest management and therefore possessing a block-grid.

In the first case—in the case of so-called primary forest management—there is no block-grid either on aerial photographs or on the terrain. Therefore the first step in the work is the laying-out on aerial photographs of a grid of proposed rides, and also of the so-

5

called sheet-polygons, i.e. groups of blocks that on a given scale should be shown on a single sheet of the forest-management plan. The proposed grid is drawn on the photographs with tooth-paste or with a ball-point pen, so that in the event of possible changes in the grid when it is later laid out in the field it can easily be changed also on the photographs (Kolosova and Raizer, 1953).

Afterwards, before the forest surveyor goes out on the survey, two rides (out of all those proposed) are cut perpendicular to each other, cutting across the whole forest massif through its centre; these are called master rides. When they are completed the forest surveyors, using local landmarks (streams, glades, clearings, etc.) fix the location of these rides on the photographs and trace them with indian ink on the face of the prints.

Later the laying-out of all the remaining proposed rides takes place. They are cut as fully in agreement as possible with the project as devised. But, regardless of this, the location of each ride should be repeatedly determined by landmarks and only after that should it be confirmed in indian ink on the photographs.

If valuation with aerial photographs has to be done a second time on territories where forest management has already been carried out and where a block-grid exists, then before an aerial photographic survey of the forest massif is made some preliminary work should be done. That consists in clearing, and partly also in extending, the ride-grid and in setting up markers (identification signs) at the angles where the rides intersect. The markers are structures of definite shape (crosses, L-shapes, etc.), made from trees with the bark peeled off, trees with light-coloured easily-noticed bark (birch), or soil that contrasts strongly with the environment (e.g. light-coloured sand). The preliminary work has as its aim the bringing of the whole block-grid into such a condition that both the rides and the localities that they cut through will be clearly visible on aerial photographs. Naturally the requirements for preliminary work differ somewhat with different

TABLE 7. REQUIREMENTS FOR CONSTRUCTION OF A BLOCK-GRID WITH DIFFERENT SCALES OF AERIAL PHOTOGRAPHS

Scale of aerial photograph	Required width of ride (metres)	Required size of markers (metres)	
		width	length
1 : 10,000—1 : 15,000	1.5	4–6	40–60
1 : 25,000	2.5	12	100

scales of aerial photographs. In the above table (Table 7) data are given on widths and sizes of markers for different scales of aerial photographs.

If these conditions are observed, the ride-grid should be perfectly clearly shown on aerial photographs.

Thus as a result of the first stage of the work, with both primary and secondary forest management, the forest surveyor should have at his disposal aerial photographs of the forest massif with the block-grid shown on them; the difference will consist only in the fact that in secondary forest management the aerial photographs will contain a picture of the grid, whereas in primary forest management the grid is entered in indian ink.

The next stage of the work is orientation of the photographs. It consists in identification of each block and each ride on the photographs and in entering the numbers of the blocks on the photographs. When there are forest-management plans from previous years (in cases of secondary valuation) this may be done in the office; in primary forest management or in cases where there are no plans of former forest management, this work is done in the field, making a circuit of the blocks and identifying each of them on the photographs by local landmarks.

After orientation of the photographs the valuation should be commenced. It begins with preliminary analysis of the aerial photographs. All parcels whose nature is beyond doubt in the analysis are traced round with indian ink and each of them is described in the valuation journal from the analysis data.

After the description has been entered, however, some blank lines remain for entering additional data when the parcels are visited in the field, and beside the text of the discussion itself a short note "anal." is made; this signifies that the description was made from analysis data and not in the field.

Boundaries of parcels whose nature was not quite clearly defined in the analysis are traced over with a soft black pencil and described as stated above.

After the preliminary analysis a circuit is made along the rides. Each parcel is given a brief additional description (in the remaining blank lines). If the length of a parcel along a ride is not more than 200 m one description is entered; if the length is from 200 to 400 m, two descriptions, and if the parcel is more than 400 m long, three descriptions.

5*

In inspecting a parcel that was not defined in the preliminary analysis, its boundaries are determined by measurement to the nearest grid marker, a description of the parcel is made, and it is shown on the photographs according to the given measurements.

If the valuation work is not in a higher category than III, field work ends with travel over the rides. With valuation in category II the forest surveyor must, besides travelling over the rides, make journeys within the blocks tc parcels in which during the past decade any economic measures have been recorded. With valuation in category I every parcel must be examined in the field.

(d) *Aerovisual Forest Investigations*

This type of work is essentially an aerovisual geo-botanical survey and includes all the stages of work described for that type of survey (compiling a basic map, selective ground work, training, survey, and office work).

In order to ensure the accuracy of the data obtained, sketches are made simultaneously during aerovisual forest observations by two persons—the forest surveyor and the pilot; the forest surveyor sketches the forest area with outlines of the forest parcels and the pilot sketches the unforested area, entering on it the general situation of localities to make orientation precise and to facilitate transfer of material from the sketch to the basic map.

Each parcel shown on the sketch should be visually appraised by the forest surveyor according to the followign characteristics: dominant species, composition, age (only five age-groups being specified—young, medium-aged, pre-mature, mature, and over-mature), quality class, density of stocking. The characteristics are given in the form of a fraction: the numerator contains the composition and age, and the denominator the quality class and density of stocking (the latter is given not in tenths, as is usual, but in whole numbers). Thus, for example, a mixed stand of pine with birch and spruce, mature, of quality class II and 0.6 density of stocking, will be designated by the following formula:

$$\frac{5P \ 3B \ 2S \ \text{mat.}}{II \ 6}$$

The formula is written directly on the parcel as depicted on the sketch.

The flight altitude in aerovisual forest observations is usually 400 m when the distance between transects is 4 km (Samoilovich, 1953). With greater distances the flight altitude is increased correspondingly: with intervals of 6 km the altitude should be 600–700 m, and with intervals of 8 km it should be 800–1000 m (Anuchin, 1952).

Material obtained from aerovisual observations is not distinguished by the same precision as that from ground valuation: it is suitable mainly for compiling diagrammatic maps of forest distribution, for discovering forest areas to be designated for exploitation in the immediate future, and for defining areas requiring precise valuation (Tyurin, 1945).

Among aerovisual forest observations we should also include cases where the forest surveyor draws the outlines of forest parcels not on a sketch but directly on a topographical map. This kind of work is used principally not for investigation of great forest massifs but for valuation of small disconnected forests in river valleys. In this case the topographical map gives a fairly precise representation of the boundaries of each such parcel, and the forest surveyor has only to examine them from the air and to determine and write on the map the formula of the stand. Naturally in this case there is no need to lay out transects strictly parallel to each other. The transects may have the most varied shape and their grid is designed only for the purpose of visiting all forest areas shown on the map.

(e) *Aero-valuation (Valuation from the Air with Aerial Photographs)*

This type of work is an aero-geo-botanical survey with use of aerial photographs. It includes the series of investigations indicated for that type of geo-botanical survey (preliminary analysis of contact prints, mounting of the latter in strips for proposed transects or preparation of mosaics, training, flying over the territory to determine the geo-botanical content of the defined areas, etc.).

Aero-valuation investigations, however, vary somewhat, depending on the scale of the aerial photographs used. If aerial photographs on a scale of 1:50,000 are used, the work is done in a way similar to that stated above in the description of aero-geo-botanical surveys with use of aerial photographs. If he has photographs on larger scales (1:10,000—1:25,000), the forest surveyor is enabled during the preliminary analysis not only to define the boundaries of parcels but also to establish their geo-botanical and valuation characteristics (for the majority, if not for all of them) and to make valuation descriptions from the aerial photographs. In this case the work during flight consists in characterizing parcels that remained unidentified during the analysis and during selective checks from the air of the results of the preliminary analysis.

For this purpose it is unnecessary to lay out a large number of transects strictly parallel to each other. The transects are laid out so that parcels not yet investigated will be visited and so that they will pass through as many parcels as possible in order to verify the preliminary analysis. The transects may then be of various shapes.

It must be remarked that for the latter type of work (with large-scale photographs) it is more convenient to have on the flight not a series of photographs mounted in strips but mosaics prepared from the analysed photographs.

Aero-valuation work is usually carried out at an altitude of 100–300 m. The minimum size of a forest parcel for aero-valuation is about 20 hectares, and the minimum size of an unforested area 5 hectares. Aero-valuation is possible in strips whose width is not more than three times the altitude of the flight (with observations from one side of the aeroplane: Samoilovich, 1955).

3. BRIEF NOTES ON INTERPRETATION OF AERIAL PHOTOGRAPHS OF FOREST VEGETATION

The purpose of forest interpretation is determination from aerial photographs of the different categories of areas and the categories and types of forests, and establishing their characteristics.

Special methods of forest interpretation are described in text-books on forest valuation with use of aircraft (Anuchin, 1952; Kolosova and Raizer, 1953; Samoilovich, 1953). We give below the interpretation characters only for the most important geo-botanical features of stands, namely the characters for analysis of the composition of stands.

Stands of spruce *(Picea)* and silver fir *(Abies)* have a number of common features in aerial photographic representation. Mature stands of these species are distinguished by their extremely dark hue—the darkest among our forest species. This is particularly notice-able in infra-red photographs. Young stands are lighter in colour and are difficult to distinguish by their hue from stands of other species.

Because of the density of the tree crowns, the boundary between the lighted and shaded parts of a crown is very sharp and straight.

Near the margins of the aerial photographs the light and dark sides of the crowns begin to be noticeable, having the appearance of elon-gated triangles.

Usually a sharp difference in the height of the trees is clearly visible (indicating differences in age, usual in stands of spruce and silver fir). Very characteristic is uneven distribution of trees, the existence of gaps in the canopy giving it a ragged and uneven appearance (due to the prevalence of windfalls among spruce). In a photograph that is indicated by the extremely unequal sizes of the intervals between the crowns of trees. These intervals are either very small or very large: their colour is very dark (extreme depth of shade).

If a spruce stand is thinned, the low position of the crowns is readily observed (the crowns almost rest on the ground).

A mixed stand of pine and spruce is difficult to identify. Pines are recognizable mainly by their height and the very pronounced round-ness of their crowns. An admixture of aspen (*Populus tremula*) is iden-tified by its very light hue and by the characteristic "flower-bed" nature (distribution in compact groups) of its occurrence. The same feature, less clearly shown, characterizes admixtures of birch.

In winter photographs admixtures of deciduous species practically defy identification.

Silver fir is distinguished from spruce mainly by its longer sharp-pointed shadow.

Pine stands are lighter-coloured in aerial photographs than spruce stands. The roundness of the crowns is very noticeable, and—in thinned stands—the high position of the crowns. The transition between the light and dark sides of the crown is not abrupt but gradual. The intervals between crowns are uniform and not deeply shaded. The surface of the canopy is smooth. In the marginal parts of the photographs one can see the usual configuration of pine crowns peculiar to them when the trees are seen from the side by an observer on the ground. Also in the marginal parts of the photographs it is easiest to observe an admixture of poplar and birch in a pine stand—in the centre of the photograph this is difficult.

Deciduous stands are distinguished by their bright light-grey colour (especially in summer photographs). The surface of the canopy is somewhat uneven (less than that of spruce, but more uneven than that of pine). The distribution of the trees in groups (from three to five trees in a group) is characteristic.

Birch stands, by their appearance in aerial photographs, rather remind one of pine stands. Their colour, like that of the latter, is light grey (darker than larch but lighter than spruce and silver fir). In infra-red photographs birch stands are considerably lighter in shade than pine. The canopy of the stand is usually smooth, without windfalls, and the spaces between crowns are small and uniform in size. The crowns are convex and the boundaries between the lighted and shaded parts of them are not sharp (in which birch resembles pine). Observation of a pine admixture is possible only in the marginal parts of the photographs, where the difference in the shape of the crowns becomes noticeable. Birch crowns there look more elongated than pine crowns; the greatest width of the birch crowns is seen, in the marginal parts of the photographs, to be considerably lower than that of the pine crowns.

Aspen stands are distinguished from stands of spruce, pine and birch by their lighter tone. The convexity of the crowns is almost unnoticeable. Separate crowns along the margins look (as it were) ragged, uneven. In thinned stands the very high attachment of the crowns is characteristic—these appear, as it were, to be hanging above the ground. Often a "flower-bed" distribution is noticeable. It must be remarked, however, that identification of an admixture of birch and pine in a poplar stand is fairly difficult, and if the area is small it is impossible.

Oak stands, particularly if well thinned out, can be identified on a photograph by the characteristic shape of their shadows, in which the unique compact, blunt top of the oak crowns is clearly visible. In early spring photographs oak produces a unique hatched-drawing effect, due to the absence of leaves from the crown. In stands of other species oaks are usually recognizable by the very large size of their crowns. On the whole, the features whereby oak stands can be identified have been little studied.

The features of lime *(Tilia)* stands have also been little studied. It is easy to distinguish lime from oak, spruce or birch in a photograph made during the flowering period, when the lime appears in light, almost white shades.

Cut-over, burnt and windblown areas in forests are also characterized by a number of features by which they can be identified. Thus, for example, cut-over areas are distinguished by their uniform white colour and their usually straight and very definite boundaries. Isolated remaining trees may be seen on cut-over areas.

Burnt areas also, like cut-over areas, are distinguished by their white colour, but their boundaries usually have irregular outlines and penetrate like tongues into the surrounding forest massif. Usually the burnt area is seen to be littered with trees lying in all directions. Individual standing trees (deadwood) cast almost no shadow.

Windblown areas are generally similar to burnt areas, but fallen trees are usually seen to be lying in one direction and the area is generally elongated in the direction of the windfall.

4. RESULTS OF VALUATION SURVEY WORK

As a result of valuation work (ground visual valuation, valuation with aerial photographs or aero-valuation), so-called "planchettes"* are drawn on the basis of the sketches obtained and the valuation descriptions; each planchette is a plan of a group of blocks, with a statement of their boundaries and the boundaries of the separate forest parcels, the lengths of rides and sightings, and also the size of the angles between them. The planchette is drawn on a sheet of standard size, 60 by 60 cm (the working area of the plan is 50 by 50 cm, with a margin of 5 cm on each side). The scale of the planchette depends on the category of valuation work (Table 8).

TABLE 8. SCALES OF PLANCHETTES FOR DIFFERENT VALUATION CATEGORIES

Category of work	Scale of planchette
I	1 : 5000
II	1 : 10,000
III	1 : 25,000
IV-V	1 : 100,000

The boundaries of parcels established visually or by aerial photographs are shown on the planchettes by dotted lines, and the boundaries established instrumentally by solid lines.

* Equivalent to "stock maps" in British forestry practice.

On each planchette is stated its number, its location by administrative district, and the names of the "leskhoz"* and the forestry administration; the geographic and magnetic meridians are shown (in the centre of the upper margin of the planchette), data concerning the area of the planchette are entered, and the compilers and the organization by which the work was done are stated.

On the basis of the planchettes, plans of the forest stands are made using a pantograph or photographically. Their scale also depends on the category of the work (Table 9).

TABLE 9. SCALES OF PLANS OF FOREST STANDS FOR DIFFERENT VALUATION CATEGORIES

Category of work	Scale of plan of forest stands
I	1 : 10,000
II	1 : 25,000
III	1 : 50,000
IV–V	1 : 100,000

All defined forest parcels are shown on the plans. Within each parcel the formula of that parcel is shown as a fraction: the numerator is the number and letter of the parcel, and the denominator the quality class and density of stocking. The parcels are coloured according to the dominant species. Standard colours for parcels are as follows:

Pine — gold   Oak—dark grey
Larch—brown   Birch—sky-blue
Pinus sibirica—red   Aspen — green
Spruce and silver fir—lilac

On the basis of the forest-stand plans, diagrams of the leskhozy are compiled. There the separate parcels are grouped into larger divisions according to their dominant species.

The plans, forest-stand plans, and leskhoz diagrams serve as basic material for compiling various forest maps.

The following types of forest maps are known: (a) leskhoz maps .on scales from 1:100,000–1:200,000; (b) regional forest maps for separate republics, regions and provinces on scales from 1:300,000 —1:1,000,000; (c) general maps of the forests of the U.S.S.R. on a scale of 1:2,500,000 (Malev, 1949; Tsvetkov, 1950).

* Literally "forest farm"—a subdivision of forest land for management purposes. Plural is "leskhozy".

Maps of leskhozy are comparatively few. Therefore in most cases it happens that there is nothing intermediate between primary material (planchettes and other plans) and regional forest maps.

To compile a regional forest map from primary material it is necessary first to enter on the map of the given province the administrative boundaries of the leskhozy. After that, within the boundaries of each leskhoz the grid of block-rides, copied from the leskhoz plan, is shown. In both the first and the second of these tasks numerous difficulties are met with, as the boundaries of many leskhozy do not accord with the national triangulation grid, and the actual configuration of the rides differs considerably from their representation on the plan of the leskhoz. Methods whereby one may overcome these difficulties are discussed in special works (Tsvetkov, 1950).

The boundaries of leskhozy and the grid of block-rides form a grid of orientation lines, relying on which one may transfer to the map data relating directly to its chief element, the forest.

For that purpose one prepares (on waxed paper) copies of the forest-stand plans, copying boundaries, rides, hydrographic and road networks, settlements and other landmarks, and the outlines of different forest divisions. The first two elements are copied in photographic colour,* the others in non-photographic colour. After that, a general outline of the divisions is drawn on the copies so obtained with a thick line in photographic colour, corresponding with the scale on which it is proposed to prepare the regional forest map.

The generalized plans so obtained are reduced photographically to the scale of the regional map. The generalization may be done all at once, with reduction to the scale of the regional map, or may have a repetitive character. In the latter case the generalization is repeated several times and the required scale is obtained gradually.

When the required reduction is achieved, the material obtained is copied on the map (with the aid of a glass-topped tracing table), using mainly the leskhoz boundaries drawn on the map, and also other landmarks.

The most important features for generalization are, first, the dominant species, and then, within the areas where the dominant species are defined, the age groups to which the stands belong.

On forest maps a system of colours and indicational symbols is generally used. The dominant species is mostly indicated by colour,

---

* i.e. a column that will appear dark when photographed for reproduction. (Editor's Footnote)

and the chief tree species accompanying the dominant species are shown by symbols. Shaposhnikov (1954) has collected data on the colours mostly used up to the present to designate various species, and also suggested a new system of colours and indicational symbols. Below, in Table 10, we give as an example the former colour symbols and some of the new ones proposed by Shaposhnikov.

TABLE 10. COLOUR SYMBOLS FOR STANDS WITH VARIOUS DOMINANT SPECIES

Dominant species	Symbol on maps of former years (colour)	Symbol according to Shaposhnikov (colour)
Spruce *(Picea)*	grey-violet	rose-grey, lilac
Larch *(Larix)*	light brown	greyish-red
Pinus sibirica	red	reddish-lilac
Oak *(Quercus)*	black	dark grey
Birch *(Betula)*	blue	sky-blue
Other broad-leaved trees	various shades of green	yellowish-green
Pine *(Pinus)*	orange	orange
Beech *(Fagus)*		dark green
Hornbeam *(Carpinus)*		snuff-coloured
Aspen *(Populus tremula)*		transparent green

5. FOREST-TYPOLOGY SURVEYS

Forest-typology survey work may be divided into two kinds: (a) reconnaissance-transect surveys and (b) detailed-transect surveys. That corresponds to the division of geo-botanical investigations of forests given in the "Programme for Geo-botanical Investigations" of the Botanical Institute of the U.S.S.R. Academy of Sciences, published in 1932. Both types of survey are essentially transect-visual surveys.

Reconnaissance-transect surveys are used in investigating large, little-studied massifs, dividing them into groups of forest types and mapping the latter.

The surveys are carried out by setting up a wide-spaced transect grid with observance of the general requirements relating to transect-visual surveys.

Of the two above types of work, however, only the first type should be included in forest-typology surveys in the strict sense of the word, since it actually differs considerably from the valuation work described above. In reconnaissance-transect work only the most elementary visual valuation is made, and sometimes valuation features are almost absent. In detailed-transect surveys valuation characteristics are given in such detail that that type of forest-typology survey really merges into reconnaissance valuation, described above.

Therefore we discuss below, as an example of forest-typology surveys, only reconnaissance-transect survey work.

In traversing parcels of different types of forest, sample plots 0.25 hectare in area are laid out in them. The plots need not be located in every parcel, but should be of such density that by the end of the work in a given district every type of forest is represented by not fewer than three plots.

The usual geo-botanical description of the forest community is made in each plot (see "Programme for Geo-botanical Investigations", 1932; Sukachev, 1931). A pit is dug in each plot and is described with a selection of samples subsequently taken from it.

The density of the transects depends on the scale of the survey and on the degree of uniformity of the forest massifs in the district studied. The space between transects should be 2 km on a scale of 1:100,000, 5 km on a scale of 1:200,000, and 10 km on a scale of 1:500,000 ("Programme for Geo-botanical Investigations", 1932; Bykov, 1953). When there is considerable lack of uniformity in the forest massifs these distances are reduced by 25 per cent.

During travel along a transect the geo-botanist distinguishes types of forest, draws the boundaries of different parcels within them, and pays constant attention to the changes in forest types connected with changes in habitat conditions. Thus each transect is converted into study of a unique ecological series. All data obtained on the transect —description of sample plots in different groups of forest types and observations on the relation of these groups to ecological conditions —are entered in the field journal. The transects serve as material for interpolation, by means of which the inter-transect areas are filled in with outlines of different groups of forest types.

The cartographic material obtained as the result of such a survey is generally called diagrammatic forest-typology maps or diagrams of the distribution of different groups of forest types. They give only a close approximation to the distribution of forests and are one of the primary phases of study of forest massifs.

The units defined on forest-typology maps may be of the following orders (Motovilov, 1955): (a) forest types corresponding to forest-management work of the first and second categories; (b) groups of types obtained by combining forest types similar in their soil conditions (they are defined in work of the third and fourth categories); (c) generalized groups of types, obtained by combining groups of types similar in their soil conditions and character of moisture-supply (they are defined in work of the fifth category).

The definition of separate types of forest in transect investigations is practically impossible, as for that purpose very detailed work is required, often acquiring the character of stationary investigations (Zhilkin, 1957).

If in a given territory forest-management work has been carried on, the diagrammatic map of distribution of different groups of forest types may be compiled in the office without field work, as according to recent departmental instructions for valuation work the forest surveyor is required to define the types of forest to which various parcels should be referred.

CHAPTER IV

GEO-BOTANICAL SURVEYS FOR THE NEEDS OF THE PEAT INDUSTRY AND AGRICULTURAL RECLAMATION OF BOGS

1. GENERAL INFORMATION ON GEO-BOTANICAL SURVEYS IN BOGS

THE economic significance of bogs is of many different kinds. Peat production is the most important type of economic activity in bogs. But in addition many bog areas (especially those that contain small supplies of peat, or peat of low quality not well suited for use as fuel) may be used agriculturally. Methods of such use are varied: (1) a bog may be drained and after appropriate fertilization used for farm crops; (2) some kinds of bogs can be used as hay-meadows or pastures; (3) bogs may be the sites of production of moss litter, berries, etc.

A bog, being one of the most difficult land areas to travel through, requires special measures for road location and road construction.

Finally, a bog is very often the location of the sources of many rivers; a large number of lakes are situated in bogs. Bogs are a link of no little importance in the transportation economy of the country and are one of the objects of hydrographical and hydrological work.

Because of the great economic role of bogs, the compiling of maps and plans of their plant cover acquires much importance.

Geo-botanical mapping of bogs has its own peculiarities, dependent on several natural features of bogs. The principal of these are as follows:

(a) In compiling geo-botanical maps and plans of bog massifs aerial methods are of particularly great importance, as the difficulty of traversing bogs impedes the laying-out of a close grid of ground transects.

(b) The compiling of geo-botanical maps (or plans) of bogs includes mapping not only of the plant cover but also of the thickness of the peat, and therefore is accompanied by special boring work (probing the depth of peat and selecting peat samples).

(c) The extreme patchiness of the plant cover of many types of bogs (alternation of small patches of different plant communities) requires the use for bog-mapping of several special methods of quantitative appraisal to establish the proportion of any community in the plant cover of the bog.

The compilation of more detailed geo-botanical plans of bogs is done: (1) for study of bogs as means of peat production, (2) for study of bogs as sites for agriculture.

In investigation of bogs for road construction and in hydrographic investigations, geo-botanical maps are not compiled; in these types of work only very diagrammatic plans of plant distribution are compiled (in hydrographic work there may also be compiled diagrams of the depth of the peat layer, diagrams of the microrelief of the bog, etc.; see Il'in, 1953).

As all the above types of geo-botanical mapping of bogs have their own peculiarities, it is necessary to discuss each of them separately.

2. GEO-BOTANICAL SURVEYS
FOR INVESTIGATION OF PEAT DEPOSITS

Investigation of peat deposits is carried out for valuation of the quantity and quality of peat resources in each of the deposits studied.

Investigation work on peat-bogs is divided into:

(a) exploratory-transect investigations,
(b) reconnaissance investigation,
(c) detailed investigation.

These three types of work are distinguished from each other by the degree of precision and completeness of the data obtained, which increases progressively from exploratory transect-investigation to detailed investigation.

All three types of work include geo-botanical mapping. In addition, however, research work includes a number of investigations relating to the determination of technological characteristics of peat, and also several other special tasks.

We discuss below only the methods and documentation of geo-botanical cartography work in all three types of peat-bog research. The description of other work may be found in special text-books on research (Tyuremnov, 1949).

(i) *Exploratory-transect Investigations*

Exploratory-transect investigations constitute the first stage in investigation of peat-bogs. They are carried out in districts where neither the location of bogs nor their features are known.

In exploratory-transect investigations it is necessary first to determine the location of the peat-bogs. The best way to do that is to examine mosaics (or contact prints) of the district under study, and thus the outlines of bog massifs can be transferred diagrammatically to the working topographical map of the district.

If the topographical map is old in comparison with the aerial photographs, considerable difference is usually noted between the shape of the bogs shown on the map and their outlines on the aerial photographs. In these cases one may show on the working topographical map, with a dotted line, outlines of the bogs corresponding with those on the aerial photographs.

After establishing the location of bog areas (and also preliminary analysis of them, when aerial photographs are available) one should organize the work so that each of the defined bogs will be visited in order to investigate it, and also so that some general traverses of the district of the work will be made.

The result of doing these tasks should be production of the following: (1) a general description of the district under study, with a list of observed peat-bogs and their characteristics (it is useful to attach to the description a diagrammatic map of the distribution of peat-bogs in the given district); (2) a diagrammatic plan of the peat-bogs, with an approximate calculation of their areas, average depths, and peat reserves in cubic metres and in tons (the results of all these calculations are stated in an explanation—a special table attached to the plan); (3) the profiles of the bogs (i.e. their vertical sections) with indications throughout of the botanical composition of the peat, its state of humification and its ash content; (4) a report on the analysis of peat samples for ash content and calorific quality.

To compile the diagrammatic plan a transect-visual survey and probes of the peat-bog are made. When the bog is elongated in shape one transect is laid out along its long axis and a second perpendicular to the first.

Every 600–1000 m along the transect (depending on the complexity of the relief and the plant cover of the bog) a description of the plant cover is made, accompanied by stratigraphic boring, i.e. boring into the peat with samples taken not more than 0.25 m apart. The description applies to sample areas. The optimum size of these is 10 by 10 m (Vlastova, 1933). The description contains notes on species-composition, average height, diameter and density of growth of the tree cover, the dominant species in the shrub, grass and moss cover with a statement of the percentage cover, and also the character of the microrelief and the amount of moisture in the bog (slight, moderate, abundant).

For each of the samples taken, the type of peat and the extent of its distribution are determined on the spot; each sample is labelled, wrapped up in waxed paper and sent to the laboratory for analysis. The number of the sample, the type of peat and the extent of its distribution are entered in the boring journal.

Every 200 m between the points of description the bog is sounded by boring, the bores being made down to the mineral soil at the bottom of the bog (which is recognized by the characteristic shock caused by the borer striking the soil and by the grating sound made by contact of the borer with the soil).

When boring, one sample is taken from one part of the bog, in such a way that the core taken by the borer includes some mineral soil (for this purpose the borer is sunk a little distance into the mineral floor of the bog). The thickness of the peat bed (from the surface to the bottom) is measured when the boring is made; if sapropel is observed its thickness is measured separately.

In the descriptions a few of the most common species are recorded for each sounding-point, with the percentage of their crown closure (for trees) or coverage (for other types of plants).

The keeping of the journal during the transect-visual survey may be assigned to one of the technical personnel doing the boring. In addition the areas between the points are described by the bog geo-botanist along a small number of selected, most typical transects.

For areas where the plant cover is very patchy and consists of small areas of different communities, a line transect estimation is made (see above).

The length of a linear estimation transect, according to Vlastova

(1933), should be not less than 30 m. Such a short transect, however, can be recommended only for extremely small complexes. Where there is a succession of larger areas transects should be laid out with a length of 250 m and even up to 500 m.

Besides all the above geo-botanical tasks, the geodesic technician attached to the transect-exploration party does levelling on the most typical main areas of the bog and lays out a survey line to the nearest watercourse, in the direction of which outflow from the bog is most probable.

The geo-botanist should also describe briefly the land adjoining the bog. For that purpose it is recommended that he should sketch by eye the relief of that land where it touches the bog, make on the sketch a profile of the sections occupied by separate communities, and state in the explanation (explanatory table) of the profile the names and dominant species of these communities, thus obtaining a diagrammatic ecological zonation of the margin of the bog and of the parts of the bog lying beside it (Vlastova, 1933).

After the completion of all the above tasks it is recommended that, before the party leaves the bog, a diagrammatic plan of it should be compiled in the field, using sketches made during the transect-visual survey.

The plan should show the boundaries of the bog, the largest streams and lakes, and also all transects, with descriptions of the sounding and boring points under their respective numbers.

After calculating the area of the bog and its average depth and peat reserves, constructing a profile of the peat deposit (see below) and obtaining analytical data, the transect-exploration investigation of the bog may be considered to be finished.

In the report on the transect-exploration research the following should be given: (1) a brief description of the natural conditions of the whole district under study, (2) a description of all bogs in that district, (3) an approximate valuation of each bog massif from the point of view of its economic utilization (for peat production, etc.).

After the conclusion of the transect-exploration work on the bogs designated as suitable for peat production, the so-called reconnaissance research on the bogs begins, and bogs designated as suitable for agricultural reclamation are subjected to special investigations to determine their economic value (see below).

Borings are made in each community noted during travel along the paths. The borings are located not only on the surface of the bog itself but also on dry ridges and islands scattered through the bog, as it is not always certain that there is no sapropelite there (Alabyshev, 1928).

In cases where the transect-exploration research has as its aim the discovery of sapropelite, the studies are conducted in almost the same way. A master transect is laid out along the long axis of the bog, and other transects perpendicular to it 100 –300 m apart (depending on the size of the bog).

Of very great importance in transect-exploration research (especially in its first stage, namely, finding out the distribution of bog massifs) are aerial methods, consisting both in analysis of aerial photographs and in aerovisual observations of bogs from an aeroplane.

In districts that are very little studied, very boggy, difficult of access and not covered by aerial photographic surveys, the chief form of use of aerial methods is in aerovisual surveys (see above), consisting in drawing the outlines of bog massifs by eye on millimetre-squared paper by an observer in an aeroplane (Dyukarev, 1948). This survey method is chiefly used only in very boggy districts with large bog massifs coalescing with each other. In these conditions, according to Dyukarev (1948) and Rumyantsev (1940), errors in the dimensions of the outlines drawn amount on an average to only 5 per cent as compared with aerial photographic surveys. If, on the other hand, that method is used to draw small discrete bog massifs, errors in the data obtained—as compared with aerial photographs—amount on an average to 50–70 per cent.

N. P. Dyukarev suggests a number of characters for identifying bogs* from the air. We present these characters in a somewhat condensed form in Table 11.

The practical effectiveness of aerovisual surveys in districts not provided with aerial photographs is very great (Olenin, 1948).

Many specialists consider it possible to distinguish Weber's chief types of mires (fen, transition, and raised bog) from aerial photographs, identifying them both by the definite tone of the photograph and by their specific appearance. In Table 12 we give some characters for identification used in such investigations.

---

* "Bog" is used throughout as a translation of "boloto", though the English word is rather more restricted in meaning, and many British and Scandinavian ecologists would prefer to use "mire" as a neutral term for wet peat vegetation. "Nizinnoe boloto" and "verkhovoe boloto" (corresponding to German "Niedermoor" and "Hochmoor") are translated as "fen" and "raised bog". (Editor's note)

TABLE 11. AEROVISUAL CHARACTERS OF SOME OF THE CHIEF TYPES OF BOGS

Type of bog	Appearance from the air
Fen	Smooth dark-green surface (the darker the colour, the wetter the mire). The colour depends on the colours of the sedge and the peat surface.
Transition bog (sedge-*Sphagnum*) without trees.	Patchwork picture of dark-green (wet peat), green (sedge) and yellow (dry sedge) patches, without sharp borders between them.
Transition bog with ridge-pool complex.	Green and light-yellow ridges alternating with dark-green or black pools (the latter with water).
Peat-group bogs.	Smooth surface, of dark-green colour, depending on the wetness of the peat surface and the sparse low herbage covering it.
Transition peat bogs with trees.	Patchwork picture of dark-green, green, and yellow patches of scattered trees (their crowns and shadows, and rarely their trunks, are visible).
Raised bog.	Narrow zigzag dark lines parallel to each other against a lighter brownish background formed by *Sphagnum*, or a grey background of lichens.
Raised bog with trees.	Trees visible against a typical raised-bog background.

TABLE 12. CHARACTERS FOR IDENTIFYING THE CHIEF TYPES OF BOGS

Type of bog	Investigator and characters proposed by him	
	N. P. Dokarev, 1934	G. G. Samoilovich, 1953
Fen	*Direct indicators* Dark tone, absence of outlines *Indirect indicators* Location of bog in river valley or near lake	Uniform tone, dark-grey; outlines elongated
Raised bog	*Direct indicators* Light-grey to dark-grey tone, light-grey predominating; the picture is nowhere uniform in tone, and sinuous parallel belts are visible; trees are seen like very small grains (separate individuals) or grainy patches (groups of trees) *Indirect indicator* Location on watershed	Wavy picture, light-coloured sinuous belts with dark intervals (ridges or pools); edges of bog irregular

Pronin (1935) believes it possible to distinguish on a photograph treeless bogs (uniform grey tone), bogs with woody vegetation (uniform granulation over the whole background) and bogs with scattered trees on ridges (grainy sinuous belts on a uniform grey back-ground).

The most detailed analysis of aerial photographs of bogs may be made using the characters proposed in the handbook "Valuator's Companion" (Tret'yakov, Gorskii, and Samoilovich, 1952). With some abridgments these indicators are given in Table 13.

TABLE 13. CHARACTERS FOR IDENTIFYING SOME MIRE COMPLEXES AND BOGS

Name of item	Identification characters
Small lake-pool complex	Dark-grey picture with sinuous belts, along which are scattered black circular or slit-like patches (pools)
Ridge-pool complex with pools not containing much water	Concentric-belt picture: dark belts correspond to ridges and light belts to pools
Ridge-pool complex with pools containing much water	Picture similar to above, but pools come out dark and ridges light-grey
Forested bogs	Crowns and shadows of trees show up against background of bog
Raised bogs	Presence of forested ring (with crowns and shadows showing up) is characteristic: on the peripheral slope of the bog, inside the ring, lies a ridge-pool complex
Sloping raised bogs	The greater part of the bog is occupied by a ridge-pool complex, reaching almost to the mineral margin of the bog

However, the possibility and expediency of identifying Weber's bog types by aerial methods have been criticized in recent years in the works of Galkina (1953, 1955). Her criticism is based on the fact that Weber's bog types are extremely comprehensive, as they include a large number of different kinds of bog massifs that developed from different causes and in different forms, grouped together only by the phase of development through which they are passing (fen, transition or raised bog phase).

In the analysis of bog massifs Galkina gives first place to the mode and conditions of formation of a bog (origin of the bog), and the reflection of its origin in the configuration and appearance of the bog. She suggests that the origin of a bog is expressed very strongly in its appearance, as, for example, a bog massif originating in a land-locked basin will have closed circular or oval outlines repeating to a great extent the configuration of the basin in which it was formed; a bog in a stream valley will have an elongated outline; bogs in basins with drainage outlets and on slopes, etc., have their own peculiar forms (Fig. 6). The appearance of the surface will also be different in bogs formed in different conditions: thus bogs in land-locked basins are characterized by a concentric-belt appearance, i.e. a succession of concentric belts enclosing each other like rings as different kinds of bog vegetation succeed each other from the periphery of the basin to its centre. Linear-belt structure is characteristic of bogs on lower mountain slopes, arising from the fact that the peat bed gradually creeps down the slope, forming folds lying along the slope. Other types of bogs originating in different ways also have a number of peculiar features.

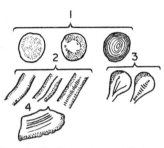

FIG. 6. Configuration of different types of bog (after Ye. A. Galkina): 1 — bog massifs in land-locked basins; 2 — bog massifs in stream valleys; 3 — bog massifs in basins with outlets; 4 — bog massifs on lower mountain slopes.

Bog massifs differing in their conditions of origin and therefore differing in their configuration and in their surface appearance are, in the terminology proposed by Galkina, "bog meso-landscapes", appearing as principal units in analysis of aerial photographs of bogs and in aerovisual observations. Meso-landscapes are easily distinguished in aerial photographs: (1) by their definite borders, (2) by their comparatively simple outlines (circular or oval, linear-belt, trapezoidal, etc.). These two characteristics of the aerial-photographic appearance of meso-landscapes are due to the fact that they are usually bounded on all sides by non-boggy territory (the boundaries of which with bogs are very definite) and have configurations repeating the outlines of the depressions in which the bogs were formed.

Galkina (1955) proposes a classification of the chief types of bog meso-landscape. For each type she presents fairly detailed characteristics both of the course of development of the bog and of the various features of its appearance in aerial photographs. In Table 14 we give a list of the types defined by her and some of the most easily observed characteristics that permit a given type to be identified in aerial photographs.

According to Galkina, we may observe different meso-landscapes both in eutrophic (rich in mineral nutrients) and in oligotrophic (correspondingly poorer) phases. Generally a nutrient-poor phase is recognized by the domed configuration of the bog surface (when aerial photographs are examined stereoscopically). In bog types 2, 3, 5 and 7, however, even in conditions of the poorest mineral nutrition the surface does not acquire a domed form, and the evolution of surface configuration for types 8, 9 and 10 has not been studied.

In addition to Galkina's classification there are also peculiar bog meso-landscapes caused by human activity and developing in various pits, excavations and workings: they are easily identified by their straight borders and rectangular shapes.

TABLE 14. TYPES OF BOG MESO-LANDSCAPE (AFTER YE. A. GALKINA)

Type of meso-landscape	Some features of its appearance in aerial photographs
1. Bog meso-landscapes developed in land-locked basins	Circular or oval form, closed outline and very slightly broken margin.
2. Bog meso-landscapes in valleys	Ribbon-like form. Much-broken margin, because of valleys debouching into one another.
3. Bog meso-landscapes in basins with drainage outlets	Fan-like form, narrowing towards the outlet.
4. Bog meso-landscapes in stream valleys	External shape of the bog circular or oval, but outline not closed.
5. Bog meso-landscapes on lower slopes of mountains	Characterized by the fact that the bog adjoins the original banks of rivers or lakes or the slopes of terraces, and by streaking with lines parallel to the foot of the slope, due to folds forming as the bog creeps down.
6. Bog meso-landscapes in river reaches	Elongated shape. Characterized by location near rivers from which the bog is separated by a narrow ridge.
7. Bog meso-landscapes on sloping banks of small lakes or silted-up bays	Ring-shaped or bean-shaped. Characteristically widespread in districts rich in lakes.
8. Delta bog meso-landscapes	Develops in streams and creeks without outlet that dissipate themselves by overflowing. Funnel-shaped, gradually widening from the stream mouth to the part of the overflow most distant from it.
9. Flood-plain bog meso-landscape	Characteristic of flood-plains of rivers in their lower reaches. Sickle-shaped.*
10. Bog meso-landscape developing through the swamping of dry stream-beds	External features very undefined (identification of this type is most difficult)

* This type has been little studied.

In localities of intensive human economic activity such bogs are not uncommon.

If several bog massifs coalesce in the process of growth, there develops (in Galkina's terminology) a "bog macro-landscape" or bog system.

On aerial photographs bog macro-landscapes are identified: (1) by their usually very considerable size, (2) by their complex configuration, due to the coalescence of a number of meso-landscapes, and (3) by their more-or-less-noticeable division into meso-landscapes (which usually do not coalesce to such a degree that their boundaries are entirely obliterated).

Finally, within meso-landscapes one may observe areas, usually with fairly indefinite boundaries, but differentiated by the appearance of their surface. One surface-appearance gradually merges into that adjoining it. Galkina calls these areas micro-landscapes. They correspond to different parts of a single meso-landscape, differing from each other in the character and composition of the plant cover and the degree of waterlogging of the soil. It may be said with some confidence that micro-landscapes correspond to complexes of two or three communities and sometimes to a single plant community.

Galkina proposes the following steps in research work on bogs with aerial photographs:

(1) Examining the aerial photographs, with classification of some bogs as meso-landscapes and some as macro-landscapes (by their size, form, regularity of appearance).

(2) Combining different concrete meso-landscapes (i.e. separate bogs) into genetically-uniform groups, shown, for example, in Table 14.

(3) Distinguishing subgroups within these groups by nutritional phases (poor, medium and rich).

(4) Careful analysis of the appearance of bogs in each subgroup, not only the larger and more common (first-rank appearance) but also the smaller and less common (second-rank), with explanation of the characters whereby each subgroup is identified. This is the most difficult stage of the work, calling for high qualifications in the person doing it.

(5) Selective checking of the correctness of the analysis by ground studies of parts of the bog, so-called "key areas" or "keys".

Naturally if it is a question of compiling a map or plan of a bog, the outlines obtained as the result of analysis of aerial photographs, after verification by ground studies on "keys", should be transferred to a topographical plan.

With all the undoubted prospects for the use of aerial methods for the early stages of bog investigations, it must be remarked that the whole system of bog investigations proposed by Galkina is quite complex and requires high qualifications in the investigator.

We would recommend to beginners in investigation, who do not have much experience in analysis, the use of aerial photographs in the following cases:

(1) to determine the locations of bogs;

(2) to determine the probable manner of formation of a bog (for that the above genetic classification by Galkina is very convenient);

(3) for field analysis carried out similarly to that discussed in the description of transect-visual surveys with use of aerial photographs (see above).

(ii) *Reconnaissance Investigation*

Reconnaissance investigation is the second stage of research on peat-bogs and is undertaken only after the exploratory transect work described in the preceding section has been done.

Reconnaissance investigation should give precision to the data of exploratory transect investigation.

As the result of reconnaissance investigation a plan of a peat bog should be drawn up, made on a background obtained as the result of a geodesic survey of the bog. Therefore geodesic work precedes the drawing-up of the plan.

As the result of the geodesic work a geodesic plan of the peat bog should be compiled, and on it should be entered the directions of the lines along which the geo-botanist will make a reconnaissance of the bog.

Therefore the larger the number of lines laid out in the bog, the fuller and more precise will be its geo-botanical description. Tyurem-nov (1949) presents data whereby one may be guided in determining the number of transects required for reconnaissance investigation on bogs according to the area of the latter (Table 15).

One transect, laid out along the longest axis of the bog and passing through its centre, is called the master transect. The other transects are laid out to cut across the master transect.

On bogs with trees, rides are cut out along the transects; on bogs without trees the transects are identified by markers.

TABLE 15. DETERMINING THE NUMBER OF TRANSECTS FOR RECONNAISSANCE
INVESTIGATION ACCORDING TO THE SIZE OF THE BOG

Area of bog (hectares)	Number of transects
Up to 100	1 or 2
100 – 1000	2 – 4
1000 – 10,000	4 – 6
Over 10,000	transects laid out every 2 km

Reconnaissance investigation differs comparatively little in the principle of its organization from exploratory transect investigation, being essentially a transect-visual survey. The most substantial differences are: (1) the carrying-out of preliminary geodesic work; (2) the much greater density of points of description, boring and sounding.

The density of points of description of the plant cover accompanied by boring may be determined from the following data (Table 16, from Tyuremnov, 1949):

TABLE 16. NUMBER OF BORING POINTS FOR RECONNAISSANCE INVESTIGATION
ON PEAT-BOGS OF DIFFERENT SIZES

Area of bog (hectares)	Number of boring points
Up to 25	2
25 – 100	2 – 4
100 – 1000	4 – 10
1000 – 10,000	10 – 20

Sounding points also should be distributed at a fixed density, which is determined from Table 17 (from S. M. Tyuremnov).

TABLE 17. DENSITY OF POINTS FOR SOUNDING PEAT BEDS IN RECONNAISSANCE
INVESTIGATION ON BOGS OF DIFFERENT SIZES

Area of bog (hectares)	Distance between sounding points (metres)
Up to 25	50
25 – 1000	100
1000 – 10,000	100 – 200 (depending on complexity of bog structure)
Over 10,000	200

At boring points peat samples are selected in the same way as described above. The type of peat is determined at each boring point (fen, transition, mixed, raised bog).

As a result of reconnaissance investigation a plan of the peat deposit is compiled by entering on a geodesic plan the limits of distribution of different types of peat beds. These limits are determined by outlining the areas on which the boring points are located and which are covered by beds of the same type. The limits of distribution of different types, as established by ground data alone, are very provisional. They may be made much more accurate if aerial photographs are available. In such cases one should enter on the aerial photographs (which may be mosaics or contact prints) all boring and sounding points, and see which of them are located in areas with a certain definite surface appearance. In such investigations, carried out carefully enough, one often observes a connection between a certain type of peat bed and a certain appearance of the bog surface. Then the outlines of the area occupied by surfaces of that appearance may be looked upon as outlines of that particular type of peat bed.

(iii) *Detailed Investigation*

As a result of reconnaissance investigation, the peat-bogs that are to be exploited are designated. Detailed investigation is carried out on these bogs in order to establish a technical project for utilizing a given peat-bog.

On the basis of detailed investigation data there are compiled:

(a) a plan of the vegetation of the peat-bog on a topographical background (map) obtained by survey of the bog;

(b) a stratigraphical plan of the bog;

(c) a series of stratigraphical profiles;

(d) a description of the bog;

(e) a technological plan of the bog;

(f) a series of reports with results of analyses of the selected peat samples to determine their different characteristics (moisture, specific gravity, ash content, calorific value, botanical composition, degree of humification, solidity, water-absorbency, tendency to crumble, etc.).

We discuss below the tasks listed under (a) and (b), as they alone are the result of geo-botanical cartography in the strict sense of the word (these tasks are combined by S. M. Tyuremnov in his work "Peat Deposits and their Investigation" under the name of geo-botanical and stratigraphical field work, separating them from strictly technological tasks).

Detailed investigation, like the types of investigation described above, is carried out by means of transect-visual survey of a peat-bog. The transects should be laid out on a background compiled as a result of topographical work. A topographical plan for massifs up to 5000 hectares in area is drawn on a scale of 1:10,000, and for larger ones on a scale of 1:25,000. On it should be shown, besides the network of transects, the general situation, contour lines (at 0.5 m intervals), and the boundaries of worthless and economically valuable beds.

With a peat-bog less than 1000 hectares in area, transects are laid out 200—400 m apart. With areas larger than 1000 hectares the distance between transects fluctuates around 400 m.

On the transects the plant cover on typical plots selected for that purpose is described, and stratigraphical borings are made there. The number of such points on a path 1 km long should be not less than four, and if the length exceeds 2 km not less than seven. The distance between the points varies from 200—500 m.

The description of the plant cover is made on sample plots: the tree layer is described on plots of 10 by 10 m, and the shrub-herbage and moss cover on areas of 2 by 2 m. In the tree layer, an estimate is made of the composition of the standing timber (on a 10-point scale) and of the average height and average diameter for each species (visually). A list of species in the herbage-shrub and moss cover is made, with an estimate of the percentage coverage for each species.

On forested bogs a valuation of the tree layer is made for the whole area of the bog.

Borings are made at points of geo-botanical description. Samples of peat are selected, not at all boring points, but over a less dense network: namely, on raised bogs at every fifth point and on fens at every fourth point. At the other points samples for analysis are not taken, but determinations are made of the kind of peat and the degree of humification and moisture content (the latter is determined approximately by the ease with which water is squeezed out: if there is free water the moisture content is considered high; if water comes out with light squeezing, medium; and if water comes out only after very strong squeezing, low).

In field conditions, days are assigned for preliminary office analysis of the material. In the process of that work a plan of the vegetation of the bog is compiled (Fig. 7). It is compiled by joining the points of description located in similar plant communities. The best result is obtained by entering all points of description on aerial photo-

No. of par-cel	Conven-tional symbol	Name of complex of associations	No. of par-cels	Total area (hec-tare)	Percent-age of total area of peat beds	Microrelief
I		Sphagnum fuscum	14	596	8.5	Tussocky
II		Ridge-pool	13	678.4	9.1	30% pools 70% ridges
III		,,	9	2935.2	41.9	50% pools 50% ridges
IV		Ridge-lake	4	179.6	2.6	70% pools/lakelets 30% tussocks
V		,,	3	300.4	4.3	25% lakelets (open water surface)
VI		Medium	6	296.9	4.1	10% inter-tussock 90% tussocks
VII		,,	11	579.4	8.3	50% inter-tussock 50% tussocks
VIII		Transition-forest	2	324.0	4.6	
IX		Transition-forest	14	1140	16.2	
X		Sphagnum-sedge	1	27.6	0.4	

FIG. 7. Plan of vegetation in a peat bog (after S. M. Tyuremnov).

graphs and drawing boundaries between communities according to the boundaries between areas of different appearance on the aerial photographs. Here, in addition to data obtained by direct observations on the bog, one may use the characters for identification of some bog communities listed above in Tables 12 and 13.

A special table (explanatory legend) in the following form is attached to the vegetation plan (Table 18).

TABLE 18. FORM OF EXPLANATORY LEGEND OF THE VEGETATION PLAN IN DETAILED INVESTIGATION ON A PEAT-BOG

Name of community	Number of habitats	Total area (hectares)	Percentage ratio to area of bog	Micro-relief

Since the plant communities in the bog are fairly fully shown on the vegetation plan, and their number is comparatively large, it is necessary to have a definite system of designating them on the plan. These designations should be readable, and at the same time should express to some extent the degree to which the plant communities approach each other in their composition.

In the instructions of the All-Union Peat Institute (Grebenshchikova, 1933) one such system of designation is offered. In it a combination of a particular tree species with a certain species of peatforming moss is designated by a colour, and the dominant species of the second (herb-shrub) story are designated by the initial letters (Latin and Russian) of the specific or generic names of the plants. Thus, for example, an association of *Pinus silvestris* and *f. sphagnicola* with *Sphagnum fuscum* is designated by a brownish colour; its association with *S. recurvum* by greenish-yellow, with *S. subbicolor* by orange, and with *S. medium* by red. Burnt areas are shown in grey, and areas not bog-covered in bright green. The letter-designations of the chief bog plants are given below:

Ledum palustre — L;
Cassandra calyculata — Cs;
Andromeda polifolia — A;
Calluna vulgaris — Cl;
Empetrum nigrum — Et;
Rubus chamaemorus — R;
Eriophorum vaginatum — PP;
Vaccinium oxycoccus — Ox;
V. uliginosum — U.

During the period of preliminary field office work the type of structure of the deposit is determined for each boring site. The most important indicator for determining the type of structure is predominance in the deposit of a particular kind of peat. For the classification of the types of deposit-structure one may use the list of different classificatory units of peat-deposit structure, compiled by the Peat Institute.

By joining up the points with the same kind of structure one obtains a preliminary stratigraphical plan of the deposit.

After completing the field investigations, during the period of office work, the plan is perfected after constructing profiles of the beds. A profile of a bed is a vertical section of the bed along the line of a certain transect cutting across the bog surface. Profiles are made for all transects. To make a profile on a sheet of millimetre-squared paper, data are entered on two intersecting axes: on the horizontal axis, the boring points (on the scale of the topographical plan); and on the vertical axis, marks denoting the surface and the floor of the bog and the stratigraphical cross-section of the peat bed from surface to floor at the given boring point, on a definite selected scale. After these data are entered the space between separate cross-sections is filled in by interpolation, and thus a probable cross-section of the whole bed along a given transect is constructed.

When profiles are constructed for all transects, by examination of them one may perfect the preliminary stratigraphical plan.

3. GEO-BOTANICAL SURVEY OF BOGS IN CONNECTION WITH THEIR AGRICULTURAL RECLAMATION

The compilation of geo-botanical maps of bog massifs for the purposes of their agricultural reclamation has a number of specific features in which it differs from the work described in the preceding section. As is seen from the above description of geo-botanical surveys for investigation of peat-bogs, the greatest attention is given not so much to geo-botanical surveying as to boring and sounding the peat beds. In a survey made for the purposes of agricultural reclamation of bogs, considerably more attention is given to study of the plant cover. The plant cover stands out as one of the most important indicators of the suitability of the surface soil layers of the bog for various agricultural measures. Attempts at agricultural reclamation of bogs without preliminary compilation of geo-botanical maps are usually unsuccessful (Galkina, 1936).

In addition, the plant cover of a bog is itself the object of agricultural utilization (pastures, hay meadows). All these considerations oblige one to give close attention to study of it.

To solve problems in the agricultural reclamation of a bog one must have: (1) a plan of the arable-surface layer, (2) a plan of the peat layer (which is also called the agro-peat-master plan or the agro-technical plan), (3) a plan of the mineral floor of the bog. If the bog is of very small size, one may limit oneself to compilation of the agro-peat-master plan alone (if the area of the bog is less than 50 hectares).

These plans are compiled on the basis of the topographical plan, which in the main should fulfil the same requirements as the plan compiled for detailed investigation on a peat-bog (see preceding section). As a minimum the topographical plan should show the outline of the peat-bog, its drainage system (streams and lakes), the results of a levelling-survey of the bog, and location of the proposed transects (sightings).

To compile the three above-mentioned plans the bog geo-botanist makes a transect-visual survey of the bog, writing down a geo-botanical description and sounding the peat bed on all transects, and selectively taking samples from the arable horizon on some transects (i.e. samples at a depth of 0.25 m from the surface).

The density of the transect grid depends on the area of the bog and may be determined from the following table (Table 19).

TABLE 19. DENSITY OF TRANSECT GRID ON BOGS FOR AGRICULTURAL INVESTIGATION

Area of bog (hectares)	Distance between transects (metres)
Less than 1	20
1 — 5	40
5 — 10	40
10 — 100	100
Over 100	200

When travelling along a transect the geo-botanist briefly describes each defined area. In that description he gives only the principal typical species that show whether the area actually is raised bog, fen or other. These typical species are, as it were, indicators of the mire type.

7

At the same time that he is making descriptions along the transect, the geo-botanist makes soundings of the peat layer with the aid of workmen. The density of sounding points is determined by the following table (Table 20).

TABLE 20. DENSITY OF PEAT-SOUNDINGS ON BOGS FOR AGRICULTURAL INVESTIGATION

Area of bog (hectares)	Distance between sounding-points (metres)
Up to 5	20
5 10	40
10 — 25	60
Over 25	100

On some of the transects samples are taken from the arable horizon at a depth of 0.25 m. The number of transects on which this work is done may be determined from the following table (Table 21).

TABLE 21. NUMBER OF TRANSECTS WITH SAMPLING OF THE ARABLE HORIZON
IN RELATION TO AREA OF BOGS

Area of bog (hectares)	No. of transects with sampling of arable horizon
10 — 50	3
50 — 100	5
Over 100	5, + 1 for each 100 hectares

On bogs less than 10 hectares in area, the arable horizon is usually not investigated.

Work on the above programme should be done on all bogs, without exception, that are designated for agricultural reclamation.

Peat-bogs over 50 hectares in area are given still further geo-botanical investigation, aimed at determining the economic value of separate groups of communities occupying different parts of the bog. Thus in forested parts of the bog the trees are specially investigated; in fen areas, suitable for grazings or hay-meadows, the herbage cover is specially investigated; and finally, in parts designated for production of moss litter, the moss cover is investigated.

Special investigation of the trees is done on areas of 25 by 100 m, not fewer than two of them being selected for each of the described communities (if a given community is represented in a great number of areas in the bog, the number of sample areas must be increased).

On the selected areas the following work is done:

(a) Count of number of trees of each species;

(b) Visual estimate of average height and average diameter, and estimate of quality class.

Special description of the herbage is done on plots of 0.5 by 1.0 m, two plots being taken for each of the described communities. Samples are taken from these plots and are analysed in the same way as is done in pasture investigation.

Special description of the moss cover is accompanied by detailed description and numerical census of the elements of microrelief of the bog—the tussocks. The description and count of tussocks is aimed at both discovering the reserves of moss litter and determining the tussockiness of the bog, which corresponds to a definite degree of difficulty in doing improvement work on it.

For the special description of the moss cover, in each part of the bog characterized by uniform tussockiness four test plots, size 5 by 5 m, are marked out. In each plot the following work is done:

(a) count of tussocks;

(b) measurement of their height, breadth and length;

(c) taking of blocks from the tussocks and the inter-tussock areas, size 20 by 20 cm; in the tussocks the blocks are taken through the depth of the tussock, and in the inter-tussock areas through the depth of the moss bed.

From the data obtained one calculates:

(a) the number of tussocks per hectare (multiplying the total number of tussocks on all four plots by 100; 8 per cent is deducted from the resulting product to correct errors in the method);

(b) the average surface area of a tussock (multiplying length by breadth);

(c) the area of tussocks per hectare (multiplying the average area of a tussock by the number of tussocks per hectare).

By special calculations one estimates the practical output of air-dried moss litter (see Neishtadt, 1937).

An important element in the agricultural valuation of bogs is the estimate of "stumpiness", i.e. of the presence of stumps and other remains of buried trees in the peat. To estimate stumpiness in all the most widespread communities in a bog (it is desirable to do so in each area defined on the plan) sample plots size 20 by 20 m are marked out. The stumpiness estimate may be made in two ways. If an exact count is necessary, Lepchenko's (1933) method of estimating

7*

stumpiness is used. For it, a very large number (over 6000) of soundings are made on the plot to a depth of 1 m with a metal rod. The
sounding points are laid out in straight lines, the distance between
points in one line and between lines being not less than 25 cm.

For observations more of a reconnaissance character it is sufficient
to make soundings only along the four sides of the test plots and
along their two diagonals. In that case the number of soundings is
reduced to approximately 500 (Anufriyev, Bogdanovskaya-Giyenèf,
Galkina and Tsinzerling, 1938).

The principal document giving the results of geo-botanical mapping
of a bog for the purposes of agricultural reclamation is the agro-peat-
master plan, as the arable-layer plan and the plan of the mineral floor
of the bog do not contain geo-botanical data.

On the agro-peat-master plan (in which, as stated above, are shown
the outlines of the peat deposits and their drainage system) one enters the transects and the outlines of parcels of the peat deposits by
their types (raised bog, transition, fen). The boundaries of parcels
between the transects are produced by interpolation, and therefore
have a somewhat provisional character. They can be made considerably more precise by use of aerial photographs.

In addition, on the agro-peat-master plan are shown a number of
economic features of the bog, namely: the boundary where the peat
ends, the boundaries of areas where the peat is not less than 0.25 m
deep, the boundaries of areas with different degrees of stumpiness,
the boundaries of areas suitable for litter production or grazing, etc.

4. GEO-BOTANICAL SURVEYS
OF BOGS FOR HYDROLOGICAL,
ROAD AND SANITARY INVESTIGATION

Bogs form one of the objects of hydrological investigations although they cannot be included either in land or in water areas,
occupying to a certain extent an intermediate position. The role of
bogs in the water economy, however, is very great, as a large number
of lakes, from which many rivers flow, lie in them. Therefore in the
method of hydrographical investigation of waters on land, attention
is given to bogs (Il'in, 1953).

In hydrological investigation of a bog, a working map is compiled
(usually on a topographical background on a scale of 1:100,000 or

1:200,000) in which, besides a number of hydrological data, are shown several elements characterizing the plant cover. Entry of those items is very important, as the plant cover of a bog is closely linked with its various peculiarities and especially with the distribution of water in it. Therefore vegetation is a sensitive indicator of the hydrological peculiarities of a bog.

To compile a working map the hydrological investigator makes a circuit of the boundaries of the bog by the surrounding dry ground and crosses the bog by several marked transects. The density of the transects should be such that there is one linear km of transect for every square km of bog surface. Transects should run both through the centre of the bog and through its swampiest parts. It is recommended that aerial photographs should be used in laying out the transect grid.

During his travel along the transects the hydrologist writes down brief data on the vegetation as well as all possible hydrological data. For the trees he estimates the closeness of the canopy, and for other layers the percentage of coverage by each layer. The condition of the vegetation is noted, and also the presence of dead wood among the trees (as a percentage of the living trees).

Not fewer than two soundings of the peat bed are made on each km of the transect. Peat samples are taken at depths of 0.5, 1, and 2 m and from the bottom layer of the peat. For each peat sample the species, colour, moisture content (by hand-squeezing) and the presence and kind of plant and mineral inclusions are recorded.

The outlines of different types of bog vegetation are entered on the working map. On it also are entered the sounding points with their serial numbers.

Bogs, being areas difficult to traverse, require special exploration when roads are being built through them. On such explorations considerable attention is given to the entering on the compiled plan of various data on the plant cover, since the latter is looked upon as an indicator of the hydrological features of the bog.

These investigations consist of two stages: (1) geo-morphological and hydrological examination of the bog to obtain general knowledge of it; (2) reconnaissance investigations, made to select a place to build a road through the bog.

In the second stage of the work a plan of the bog is compiled, giving the depth in different parts of it; if the bog covers not more than one square km the plan covers the whole of it, but if it is larger the plan covers an area of from one to 3 km² in the district of the proposed road through the bog. If the road cannot be marked out earlier, several different areas are selected, representing different possibilities for the road site.

The plan is compiled on the basis of an instrumental survey of the bog (the survey is made either by traverses or by circuit).

To determine the depth of the bog, that part of its surface shown on the topographical plan is divided up into large groups, very uncertainly known, of plant communities. The greatest attention is given to those plants that may serve as indicators of the water regime of the bog. In "Instructions for Investigating Bogs in Seeking Routes for Roads" (1939) the indicators of flooded bogs, having depths not over 3 m, are given as large-stemmed sedges, reeds, bogbean *(Menyanthes trifoliata)*, water arum *(Calla palustris)*, bog iris *(Iris pseudacorus)*, green mosses and partly sphagnum, and characteristic absence of trees. For bogs filling up the whole of a lake basin, *Sphagnum* cover with *Pinus silvestris f. sphagnicola* is characteristic. *Alnus glutinosa* is looked upon as an indicator of fairly lively movement of underground water in fens and transition mires. For raised bogs an indicator of that phenomenon is good development of pine timber; suppression of pines is considered an indicator of stagnant conditions.

In each of the large plant community groups from two to four borings are made (but not more than 100—250 m apart). The holes are sunk to the floor of the bog. Peat samples are taken from the holes at every 0.5 to 1 m of depth. From the peat samples estimates are made, visually on the spot, of the kind of peat, degree of humification and moisture content (by squeezing). All data from the boreholes are entered in the boring journal.

In a special field journal for reconnaissance work, among other sections, columns are provided for "Type of bog and predominating vegetation" and "Average density of trees". Brief data are entered in these columns about the plant cover in each of the investigated areas of the bog. Each area occupied by a large plant group is entered on the plan, and the location of that group on the future road site is stated in the field journal (the serial number of the road and the numbers of the marker stakes nearest to the group). On the area as entered in the plan, the various depths of the peat beds therein are stated.

Sometimes bogs become the object of sanitary investigations in connection with the necessity for partial use of bog water for human consumption. Such cases are very rare, and special instructions for them have not been worked out. The limited personal experience of the author, however, in such work (Viktorov, 1948) permits him to recommend the following measures:

(1) A grid of foot transects is laid out on the map or on aerial photographs so as to visit all water areas and water sources in the bog (lakes, springs, drainage channels, rivers) and also to cross the bog at least along its two greatest diameters.

(2) During the transects the observer enters visually on the map the boundaries of areas of raised bog, fen and transition types of bog traversed by him and the location of water areas. In the absence of a topographical map a circuit of the bog is first made around its edges, its outlines are noted visually on millimetre-squared paper, and during the transects through the bog the sketched area is visually filled in with the outlines of various types of bog and also the outlines of water areas.

(3) The defined areas of various types of bog are numbered. A brief general description of each area is made, with a statement of several of the most widespread species of trees, shrubs, herbage and mosses. The descriptions are made under the same numbers as the areas.

(4) Water samples are taken from all water areas visited (not less than 0.5 litre). From each area with abundant pools a water sample is taken from one pool. The samples are analysed in the laboratory.

After the results of the analyses are obtained, the waters from bogs of each type are evaluated for suitability for human consumption (for that the results of not only chemical but also bacteriological analysis are required). Later, on the diagrammatic plan compiled during the survey all types of bog whose waters were found unfit for human consumption are coloured with one general colour, and types of bog whose waters were found fit for human consumption with another colour.

The plan so compiled gives a sanitary evaluation of the quality of bog waters.

CHAPTER V

GEO-BOTANICAL SURVEYS
FOR STUDY OF PASTURES

1. GENERAL INFORMATION ON PASTURE MAPS

THE compilation of maps of pastures and hay-meadows is one of the most important prerequisites for rational organization of animal husbandry in the U.S.S.R. Without use of pasture maps it is in many districts impossible to organize proper pasture rotation and to calculate the fodder resources in pastures and hay-meadows. Especially important are maps of pastures in tundra districts and in desert or semi-desert districts, where livestock remains on pasture all year round or for a large part of the year.

Geo-botanical special maps, compiled for the needs of the pasturing industry, are usually called maps of pasture types. Maps of pasture types are not purely geo-botanical maps. On these maps plant communities, similar in their value as fodder resources, in the season and in the nature of their use as pastures, are combined into definite economic units—types of pasture. Maps of pasture types express, besides their geo-botanical content, a number of other elements not related to plant cover.

Thus, for example, there may be shown on the map seasonal fodder resources in each type of pasture (better—in each definite community habitat), and pastures recommended for different species of livestock are indicated separately. In addition, there may be shown on it existing and proposed livestock farms, wells (especially in arid regions), veterinary stations, pens (enclosures) and places with possible natural shelter for livestock. In cases where the map covers a very large territory livestock-driving routes should be shown (the latter are especially important in desert districts, where selection of unsuitable driving routes, inadequately provided with wells and fodder, may lead to catastrophic results).

Unfortunately it must be remarked that in many cases geobotanists have up to the present limited themselves to showing on the map only pasture types, ignoring all the necessary economic elements of the map mentioned above.

Maps of pasture types are in their turn material for compiling other graphic documents having a predominantly economic character—pasture-rotation charts, i.e. charts showing the succession of grazing in pastures either during the year or over a longer multi-annual cycle.

The first of these pasture-rotation cycles is called a minor cycle, the second a major cycle (usually by "pasture rotation" one means only a major cycle). Pasture-rotation charts, being of great importance with regard to proper use of pastures, are compiled not so much by a geo-botanist as by a zoo-technician (and, in deserts, with participation by a hydro-technician). But the geo-botanist must also take part in compiling these charts, since a map of pasture types is a most important starting-point for devising pasture rotations.

Transect and aero-geo-botanical surveys are used in compiling maps of pasture types. To compile large-scale maps of "key" areas on pastures, grid and continuous-outline surveys are used.

Maps of pasture types are made for various geographical zones. The characteristics of the zones and the special features of the branch of animal husbandry for which the map is compiled (reindeer-herding, sheep-breeding, etc.) impose a particular form on the method of compiling maps of pasture types in different conditions. There are, however, certain general features in the methods of compiling any maps of pasture types.

These features are as follows:

(a) To compile a map of pasture types, an estimate of the fodder resources in each type of pasture must be made by the sampling method. It may be made either in great part by determining the areas occupied by various types (if the survey is made by ground methods) or merely on a comparatively few "key" areas (if it is made by aero-geo-botanical survey). In the latter case data obtained on "keys" for a specific type of pasture are extrapolated visually by the surveyor on areas belonging to the same type and observed by him from the air.

(b) To compile a map of pasture types it is desirable that each type should be characterized not by a single figure for fodder resources but by a number of figures. For that purpose one must collect samples characterizing a given type not at one point but on various areas belonging to that type.

(c) It is necessary to have data on the dynamics of fodder resources, i.e. on seasonal fluctuations in these resources. Usually it is impossible to collect such data in the conditions of a geo-botanical survey of pastures, as that would necessarily call for numerous visits to a number of areas, which in practice is unrealizable. Therefore one must limit oneself to a single census of fodder resources, and estimate resources at other seasons from tables that have been compiled for the majority of pasture types and the principal fodder plants (see, for example, Nechayev, Mordvinov and Mosolov, 1943).

(d) By analysis of data for the nearest meteorological stations one must discover whether the given year (in which the survey is made) is typical in amount of precipitation and temperature. These data must be supplemented by questioning local livestock breeders. If the year is not typical in the amount of fodder supplies as determined by mapping the pastures, corrections must be made, using the correction coefficients established for such cases (see Larin, 1932, 1952).

(e) It is necessary that each of the pasture areas should be classified with regard to the presence in it of harmful and poisonous plants and also of causative agents of any infectious animal diseases: therefore the geo-botanical investigation of pastures should be combined with zoo-technical and veterinary investigations (for which it is necessary to add the appropriate specialists to the staff of the survey party).

(f) In determining pasture types it is necessary to approach the problem of identifying them from as many directions as possible, taking into account not only plant cover and fodder supplies but also the soil and the relief of the pasture, evaluating the possibility of improving the quality of the pasture by an appropriate series of ameliorative measures, at the same time guarding against the danger of injuring the pasture by excessive and improper exploitation of it.

2. FEATURES OF SURVEYS IN SEMI-DESERTS AND DESERTS

The most important elements in the work of the geo-botanist-surveyor in compiling maps of pasture types in semi-deserts and deserts are the following: (1) compiling a geo-botanical map, later converted into a pasture map, (2) collecting data regarding fodder supplies, (3) collecting, by questioning, botanical, meteorological and zoo-technical data, (4) interpreting all the collected material for the purpose of devising a pasture-rotation chart.

We discuss each of these elements briefly below.

(i) Compiling a Geo-botanical Map

The optimum scale of maps of pasture types for one of the most important kinds of animal husbandry in the deserts of Central Asia —sheep-breeding—is considered to be 1:100,000 (Amelin, 1943). That map scale is used also for other kinds of animal husbandry in arid regions.

The compilation of a map of pasture types in semi-deserts and deserts in usually done either by transect-visual surveys or by transect surveys with use of aerial photographs, both kinds of surveys being made by automobile and supplemented by transects on foot. Aero-geo-botanical surveys are used to a smaller extent.

Use of automobiles for surveying considerably raises the productivity of work and makes possible precise measurement of distances covered on transects (in view of the use of very precise speedometer readings).

The organization of surveys by automobile has been briefly described above (see the chapter on "Geo-botanical Surveys"). A detailed description of that work may be found in Tsatsenkin (1949), who was the pioneer of that kind of survey. It is necessary, however, to remark that calculations by speedometer, although they enable one to establish with great precision the boundaries of different complexes or large non-complex areas, do not provide a trustworthy picture of the relations of communities within a complex. To determine these relations one must lay out foot transects, accompanied by linear valuation.

The density of survey transects in work in semi-deserts should be considerable. Tsatsenkin (1952) considers that on a scale of 1:100,000 a sufficient distance between transects is not less than 2 km. Such a density of transects, however, is suggested by him for surveys made with use of aerial photographs.

Larin, Byeidyeman and Shiffers (1952) recommend that—for surveys made not only without aerial photographs but even without a sufficiently detailed topographical map on a scale corresponding to the survey—the following densities of transects should be used with various scales, in level-relief conditions (Table 22).

TABLE 22. DENSITY OF TRANSECTS FOR GEO-BOTANICAL SURVEYS ON PLAINS

Scale	Distance between transects (km)
1 : 100,000	1 — 5
1 : 50,000	0.5 — 1.5
1 : 20,000	0.25 — 1

Comparing the above transect density used by Tsatsenkin, on the one hand, and that used by the three investigators mentioned above, on the other hand, it is easy to note that the norms of density given in Table 22 are fairly low. In our opinion these norms are to be used only if the survey is made with use of aerial photographs. In the opposite case transects should be laid out at distances approximately half as large as those stated for the respective survey scales in Table 22.

In departmental instructions there are other norms, which fluctuate considerably from year to year in accordance with changing requirements for maps.

As a general statement it must be remarked that the density of transects obviously should not be the same in all territories surveyed. It should be increased in more chequered areas and may be considerably decreased in uniform areas. Invaluable help is given there by aerial photographs, which enable transects to be spaced rationally.

For sands and sandy plains, the relief of which is in places considerably dissected, Gayel', Dubyanskii, Petrov and Yakubov (1932) recommend the following density of transects when aerial photographs are lacking (Table 23).

TABLE 23. DENSITY OF TRANSECTS FOR GEO-BOTANICAL SURVEYS ON SANDS

Scale	Distance between transects (km)
1 : 25,000	0.5
1 : 100,000	3.0 — 4.5
1 : 200,000	5.0 — 8.0
1 : 400,000	10 — 15

The above numbers of transects are recommended not only for mapping of pastures but also generally for any geo-botanical surveys on sands.

Later Gayel' and Kolikov (1937) proposed another, slightly larger number of transects for investigations on sands (including sandy pastures). They are given in Table 24.

TABLE 24. DENSITY OF TRANSECTS FOR GEO-BOTANICAL SURVEYS OF PASTURES ON SANDS

Scale of survey	Distance between transects (metres)
1:10,000	75–200
1:25,000	200–750
1:50,000	750–2500
1:100,000	2500–5000
1:200,000	5000–7000
1:400,000	7000–10,000

The personal experience of the compiler of the present guide enables him to consider the norms given in Table 24 acceptable for mapping of sands. The norms given in Table 23 apparently are acceptable only when it is a question of compiling a sketch map from reconnaissance work.

Each community encountered on a transect should be described according to the usual requirements relating to geo-botanical description. Attention should be given especially to description of vegetation, and also of relief and soils, as these elements are of primary importance in devising pasture rotation in semi-deserts and deserts (especially in sandy areas). One must also carefully consider not only the abundance of fodder plants but also that of plants without food value by which one may determine the nature of the soil and hydrological and other conditions (plant indicators, see below).

Good results are obtained when a map of pasture types is compiled by a geo-botanist together with a soil officer or a geomorphologist. An experiment in such co-operative mapping was conducted by an expedition of the Geographical Institute of Moscow State University (Tsatsenkin, 1952). The work was done in such a way that in the process of field analysis of aerial photographs areas uniform with regard to their plant cover and also with regard to their soil and geomorphological conditions were defined; by transferring these areas to a topographical map of scale 1:100,000 one could obtain a geo-botanical map of very high accuracy.

Each of the defined areas should be characterized with regard to fodder resources (see below).

Transferring the outlines of communities to the map is done by the usual methods of geo-botanical transect surveys (see above). There is, however, great difficulty for the surveyor in the question of just what to enter on the map, as the plant cover of semi-deserts, and to a certain extent of deserts, is complex in nature, i.e. is composed of a succession of small patches of different communities frequently repeated. It is impossible to show all these very small patches on the map. In that case one must show on the map complexes, not separate communities. The scale of the map does not always permit the showing of the boundaries of separate complexes, and the need arises to combine complexes into units of higher order.

The method of such generalization of complexes on pastures on deserts and semi-deserts has so far not been well worked out. Dokhman (1936, 1954) made an experiment in combining different complexes. Dokhman (1954) named these combinations macro-complexes.* Dokhman proposed to combine is one macro-complex complexes distributed within one definite unit of relief (a river valley, a lake basin, a watershed, an outcrop ridge) and possessing a certain physiognomic similarity. Up to the present, such larger complex units of plant cover in semi-deserts have seldom been defined on pasture maps.

Complexes should be named from the dominant one or two communities. Thus, for example, one may speak of "complexes with dominance of *Artemisia incana* communities", of "complexes with dominant *Stipa—Artemisia incana* associations", etc.

It is therefore quite natural that in studying and mapping complex plant cover one of the most important elements of the work is determining the percentage ratios of communities forming a complex. That is done by means of line transect estimation (see above).

The optimum length of a transect for linear valuation on pastures in semi-desert conditions is held by Kunitsyn (1933) to be 250 m. With such a length, he proposes to have only one transect (if the community habitat is fairly small). With a shorter transect length it is desirable to lay out from 2 to 4 transects, making them perpendicular to each other or in the form of a star (see above). Evidently such small transect-lengths are acceptable only where very small patches of different communities alternate, their diameters being not more than 5 m (i.e. when the plant cover has a "micro-complex" struc-

---

* Earlier (1936) Dokhman had defined, besides macro-complexes, still smaller units—meso-complexes.

ture). When there is an alternation of larger habitats (which happens very often) such transect-lengths are insufficient.

Smirnov (1934), in investigating semi-desert complexes in which the average diameter of separate elements of a complex fluctuated from 12 to 18 m, used valuation transects whose average length was 400—600 m.

According to the observations of Zdanchuk and Artamonova (1937), for the most chequered semi-desert complexes the smallest transect-length that guarantees the obtaining of data close to the natural conditions of the area is 1500—2000 m. The best location of transects is distribution of them along the diagonals of the area selected for linear evaluation. That transect-length is also recommended for semi-deserts by other investigators (Prozorovskii, 1938; Pel't and Chirvinskii, 1956.)

Aerial methods for compiling maps of pasture types in deserts and semi-deserts are, so far, little used. For semi-deserts, the investigations of Kunitsyn (1934) and Tsatsenkin (1952) are well known. According to Kunitsyn's data for the lower Volga region, one can well discern on aerial photographs meadows *(Agropyrum, Calamagrostis epigeios,* etc.) by their dark colour, and rush and reed beds by their very dark (almost black) colour; sands in various stages of development and saline soils also are well distinguished; communities of grass and *Artemisia incana,* and of *Artemisia incana,* give a uniform grey tone, in which separate groups of associations are practically indistinguishable.

According to the observations of Tsatsenkin (1952), *Artemisia incana* and *Artemisia incana*-grass stands in semi-deserts are easily distinguished if they are located side by side in photographs taken in late spring or in a rainy period; in these cases the green colour retained by the grasses gives a dark tone to the aerial photographic picture of *Artemisia incana*-grass communities.

In spite, however, of the fact that grass and shrub vegetation in desert landscapes is much less distinguishable in aerial photographs than are forests or specific features of different bogs, examination of aerial photographs still gives very much valuable information. It enables one to identify depressions occupied by moisture-loving vegetation, to separate complex areas (revealing a clearly spotted picture, see Fig. 8) from more homogeneous areas, which show on a photograph a monotonous background with ill-defined patchiness (Fig. 9), to identify areas of saline soil (Fig. 10), beds of large shrubs and sand massifs—in other words, to break up the territory of the work into a number of separate parcels differing from one another in natural conditions. Separate plant communities are identified on aerial photographs with great difficulty.

Therefore the well-known investigator of Central Asian deserts, M. P. Petrov, allots decisive importance in the analysis of desert vegetation not to aerial photographic representation as such but to geomorphological indicators. In his opinion, in a desert the analysis should be done "not from the photographic representation of the plant cover as such, but on the basis of geomorphological analysis of the locality from aerial photographs and of the economic character-istics of geomorphological divisions by terrestrial methods" (Petrov, 1936, p. 20).

Thus in Petrov's opinion an outline of the work of a geo-botanist with use of aerial methods in desert pastures is as follows: first he studies in ground conditions the adaptations of different communities to various elements of the relief; then he makes a geomorphological analysis of aerial photographs and from the data obtained he pro-vides a geo-botanical description.

TABLE 25. IDENTIFYING FEATURES OF SEVERAL DESERT COMMUNITIES
BY CHARACTER OF RELIEF

Groups of plant communities	Identifying features
Communities of *Haloxylon persicum* and *Carex physodes*	Identified mainly by typical relief of sands with hill-ocks, with hillocks and hollows, and with ridges and hillocks. May be most clearly identified if surroun-ded by massifs of shifting or semi-shifting sands.
Small-shrub vegetation on Tertiary plateaux (mainly *Astragalus* communities)	Identified by the north-and-south elongated relief of the ridges, associated with Tertiary strata.
Stands of *Haloxylon aphyllum* on sandy loam with gypsum	Identified mainly by adaptation to broad level de-pressions and by the considerable density of the beds of *Haloxylon aphyllum*.
Vegetation of crusty-puffy solonchak soils	Identified by sharply-marked outlines bordering them, dark colour and level relief of the saline soil.
Haloxylon aphyllum stands on takyr (desert soil)	Identified by clear outlines and light colour of the takyr.
Communities on sand dunes (communities of *Aristida pen-nata* and *Calligonum* spp., etc.)	Identified by sand dune topography and by the sparse large bushes of *Calligonum* spp. and *Salsola* spp. in the hollows between dunes.

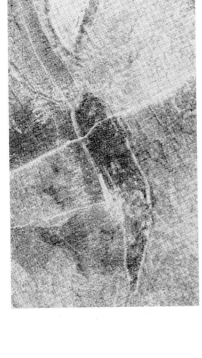

Fig. 8. Aerial photograph of plant cover in a semi-desert with strongly-defined complexity.

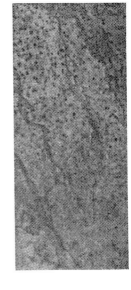

Fig. 10. Saline depression in a semi-desert.

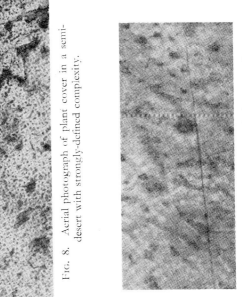

Fig. 9. Aerial photograph of plant cover in a semi-desert with vague, ill-defined complexity.

Fig. 11. Aerial photograph of communities of black saxaul (*Haloxylon aphyllum*) and tamarisk (*Tamarix*).

Petrov explained the geomorphological adaptations of a number of desert communities (1936).

As an example of the correlations discovered between relief and vegetation, we give below the identifying features (for aerial photographs on a scale of 1:16,000) of several desert communities, according to Petrov (1936), for the Kara-Kum desert (the indicators are given by us in Table 25).

Another outstanding investigator of Central Asian deserts, Leont'ev, suggests that many desert plant communities could be identified on aerial photographs without special difficulty (such as stands of black and white saxaul *(Haloxylon aphyllum* and *H. persicum)*, tamarisk *(Tamarix)*, *Elaeagnus* willow, *(Salix)*, poplar *(Populus)*, etc.—see Fig. 11). Aerovisual observations, in Leont'ev's opinion, are of very great importance in the study of desert vegetation, as the large number of clear days, the sharp contrasts in desert landscape, and the wide spacing of trees and plant stands create much more favourable conditions for such observations in the desert than in other types of landscape (e.g. in forests, etc.)

Personal experience of work in semi-deserts and deserts has convinced the authors of the present guide that the best results in these zones come from transect surveys with use of aerial photographs, made in strict accordance with the description of them given above. The geo-botanist must first analyse mosaics, tracing round all community habitats on them (even if the geo-botanical content of them is originally unknown to him), and must lay out transects so that he visits most of them, identifying them in the field and determining their geo-botanical content and their characteristics as pastures. At the same time he enters in the descriptions, together with other data, the identifying features of communities (depth of tone, configuration of habitats, appearance, structure). After establishing the identifying features and verifying them on various habitats, areas that were not directly visited by the investigator may be analysed. The work is done similarly to that described in Chapter II.

Aerovisual observations in semi-deserts and northern types of desert give very good results, although as yet they have been little used in compilation of pasture maps. According to Kas'yanova (1955), in Ust-Urt and Mangyshlak many communities are well distinguished in aerovisual observations in summer from a height of 200 m. Thus *Artemisia* gives a uniform grey colour. An admixture of grasses is revealed by a yellowish tinge. If the grasses are dominant the colour

8

of the plant cover is yellow. *Anabasis aphylla,* which is frequently found in *Artemisia* communities, is well distinguished in the form of small evenly-distributed bright-green dots on the grey background of the *Artemisia. Anabasis salsa* is difficult to distinguish from *Artemisia* by its colour in summer, but is well distinguished in autumn, when it begins to redden. In summer areas of *A. salsa* alternating with *Artemisia* may be identified mainly by the fact that beds of it look to the observer like flat expanses, while *Artemisia* beds lying beside it look somewhat higher (raised, as it were, above the *A. salsa)* and arc not so smooth.

The principal grass communities in semi-deserts—*Stipa* and *Agropyrum sibiricum* communities—are not well distinguishable. To identify them one must fly low, and then one can identify the plants immediately.

TABLE 26. AEROVISUAL IDENTIFYING FEATURES OF SOME DESERT COMMUNITIES

Plant community	Features of the community in aerovisual observations
Black saxaul (*Haloxylon aphyllum*)	In summer and late spring is distinguished by bright green (malachite) colour, extremely dense (for desert vegetation) crown, usually very compact. In late autumn and early winter the colour is brownish with an orange tinge, later darkening to brown (with shedding of the assimilating shoots).
White saxaul (*Haloxylon persicum*)	Somewhat similar to black saxaul but differs in its dove-grey hue and its more glaucous crown, and is generally less compact.
Stands of *Calligonum* spp.	Among large plants of sandy deserts, *Calligonum* is distinguished by the brightest colour and the most glaucous crown. Usually the characteristic reddish colour of the bark of the branches shows through the crown.
Stands of sand acacia (*Ammodendron*)	Identified by the characteristic "weeping" form of the crown, which is especially well observed in the shadow cast by this plant. The colour of the crown is bright silvery. In the flowering period abundant masses of dark-violet flowers are seen.
Stands of tamarisk (*Tamarix*)	Distinguished by deep yellow colour and usually by great density of growth and small height. In the flowering period the characteristic lilac colour of the crown is visible (separate large tree-like specimens are difficult to distinguish from black saxaul).
Stands of *Elaeagnus*	Identified by the compact circular silvery crowns (not having a "weeping" form, unlike sand acacia); in the flowering period the yellow colour of the flowers is noticeable.

Leont'ev (1952) also gives a number of features whereby one can identify various desert plant communities in observations from the air. Some of them are given above in Table 26.

The best height for aerovisual observations in the desert, in the opinion of V. L. Leont'ev, is from 400 to 600 m.

In the compilation of a pasture map certain difficulties attend the working out of symbols for complex vegetation on the map. Some investigators use different colours or hatching to denote the various areas of complexes, and thus the participation of different communities in a complex is shown directly on the area on the map. A community in that case is designated by a figure or a letter, and against its symbol is stated the percentage of the given area of pasture that it constitutes.

A somewhat different method is used by N. N. Pel't (Pel't and Chirvinskii, 1956) in compiling a pasture map of Ust-Urt. Different types of pasture are there shown by hatching, the latter mainly expressing only the presence in a given type of pasture of a certain dominant community, from which the pasture type is named. If, besides the plants giving their name to the pasture type, a considerable admixture of other plants occurs in a pasture or parts of it have stretches without any vegetation, a symbol (a Roman or Arabic numeral) is placed on the area. If that admixture is concentrated in a definite part of the area, the latter is defined.

Dokhman (1940) proposes the following system to designate the participation of various communities in a complex. In the legend of a map each complex as a whole or each of the communities found to occur in it is given its own colour. An area occupied by any complex is given the colour of that complex. On that background are

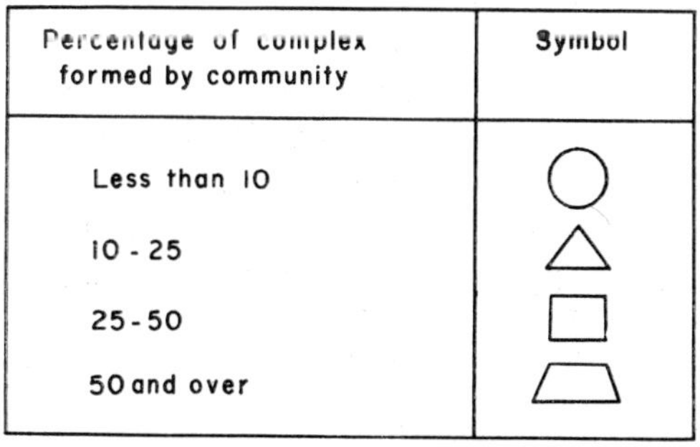

Percentage of complex formed by community	Symbol
Less than 10	◯
10 - 25	△
25 - 50	▢
50 and over	⏢

FIG. 8. Symbols denoting degree of participation by communities in complexes (after G. I. Dokhman)

8*

entered the colour symbols, not drawn to scale, expressing the participation of the various communities in the complex. The shape of the symbols indicates the proportion (percentage) of the complex represented by a given community, and the colours of the symbols indicate the communities composing the complex.

G. I. Dokhman suggests the symbols shown above in Fig. 8.

(ii) *Collection of Data on Fodder Resources*

At the same time that he enters the various outlines on the map, the geo-botanist collects data relating to the fodder resources in the outlined areas. Fodder resources are estimated by taking samples (i.e. clippings of all herbage) from sample plots or on transects, i.e. long narrow sample strips.

Different investigators have used different sizes and different numbers of plots. The data given by Larin (1952) on that subject are presented in Table 27.

TABLE 27. DIMENSIONS AND NUMBERS OF PLOTS FOR DETERMINING FODDER RESOURCES IN PASTURES

Area of plots (in m²)	Number of plots	Investigator or organization
0.25–0.5	12	A. V. Shennikov*
0.25	10	P. A. Voshchinin*
1.0	3	I. V. Larin
2.5	4	Fodder Institute
1.0	10	Orenburg Inst. of Meat-animal Husbandry
50.0	1–5	L. G. Ramenskii (for deserts)

* Data given by these authors refer to pastures in temperate latitudes.

In the opinion of Larin (1952), the most accurate data are obtained from samples taken from ten plots each of 1 m². N. N. Pel't (oral communication) recommends sampling twelve plots each of 0.25 m². With considerable complexity of the plant cover, it is better to lay out in each type of complex a transect so designed that all members of a complex are found in the area of the transect in proportions typical of that complex. Determination of fodder resources in that case is undertaken in the following way: samples are taken from small plots in each component of the complex; the amount of fodder is calculated for each community composing the complex; the proportion of each community in the complex is then estimated by the line transect method (see above) along a transect; and from these data the fodder resources in the whole complex are calculated.

Some investigators (N. N. Pel't—oral communication) limit themselves to a linear valuation of the whole complex, and lay out transects only in its separate elements.

Determination of crop production from samples taken from small plots, however, often gives results somewhat too high. Therefore Larin (1952) recommends deducting 10 per cent from the crop calculated from the samples, to bring the calculated result closer to the actual crop production.

In taking samples one must distinguish between the gross and the edible mass of the samples. Different parts of plants are eaten to a different extent by different species of livestock. Therefore for each sample taken it is necessary to determine separately the edible and inedible parts. The results of special studies are required to correct investigational data in tables compiled by geo-botanists on the basis of generalization of a large quantity of experimental material (see Nechayeva, Mordvinov and Mosolov, 1943; Larin, 1952).

In calculating the edible and inedible quantities one must give particular attention to valuation of fodder resources in communities composed of sub-shrubs and shrubs, where the edible mass is mainly the non-woody parts of the plants. Sample-taking there usually consists in cutting off (or breaking off) these non-woody parts (especially in large shrubs, where cutting the whole plant is practically useless). The seasonal dynamics of edible and inedible masses differ considerably and should therefore be taken into account separately.

In determining the crop in grassy phytocenoses that it is proposed to use for hay, good results depend to a large extent on the height at which the grasses are cut in taking samples. That has great economic importance, as different agricultural machines used for hay-cutting cut grass at different heights (mowers mostly from 5 to 12 cm, reapers not below 7 cm); therefore to know the fodder resources at different cutting heights Larin (1952) recommends the following method: a sample from a test plot is cut off at the root, and in the form of a sheaf is cut with knives into the following sections (measured from the root end): 0—2 cm, 2—5 cm, 5—7 cm, 7—10 cm, 10—15 cm, and over 15 cm. These parts are weighed in both the fresh and the dry state.

It is necessary that any sample, whether from a hay-meadow or a pasture, not only should be weighed as a whole but should be separated at least into groups (grasses, sedges, legumes, and mixed herbage), and the weight of each species or group should be determined. In doing that one may select (instead of the whole sample) only one-third of it, taken as an average sample after mixing the whole.

In order to bring the crop production as estimated from samples closer to the actual figure, it is recommended that a number of correction coefficients should be employed, especially if it is a question of estimating the production of hay-meadows. The corrections there refer mostly to allowance for losses in mowing and raking hay. In the mixed-herbage stands of steppes and deserts mowing losses vary from 2 to 4 per cent, and in grassy stands on the steppes from 7 to 20 per cent. Losses in raking and stacking mixed-herbage and sedge stands vary from 2 to 15 per cent.

Very detailed tables for estimating losses in different conditions are given by Larin (1952).

In sandy deserts, when determining fodder resources in different types of pasture it is very important to make estimates of ephemerals and shrubs, as both groups of plants are very important items of fodder. To make estimates in that case transects are laid out, the size of which depends on the density of the shrub stands: with thin stands the transect has a length of from 200 to 500 m and a width of from 5 to 10 m, and with dense stands of shrubs the transect is 100—200 m long and 2 m wide. The transect is laid out across the relief. Within the transect from twenty to fifty plots each of 0.25 m² are laid out, and from them the ephemerals and other small herbage are cut. All shrubs and large-stemmed plants on the transect are counted, divided into three classes (small, medium, and large). From each class of each species, ten (less often twenty) typical specimens (so-called model specimens) are selected, and from the largest shrubs five model specimens, from which the edible parts are cut. Then the samples are weighed (in air-dried condition); the crop of ephemerals is calculated directly on the pasture area, and the crop of edible parts of shrubs and large-stemmed plants is calculated from the number of plants of each type and class on a unit of area.

In order to obtain data on the seasonal dynamics of the fodder resources, it is necessary to calculate the fodder crop at least twice. If it is not possible to make such a double count on each area, then it is necessary to do it at least on parts of the habitats of the most widely distributed communities and complexes. Data on the seasonal dynamics of fodder resources must be supplemented by data on seasonal fluctuations in the mass of the edible parts of the most important fodder plants: these data are published in various reference books. For desert plants a collection of such data may be found in Amelin (1943).

The time required for making repeated samplings may vary considerably, depending on the individual features of development of the chief food plants in a given pasture. Thus, for example, for many pastures it is advisable to take samples in early spring (for counting ephemerals) and in autumn (for counting *Artemisia* and *Salsola* plants). On different types of pastures, however, the dates of taking samples should be different.

It must be remarked that even such elementary observations on the dynamics of fodder resources become possible only if a survey is supplemented by work of a semi-stationary character, as repeated samples should be cut on the same areas. If there is no possibility of such semi-stationary work, the dynamics of fodder resources should be calculated with use of data taken from tables.

In order that the results of sampling may be trustworthy, special attention must be given to rational location of sample plots. Sample plots should be located in typical habitats. Each plot should relate to a single defined community. If it is required to determine fodder resources in a complex of communities, then it is necessary to have perfectly accurate data on the amount of fodder in each member of the complex and on the proportion (percentage) of the complex formed by that community. One must guard against unconsidered "mechanical" location of test plots and random scattering of them at distances of a fixed number of kilometres, as is now done, unfortunately, in several pastures under investigation.

(iii) *Collecting Information by Questioning and Otherwise*

Of great importance for successful survey results is the collection of various data regarding investigations of pastures in earlier years, and also collection of information by questioning. In the first place the geo-botanist must familiarize himself with material available in local land-management offices and on state and collective farms— from various maps and plans of pastures compiled in earlier years.

Collection of information regarding the season of use of certain pastures by different species of livestock is very important. Much material on that subject may be found in the literature, but one must not fail to question local residents.

Besides information on the eating of certain plant species by live-stock at different seasons of the year, one should collect information about stock-driving routes and about use of certain territories, of separate parcels of land, and of sandy areas under pasturing in former years. Collection of such information is of great economic importance, as it is a generalization of the experience of animal breeders in the desert.

Here also one must include collection of information about wells (many of which are not shown on maps, as they were filled in during the period of civil war and banditry). Those knowing most on that subject are old shepherds and hunters.

When during a survey one comes upon any kind of area that has been abandoned for any reason—with traces of deserted farms, stock-pens, wells—one must try to discover the reason for the departure of herds from that point, as one may often succeed in that way in dis-covering the infestation of pastures by disease-producing organisms, the existence of plants harmful to livestock, low quality of water, etc.

The results of all questioning are entered in the working journals.

(iv) *Interpretation of Material*

A geo-botanical map compiled during a survey is subject to con-version into a map of pasture types. In order to make such a conversion a geo-botanist should at least have at his disposal data on fodder resources in each type (desirably, in each defined area) and on the season of use. The geo-botanist may obtain the latter information from answers to questions, from reference books, and also from his personal expe-rience in work in districts similar to that under investigation. The geo-botanist obtains information on fodder resources either directly in the field (if samples are dried and weighed on the spot) or at the end of the job, during the office-work period. In the latter case the conversion of a geo-botanical map into a map of pasture types also must be de-ferred to the office-work period. It consists in combining community habitats, similar in crops and identical in season of use, into the same type of pasture. If these communities that are referred to the same type of pasture differ in the presence of species having no fodder value but important as indicators of ecological conditions, it is recommended that they should be combined only in their general colouring, retaining for them their own indexes and the individual boundaries of each community habitat (Amelin, 1943). In general it is better to keep all community boundaries on the map, combining them into pasture types only by colouring.

The chief indicators for identifying pasture types are: similarity of plant cover, fodder resources and season of use of the pastures. One must also take into account, however, soil and geomorphological conditions and to a certain extent also the prospects of evolution of pastures during their future exploitation. Thus that work requires complex geographical methods.

Compilation of a map of pasture types concludes the work on geo-botanical survey of them. Sometimes, however, geo-botanical survey is followed by one further stage of the work—devising a pasture-rotation chart. In that stage the greater part of the work is done not by the geo-botanist but by the zoo-technician. But since the geo-botanist takes part (sometimes a very large part) in that work, he must be familiar with the problems met in compiling such charts.

Brief information on pasture-rotation charts is given below.

Amelin (1943) defines pasture rotation as a periodical change in the method or season of use of pastures in order to prevent their deterioration. He distinguishes minor pasture rotation, or seasonal change of pastures, from major pasture rotation, i.e. change in method or season of use during a whole series of years.

To compile a pasture-rotation chart one must have the following material:

(1) a map of pasture types on a scale of not less than 1 : 100,000;

(2) characteristics of pastures with relation to relief, soils and vegetation (this may take the form of explanatory notes on the map);

(3) data on the dynamics of fodder resources in all types of pastures;

(4) data on the edibility and nutritive value of different kinds of fodder;

(5) data on water supplies in pastures, output of wells and quality of water (it is desirable to show these data on a special map, compiled by a hydro-geologist or a hydro-technician);

(6) data on provision of feeding equipment for livestock;

(7) data on the number of livestock, their age-composition and veterinary condition, time of carrying out zoo-technical measures and distribution of livestock in the state or collective farms;

(8) data on farm location, road conditions, etc.

From the above list of information it is evident that a pasture-rotation chart is compiled jointly by a zoo-technician, a hydro-technician, a geo-botanist, and representatives of the administration of the appropriate economic and land-management organizations.

The actual process of compiling a pasture-rotation chart consists mainly in the following measures:

(1) distributing the pasture areas among the farms in proportion to the number of livestock present on each farm;

(2) locating the herding areas in such a way that the livestock are provided with watering-places (in deserts and semi-deserts this condition is the most important and decisive in the construction of a pasture-rotation chart);

(3) dividing up the pastures belonging to the farms for seasonal use in such a way that the herds of livestock present will be provided with the necessary amount of fodder throughout the whole season;

(4) confirming on the map the boundaries of herding areas of a given farm and dividing these herding areas into parcels to be used at different seasons of the year.

Without dwelling on calculations dealing only with fodder and zootechnical matters, we shall mention the chief tasks of the geo-botanist in compiling a pasture-rotation chart. These tasks are basically as follows:

(a) He must have absolutely accurate data on fodder resources in each area in the pasture, after using all correcting coefficients to obtain the precise data, and also data on the season of use of each area;

(b) He must have data enabling him to set apart areas suitable for haying and for the creation of emergency supplies of hay for use in case of ice-crust formation or other natural calamity;

(c) He must have information about all areas where livestock pasturing can lead to catastrophic deterioration of the pasture—that refers specially to sandy areas subject to wind erosion and unfit for pasturing;

(d) To assist in the organization of water supply to pastures he must have available information on the location of plant communities indicating the presence at no great depth of water suitable for human or animal consumption (see below) and he must recommend these locations for well-sinking;

(e) He must know the places where the vegetation and relief favour retention of snow, as melt-waters sinking into the soil there lead to formation of lenses of fresh underground water, usable later for stock-watering.

All these data should be both shown in detail on the map and entered in detail in the necessary notes on it, and in part also entered in field journals; the results of weighing and examination of samples should be presented in tabular form.

Thus as the result of survey of pastures in arid districts the following material should be produced:

(1) a map of pasture types;

(2) explanatory notes on it;

(3) field journals;

(4) tables with the results of analysis of samples.

It is desirable that the work should be continued up to the compilation of the pasture-rotation chart.

3. FEATURES OF SURVEYS ON THE TUNDRA

The work of a geo-botanist-surveyor in compiling maps of tundra pastures consists mainly of the following elements:

(a) compilation of a map of the major territorial elements—"pasture ranges" or "districts";

(b) characterizing each pasture according to a number of economic indicators;

(c) wide use of aerovisual indicators and analysis for characterizing pastures;

(d) interpretation of the data obtained in order to compile a pasture map.

These are briefly discussed below.

(i) *Compiling a Map of Pasture Ranges*

The most widely used method of compiling a map of types of tundra pastures is aerovisual survey. As a result of the development of topographical work in the North, geo-botanists generally use topographical maps in surveys, not resorting to compilation of "diagrammatic basic maps" (see above).

In recent survey practice the use of aerial photographic material (including mosaics and aerial photographs) has been constantly increasing. In such cases the work is done as in an ordinary aero-geobotanical survey with use of aerial photographs, with only this difference, that there is no preliminary analysis and the geo-botanist flies out on transects possessing mounted, but not analysed, photographs. During the flight the geo-botanist makes a number of notes on the various natural areas visible on the photographs, specifying the geo-botanical content of the areas and the nature of their fodder resources.

The analysis, with tracing over the boundaries of the various pasture areas in indian ink, is done after return from the transects (Andreyev, 1952).

Thus a survey of tundra pastures even with use of aerial photographs has certain features similar to those of an aerovisual survey.

In compiling a map of tundra pastures, one enters on the map not the outlines of separate types of pasture (since, with the great patchiness of the plant cover of the tundra, that would be difficult) but natural major pasture areas, in which may be combined areas of different types of pastures. Such natural areas are called "pasture ranges", "elementary districts", or "districts of the first order" (Andreyev, 1938). The identification of such ranges is done from the air both by their plant cover and by other indicators, among which geomorphological indicators are very important.

Such division of territory into separate districts with definite geomorphological boundaries is also recommended by Bogdanov (1954) for the pastures of Chukotka. In determining the districts, that investigator also recommends use of the method of questioning local residents in order to discover the zones of pasturing that have already been established.

In the survey of tundra pastures V. N. Andreyev distinguishes two kinds of observations on pastures: reconnaissance and detailed.

In a reconnaissance study of pastures the survey is made over a widely-spaced transect grid; in some cases that grid may be so open that not all of the territory is viewed by the surveyor, and between the transects there remain gaps (up to 15 or 20 km) to be filled by interpolation. The survey is made at a considerable altitude (900–1000 m). As a result of such reconnaissance observations one may obtain a map on a scale not larger than 1 : 500,000. On such a map one may define zones and subzones of vegetation and large landscape units, which V. N. Andreyev called "districts of the second order". On the basis of such a map one may give only general characteristics of pastures in the territory without valuation of fodder resources or with only a rough visual approximation of them. State and collective farms cannot carry out pasture management within their boundaries on the basis of such observations. Thus such work should be done only on unsurveyed territories for the purposes of the first stage of their reclamation.

Detailed observations presuppose such an organization of aerovisual surveys as will make possible examination of the whole territory of the work over a dense transect grid, enabling observation of all inter-transect areas to be made. With that type of work there should be no areas left unexamined. For that reason the spaces between transects should not exceed 5–6 km; the altitude of flight should be 300–500 m.*

In that kind of work one may obtain a map of pasture types on a scale of 1:200,000, showing on it the smaller units—"districts of the first order" or "elementary districts", which should be looked upon as different pasture ranges (Andreyev, 1938, p. 47), as internal management of pastures on collective and state farms is mainly done on a scale of 1 : 200,000, and to a very much smaller extent on a scale of 1 : 100,000. The average size of such pasture ranges, according to Andreyev, in the Yamal'skaya tundra is about 1000 hectares (Andreyev, 1938, p. 49).

In mountain districts, with very irregular relief and considerable patchiness of the plant cover, a map scale of 1:200,000 for internal management of pastures (within separate collective and state farms) appears to be insufficient. Bogdanov (1954) recommends for those districts compilation of maps of pasture types on a scale of 1 : 100,000.

(ii) *Fodder Characteristics of Pasture Ranges*

Each pasture range defined by a geo-botanist and entered on his sketch is usually not at all uniform, i.e. is not occupied by a single type of pasture. If by visual estimate from the air any one type of pasture seems to occupy more than 85 per cent of the range area, then the whole range is referred to that type of pasture (excluding only cases where there are particularly valuable localities in the remaining 15 per cent). In all other cases the surveyor is bound to enumerate all types of pasture in a given range, and to determine visually the percentage of each type.

In addition, the surveyor should make a visual valuation of the fodder on each range, i.e. estimate the following from the air:

(1) the percentage of the surface of the range covered by lichens (the principal fodder in the tundra);

* For internal management of pastures within separate collective and state farms, without use of aerial methods, Bogdanov (1954) considers that in the Chukotsk peninsula it is normal to have a distance of 3 to 8 km between ground transects to compile a pasture map on a scale of 1:100,000.

(2) the category of the lichen resources;

(3) the condition of the lichen carpet;

(4) the dominant species of lichens;

(5) the presence of green fodder;

(6) the composition of the tree stands (in forested ranges).

The percentage of the range covered by lichens is estimated to the nearest 5 or 10 per cent. With regard to category of resources, ranges are divided into category III (up to 1 ton of lichens per hectare), category II (from 1 to 4 tons of lichens per hectare) and category I (more than 4 tons per hectare).*

The amount of lichens depends primarily on their height and density. In different districts the height and density of lichens corresponding to various categories of lichen resources vary somewhat. For the district of the Pechora basin Andreyev (1952) states that, for example, ranges with resources of the highest category have lichens 5—8 cm tall and density about 90 per cent; in ranges with resources of medium category the height is 4—6 cm and the density fluctuates around 70 per cent; with the lowest category of resources the height does not exceed 3 cm and the density 40 per cent.

According to its condition, lichen cover is divided into: entire (undamaged), slightly grazed, heavily grazed, and completely stripped.**

The dominant species of lichens are distinguished mainly by their colour.

All data about each range are entered on the sketch by writing them within the outline of the range in the form of a formula. The formula consists of two parts—the left side (which is written as a fraction) and the right. The numerator of the fraction consists of types of pasture found in the given range, and the percentage of the range represented by them: types of pasture are denoted not by letters but by conventional symbols (these symbols are listed below, in Table 29). The denominator of the fraction consists of the composition of the tree growth, shown in the way usual in valuation of forests. After the fractional part of the formula stands the contraction "yag." ("lich."), signifying that the data following it refer to the lichen ("yagel'") cover. After the contraction "yag." a fraction is written, in which the numerator shows the percentage of the area

* In later works by Andreyev (1952) the first category includes ranges with the smallest supplies, and the third category those with the largest.

** On mountain pastures (Chukotka) where there is comparatively little development of lichens, the greatest attention should be given to calculating resources of grassy fodder, especially cotton grass (Bogdanov, 1954).

of the range covered by lichens and the denominator shows the category of the resources (in Arabic numerals); beside the fraction one writes the contracted Latin name of the dominant species, and after it a note on the resources of green fodder.

Andreyev (1940) gives the following example of construction of a formula: let us suppose that there were recorded on a range 70 per cent of lichen tundra (symbol 0), 10 per cent thin larch forest (symbol $\overset{+}{\circ}$), 10 per cent dwarf birch (symbol $\downarrow$) and 10 per cent lakes; composition of the forest: larch 9, spruce 1; lichens cover 80 per cent of the area and the resources are of category II; *Cladonia rangiferina* (abbreviated name *Cr)* is dominant; along the streams there is abundance of green fodder.

The formula for that range would be as follows:

$$\frac{0\ 70,\ \overset{+}{\circ}\ 10,\ \downarrow\ 10,\ \text{lak.}\ 10}{\text{L }9\quad\text{S }1}\ \text{lich.}\ \frac{80}{2}\ Cr\ \text{ab. gr. along str.*}$$

To obtain a more detailed valuation, the lichen coverage of the soil may be given more precisely by visually estimating the density of the lichens. Therefore the lichen coverage of the soil is estimated not for the whole pasture range at once but for each type of pasture on the range. For that, two characteristics are used: one of them shows the area occupied by patches of lichen within a given type of pasture, and the other is the density of distribution of lichens within these patches. In such closer estimates of lichens the formula is written as a fraction, where the numerator gives the different types of pastures (symbols) and the percentage of them in the area of the range, and the denominator gives under each type the two above-mentioned characteristics, also as a fraction: the percentage coverage of the

TABLE 28. DENSITY OF LICHENS IN PERCENTAGES AND POINTS

Density of lichens (per cent)	Points
30	0 — 1
40	1
50	1 — 2
70	2
80	2 — 3
90	3

* "ab. gr. along str." means "abundance of green fodder along the streams".

soil by lichen patches is given as the numerator, and the density of lichens within the patches is given by points (on a 3-point system) as the denominator. Besides whole points, transitional stages are also used. The actual density of lichens in lichen patches corresponding to the various points and transitional stages is shown in Table 28.

As an example of the construction of such a more precise formula, we may examine a case taken from the work of Temnoyev and Shirokovskaya (1955).

Let us assume that we have an area containing 40 per cent spruce-lichen forest (symbol ↑), 30 per cent with scattered pines and moss (symbol Y) and 30 per cent spruce-lichen sparse-forest (symbol ↑p); in the spruce-lichen forest the lichen patches occupy 50 per cent and the density of lichens within these patches is also 50 per cent and is expressed as 1—2 points; among the pines and green moss there are no lichens; in the sparse-forest there is 10 per cent of lichen patches, and the density of lichens in these patches is 40 per cent, expressed as 1 point.

The formula of that area would be as follows:

$$\frac{↑\ 40\quad Y\ 30\quad ↑p\ 30}{\dfrac{50}{1-2}\quad \dfrac{10}{1}}$$

To obtain the precise actual lichen coverage in a range it is necessary: (1) to multiply the index of coverage of the soil by lichens at the given distribution by the density of lichens in the patches (converted from points to percentages as in Table 28) and divide the product by 100; (2) to multiply the figure obtained by the percentage of a given type of pasture in the pasture range and divide the product by 100; (3) having thus determined the lichen coverage of the soil in each type of pasture, to add together the amounts obtained; the total will show the actual lichen coverage of the soil in the whole given range.

In the example that we gave above, such a calculation will have the following form:

(1) for the spruce-lichen forest we have:

$$\frac{50 \times 50}{100} = 25 \text{ per cent;} \qquad \frac{25 \times 40}{100} = 10 \text{ per cent;}$$

(2) for the spruce sparse-forest we have:

$$\frac{10 \times 40}{100} = 4 \text{ per cent;} \qquad \frac{4 \times 30}{100} = 1.2 \text{ per cent;}$$

(3) as the total for the whole range we have:

$$10 + 1.2 = 11.2 \text{ per cent.}$$

Naturally such a precise calculation of the lichen coverage of the range is used only in detailed study of pastures, usually when the scale of the survey is of the order of 1:100,000.

The formula may vary considerably, depending on the character and types of pastures. One may familiarize oneself with different kinds of formulas and methods of compiling them in the work of Andreyev (1940).

(iii) *Use of Aerial Methods for Compiling Maps of Estimates of Fodder Resources*

The most important condition for success in an aerovisual survey is accurate identification of different types of pasture from the air, and also determination of categories of resources in the pastures. For that it is necessary to know the aerovisual indicators of types of pastures and categories of resources.

To determine categories of resources from the air, V. N. Andreyev gives the following indicators: pastures with resources of category III have a very pale and not easily noticeable colour on the area covered by lichens, with the colour of the dominant species almost unnoticeable; pastures with resources of category II have a brighter background with the colour of the dominant species clearly visible; pastures with resources of category I have an extremely bright colour, visible far away, so that the dominant species is easily identified from a considerable distance.

The aerovisual indicators of different types of pastures are of several kinds. For the Archangel and Omsk North, Andreyev (1940) distinguishes 36 types of pasture; he also describes their characteristics for investigation from the air.

In Table 29 we give the aerovisual indicators established by him (with some abridgment) for ten of the types of pastures most important from a fodder point of view, and also conventional symbols used to designate these types in formulas in working sketches.

9

TABLE 29. AEROVISUAL INDICATORS FOR THE CHIEF TYPES OF TUNDRA PASTURES

Type of pasture, nature of use, and distribution	Aerovisual indicators	Conventional symbol
Lichen *Cladonia* tundras; valuable winter pastures; southern tundra and northern forest-tundra	White or whitish background of different tints	
Lichen-dwarf-birch tundras; autumn, winter and summer pastures; southern tundra, northern forest-tundra	General background light-grey or whitish; depressions with dwarf birch, dark-green	
Moss-lichen tundras; year-round pastures; southern and typical tundra, partly Arctic tundra	Pepper-grey background with brownish or greyish tints; rectilinear cracking visible	
Tussocky lichen tundras; spring and autumn pastures; southern tundra, northern forest-tundra	Greenish-whitish background; depressions dove-grey or dark-green; dense network of dendroid depressions visible	
Moss-dwarf-birch tundras; summer and early autumn pastures; forest-tundra, southern and typical tundra	Surface micro-cellular, cells greenish-whitish, sometimes with brown patches; green borders around the cells	
Moss-willow tundras; summer pastures (middle and late summer); southern and typical tundra	Brownish-green background, speckled; patches of willow—dove-grey-green or glossy dark-green; speckled with brown or orange dots due to presence of tussocks	
Sedge-willow beds; year-round pasture, particularly valuable in summer; typical and southern tundra	Dove-grey-green background; willow bushes produce the dove-grey-green background, sedges are light-green with glints of water	
Tundra-mixed-herbage meadows; summer and early autumn pastures; in all tundra subzones	Light-green uniform surface*	
Spruce-larch lichen forest; winter pasture, sheltered from winds; southern forest-tundra and taiga	Snow-white background of the ground cover with green curtains of shrubs	
Peat bogs with lichens; winter pastures; sparse taiga and southern forest-tundra.	Smooth surface of white, greyish or greenish-white colour with patches of brownish-green pools	

* Andreyev (1940) gives no conventional symbol for this type of pasture.

As is seen from Table 29, the colour and form of the surface are very important indicators for aerovisual identification of types of tundra pastures, and it is also important to note the configuration of areas and their location in the relief.

To determine the degrees to which pastures are grazed one may use the following aerovisual indicators: light grazing is shown by a slight greying of the lichen background; heavy grazing by a dense network of tracks, abundance of dark patches on the sites of broken tussocks and general heavy darkening of the background; complete stripping becomes evident by the very dark colour of the area.

Use of aerial photographs may give considerable aid in compiling maps of tundra pasture types. However, the indicators for analysis of aerial photographs of tundra pastures have not been sufficiently clarified. Interpretation indicators for lowland Arctic bogs, for tundra peat-bogs and for Arctic tundras on mineral soil have been the most studied. The most important indicator in interpretation, according to Andreyev (1955), is the formation of crevices by frost, which produces characteristic patterns on the tundra surface.

Andreyev has worked out in detail interpretation indicators of various polygonal bogs, which are presented in Table 30.

TABLE 30. INTERPRETATION INDICATORS OF POLYGONAL BOGS

Type of polygonal bog	Appearance in aerial photographs
Arctic bog	Uniform surface, sometimes with noticeable network of frost crevices and with a few lakelets of various forms and sizes.
Ridged bog	Surface with narrow light-coloured strips between separate polygons having a darker background. Scattered lakelets of very limited size, of polygonal form (the light strips are ridges at the edges of the polygons, caused by accumulation of ice along cracks).
Ridge-and-lake bog	Similar to above, but the majority of the polygons are flooded.
Hillock-and-pool bog	Polygonal surface with wide dark belts between light-coloured polygons; in the central parts of the polygons there are many lakelets
Ridge-polygon-pool bog	Narrow belts in the form of streaks not joining one another; laid out in two mutually-perpendicular directions; sometimes lakelets in the areas between the belts.

Unlike polygonal bogs, peat bogs and peat tundras are distinguished by the following features: (1) the whole system of crevices often does not have such a regular geometrical form, the polygons varying in size and shape; (2) ridges are never visible along the crevices; (3)

9*

the crevices are not filled with vegetation; (4) the crevices are dis-
integrating and therefore vary greatly in size and shape.

Among creviced tundras on mineral soil, the following may be
distinguished by the nature of their polygonal appearance: (1) Arctic
polygonal deserts; (2) creviced lichen and shrub-lichen tundras; (3)
moss-lichen tundras. In the first type the crevices develop directly
in the barren mineral soil; plants grow only along the crevices, forming dark borders interlacing the polygons. In lichen and shrub-lichen
tundras the polygons are evenly covered with lichens, which gives
them a monotonous light colour. Tundras of that type are distinguished from peat tundras by identical wide crevices around all polygons, and from polygonal bogs by the absence of noticeable ridge-
like elevations along the sides of the polygons. In moss-lichen tundras
a darker mossy border develops around the lichen-covered polygons:
therefore their appearance in aerial photographs is somewhat re-
miniscent of Arctic deserts, but differs in the fact that in the latter
the bare mineral soil is clearly visible, whereas in moss-lichen tundras
the presence of a lichen carpet on the ground is evident.

On the whole polygonal tundras may be easily distinguished from
bogs, as there are comparatively few lakes on their surface and the
polygons are not so regular in shape as in the bogs.

(iv) *Interpretation of Data*

In the process of aerovisual survey with use of the above aerovisual
indicators (and also of analysis of aerial photographs, if that   has
been done) pasture ranges are drawn on a sketch. By transferring
them to a topographical base one obtains a map of pasture types.
That map, however, is distinguished by the considerable mass of
detail in the items shown on it. Therefore in order to facilitate division
of the territory into areas with similar economic features, some generalization of the map of pasture types is expedient. For that purpose a new map—a pasture-valuation map—is compiled on the
same scale as the former one. On it types of pastures are combined
into groups of types (e.g. in one group all lichen types are combined,
in another grass-shrub groups, in a third grass-sedge groups); the
groups of types may be combined into classes of pasture: the chief
of these are the following—tundra, sparse-forest, bog, taiga, and
forest pastures. Within each group of pastures areas are combined
not according to their geo-botanical character but according to the

category of fodder resources and the degree to which they are grazed. Thus a pasture-valuation map shows fodder resources to a greater extent than does a map of pasture types, and is more suitable for planning pasture rotation.

The procedure of office work should include, besides the compilation of maps, correction of the contents of formulas written on various areas on the sketch. The correction is done on the basis of ground investigations of étalon areas, which are always accompanied by aerovisual surveys. In investigation of tundra pastures on étalon areas the proportions of different pasture types in the same district, and especially the fodder resources in different types, are estimated. The estimate of fodder resources is made by taking samples (see above for details). Thus the surveyor, possessing material from ground work, can correct data both regarding the proportions of different types of pasture in a certain range and regarding the categories of fodder resources in them.

For all areas of types of pasture shown on the map, i.e. for all pasture ranges, an area report should be drawn up in the office with quantitative data on the fodder resources in each area.

Thus as a result of aerovisual survey of types of tundra pasture the following basic material should be presented:

(1) a map of pasture types;

(2) a map of economic valuation of pastures;

(3) strips with analysed sketches, on which are shown all corrections made from the results of ground investigations;

(4) a diagrammatic map of transects made;

(5) an area report;

(6) characteristics of types of pastures (in the form of explanatory notes to the map).

As excessive accumulation and packing of snow and also ice-crust formation present serious impediments to the obtaining of winter fodder by reindeer (especially in mountain districts), Bogdanov (1954) considers it expedient to supplement maps of pasture types in these districts with the following special sketch-maps: (1) a sketch-map of the location of areas of packed snow, (2) a sketch-map of the location of beds of snow that persist in summer, (3) a sketch-map of the location of areas most often subject to ice-crust formation, (4) a sketch-map of the location of areas subject to flooding. These sketch-maps are compiled by collecting data from questioning, by examining the relief on the map, or by personal observations of the geo-botanist-surveyor.

CHAPTER VI

GEO-BOTANICAL SURVEYS
FOR INDICATIONAL PURPOSES

1. GENERAL INFORMATION ON INDICATIONAL
GEO-BOTANICAL SURVEYS

PLANT cover exists in very close and indissoluble connection with its environment. Therefore the composition, structure, and other features of the plant cover may often serve as indicators of various environmental conditions. The concept of indicator-plants and indicator-communities of plants has won for itself admission into modern science. Because of that, indicational geo-botanical investigations (i.e. investigations directed towards study of the indicational significance of plant cover) have become fairly widely used.

The concept of the indicational significance of plant cover has been developed by a large number of investigators. Thus, for example, the significance of plant cover as an indicator of the whole complex of ecological conditions was particularly clearly stated in the works of Vysotskii (1904, 1909). That investigator proposed to construct special "phyto-topographical" maps, which essentially should be maps of original (not altered by human activity) plant communities. Vysotskii suggested that in that way any territory could be divided into natural types of habitat, which would be elementary landscape units. The vegetation there would be an indicator for physico-geographical division into districts.

The use of plants as indicators of underground water was known in distant antiquity; mention of it is found in the works of the learned Roman Vitruvius Pollio.

The significance of plant cover as an indicator for geological investigations has been shown in the works of Lomonosov (publ. 1949), Karpinskii (1841), Vysotskii (1904) and Ososkov (1899). At present geo-botanical investigations are widely used as an accessory method in geological and hydro-geological research (Priklonskii, 1935; Viktorov, 1955).

Vegetation is also used as an indicator of soil conditions and of the prospects of agricultural reclamation of territory (Ramenskii, 1938; Larin, 1926; Clements, 1920).

Geo-botanical indicational investigations have come into especially wide use since aerial methods have been introduced into geology, soil management and agriculture. That is due to the fact that vegetation is one of the most important and most noticeable elements in an aerial photograph. Use of it as an indicator of soil, geological and hydro-geological conditions considerably facilitates interpretation of aerial photographs by the investigator. Therefore in modern text-books and works on aerial methods (Gaveman, 1937; Petrusevich, 1954) much attention is given to questions of geo-botanical indication.

2. KINDS OF GEO-BOTANICAL INDICATIONAL MAPS

In the process of indicational investigations, various geo-botanical maps are compiled. In most cases these maps have no independent value, but are ancillary to the compilation of geological, hydro-geological, soil and other maps.

We list below the most widely-used kinds of geo-botanical indicational maps compiled at the present time.

(i) *Hydro-indicational Maps*

Hydro-indicational geo-botanical maps show the distribution of plant communities that serve as indicators of shallow underground water of various degrees of mineralization. On these maps the distribution of other geo-botanical indicators of underground water may also be shown. Thus, for example, if two habitats of the same community have different vegetative periods (one remains green for a long time, and the other dries up quickly) and the investigator has grounds for supposing that the reason for those differences is a difference in moisture conditions in the habitats, the habitats are differentiated on the map.

The most important geo-botanical indicators of underground water are communities in which the dominant plants are phreatophytes, i.e. plants that throughout the whole year are connected by their root systems to underground water. Therefore hydro-indicational maps show mainly the distribution of cummunities in which phreatophytes predominate (Fig. 9).

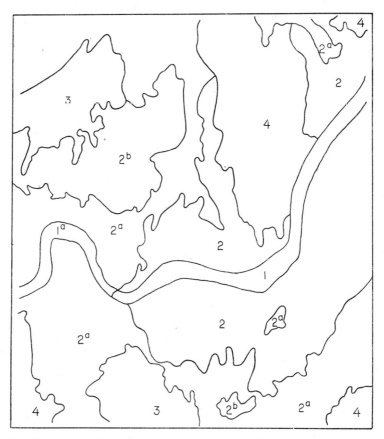

Fig. 9. Hydro-indicational map of the ancient delta plain of Syr-Darya.

1 — *Haloxylon aphyllum—Tamarix* community along the bed of a dry stream— underground brackish water at a depth of 10—15 m;

2 — dense beds of *Haloxylon aphyllum* along a dry stream-bed—brackish or salt water at a depth of 15—20 m;

1a— groupings of suppressed *Tamarix* and *Haloxylon aphyllum* along the bed of the stream;

2a— suppressed and partly dying-off *Haloxylon aphyllum* beds along the bank;

} minor horizons of underground water or only slightly increased moisture in the soil;

2b— dead beds of *Haloxylon aphyllum* on the level—extinct or dried-up permanent stream-beds of underground water;

3 — scattered specimens of *Anabasis aphylla* on takyr soil—places with temporary pools of surface water and formation of small lenses;

4 — groupings of psammophytes on the sand—they do not indicate water.

Hydro-indicational maps provide an ancillary method in the search for underground water. They are of greatest importance in deserts and semi-deserts, where the search for water is of the greatest economic interest. In addition we must remark that in these zones the compilation of hydro-indicational maps is easiest, as the vegetation there reacts sharply to the smallest changes in hydro-geological conditions.

On a hydro-indicational map all communities that indicate the nearness of underground water are shown. The legend of the map states to what depth of underground water and to what degree of mineralization each community is adapted. Thus by use of the hydro-indicational map the hydro-geologist can most rationally locate the points for boring in search of water.

The scales of hydro-indicational maps vary. The smallest scale on which they are compiled is 1 : 200,000; in particular localities where detailed water research is carried on, hydro-indicational maps are compiled on scales from 1 : 2000 to 1 : 25,000.

Hydro-indicational maps are compiled by geo-botanical parties and detachments working on the staff of hydro-geological and geological expeditions.

The method of compiling these maps is described in detail in the work of Vostokova (1955).

(ii) *Lithological-geo-botanical Maps (Lithological Maps with Geo-botanical Data)*

The distribution of plant communities depends in considerable measure on the physico-chemical features of the soils and of the soil-forming strata underlying the soils. In the ecology and geography of plants the unique features of plants growing on gypsum-bearing strata, sands, carbonate strata and saline soils have long been known. So unique is their character that in plant ecology one speaks of special ecological plant groups of gypsophytes, psammophytes, calciphytes, halophytes, etc. Therefore by studying the plant cover of any district, and knowing the connection between vegetation and various soil-forming strata, one may use vegetation as an auxiliary indicator for constructing a lithological map (i.e. a map showing the distribution of different soil-forming lithological types). Such a geo-botanical map, compiled in aid of lithological cartography done by geologists, is called a lithological-geo-botanical map or a lithological map with geo-botanical data.

In the legend of such a map are listed all communities found in it; for each community, the lithological variety to which it is adapted in its distribution is stated. Communities adapted to the same variety of rock strata are combined under the same colour, but its own index (a figure or letter symbol) is kept for each community.

It must be remarked that after studying the soil adaptations of plant communities we may in the same way compile a soil map with geo-botanical data. The works of Ramenskii (1938) and Larin (1926), which discuss in detail the soil adaptations of plants, and also the work of Clements (1920) disclose the full possibilities of such investigations. So far, however, these possibilities have not been fully realized, although geo-botanical indicators are of great importance in soil surveys.

Lithological-geo-botanical maps are compiled mainly in plains districts, where the native rock strata are not greatly denuded and where their lithological composition is very chequered. It is especially expedient to construct such maps in the mapping of Quaternary sediments in arid regions on the ancient alluvial plains of Amu-Darya and Syr-Darya (Viktorov, 1955); compilation of such maps is possible, however, also in forest districts (Ososkov, 1899; Vysotskii, 1904).

Lithological maps with geo-botanical data are compiled by geo-botanical parties working on geological expeditions. The scale of these maps usually varies between 1 : 100,000 and 1 : 300,000.

(iii) *Maps of Salinity of Soils*

In deserts and semi-deserts, where one of the most important factors in plant distribution is the degree of salinity of the soils (i.e. the total amount of soluble salts in them) and the type of salinity (i.e. the predominance of certain ions), it appears to be possible to use vegetation as an indicator of salinity. In the legend of such a map it is stated to what degree and to what type of salinity a particular community is adapted. Such maps are usually made for districts in which it is proposed to take some kind of hydro-improvement measures. The aim of such maps is to reveal areas with highly saline soil and also areas practically without salts. These maps have not been widely used up to the present and have been made for only a few districts of the U.S.S.R.

(iv) *Geo-botanical Maps of an Exploratory Character*

This type includes all maps showing the location of geo-botanical indicators of various useful minerals. These indicators are of various kinds. Thus, for example, it is known that if there is petroleum bitumen in the soil the vegetation shows a large number of abnormal features—gigantism, formation of diseased swellings, disturbance of the normal processes of development (for details see Nesvetailova, 1955). These indicators may to some extent be used in the search for oil (Kartsev *et al.*, 1954).

Pathological changes are also known to occur in plants in the presence of boron (breakdown of the root neck in some species, changes in size and colour in others). They may serve as indirect indicators in the search for boron (Buyalov and Shvyryayeva, 1955). The same phenomena are observed in plants in the presence of cobalt and nickel (Malyuga, 1950). Finally there are a number of plants closely adapted to certain ore veins (zinc, copper, etc.) (Nesvetailova, 1955).

All of these geo-botanical exploration indicators may be shown on maps. These maps are not geo-botanical in the strict sense of the word, as there the question is one of the distribution of one or a few species of plants or even of the distribution of specimens with certain disease symptoms. They have very limited use at the present time and are on the most varied scales. For detailed illustration of the boundaries of separate veins they are drawn on scales from 1 : 2000 to 1 : 10,000 (these are often not maps but plans). Cases are known, however, where such maps have been made on a scale of 1 : 500,000 (thus, for example, some maps of geo-botanical bitumen indicators have been made on that scale).

(v) *Other Geo-botanical Indicational Maps*

There are still a number of other geo-botanical maps of an indicational nature, so far not widely used, but of considerable interest from the point of view of practical application. Thus, for example, certain species and plant communities are used as indicators for determining the degree of traversability of bogs in road investigations, and in sanitary valuation of bog waters (with regard to these maps see above).

We also know of experiments made in compiling maps of recent tectonic faults (mostly of disjunctive character) from geo-botanical data. They are based on the fact that tectonic faults produce such serious changes in hydro-geological conditions and the process of soil-formation that communities differing sharply from the surrounding vegetation develop along the fault line (Viktorov, Vostokova, and Voronkova, 1955; Vinogradov, 1955). These communities can easily be identified on aerial photographs and later entered on the map.

3. METHOD OF MAKING GEO-BOTANICAL SURVEYS FOR INDICATIONAL PURPOSES

The method of making geo-botanical surveys for indicational purposes includes: (1) discovering the indicational significance of plant communities, and (2) use of indicators for compiling geo-botanical indicational maps.

(i) *Discovering Indicator Species and Communities*

The discovering of species and communities that are indicators of specific conditions is done on so-called "étalon parcels" or étalons. Étalon is the name given to an area where the object indicated is known to exist.

Thus, for example, in the compilation of a hydro-indicational map étalons are areas where water is found by boring or digging, and also areas near wells and springs (if these areas are not too overgrazed). In the compilation of lithological maps or maps of soil salinity, étalons are areas where boring or mining work has exposed bed-rock and soils formed from it, and their physico-chemical features have been studied. For geo-botanical exploration maps étalons are areas where the objects of exploration (bitumen, boron, etc.) are known to have been found. Thus when working on an étalon the investigator knows beforehand its physico-chemical and hydro-geological conditions.

These areas are subjected to detailed geo-botanical investigation, description of the methods of which does not enter into the scope of the present guide, as it has no direct relation to geo-botanical surveys (one may learn the methods of that work from the compendium *"Geo-botanical Methods in Geological Investigations"*, Gosgeolizdat, Moscow, 1955).

As a result of investigations on étalons an indicational chart should be prepared, i.e. a table showing the indicator communities and their indicational significance. As an example we give a portion of an indicational chart for one of the semi-desert districts of the U.S.S.R., taken from the work of Vostokova and Zhdanova (1955) (Table 31).

An indicational chart serves as the basis for constructing the legend of a future map. Sometimes it is transferred almost in entirety to the map.

The number of étalons required varies greatly. If an indicational chart is to be compiled in a district where the basic principles of indication are already known (or have been studied for similar districts),

TABLE 31. PART OF INDICATIONAL CHART OF AKTYUBINSK PRIURAL'YA (ABRIDGED)

Vegetation	Geo-indicational significance		
	lithological characteristics	salinity	age
Complexes of *Artemisia pauciflora*, *Anabasis salsa*, and *Camphorosma nouspetiacum*	grey and black gypsum-bearing clays	heavily sulphated	lower Abbian and Aptian
Shrubby steppe with *Caragana*	phosphorite-bearing sands	negligible	Santonian
Tussocky *Anabasis salsa*	green gypsum-bearing clays	heavily sulphated	Tas-Aran palaeogenic

only a few étalons are needed, for control purposes only. If there are no published indicational data at all the number of étalons must be increased (as a minimum for establishing the indicational significance of each community we may recommend at least five étalons). In rare cases, if a certain indicational method has been worked out first, the geo-botanist is enabled to dispense with survey work in the first year and to occupy himself only with the discovery of indicators.

The sizes of étalons vary. Usually étalons are laid out within the boundaries of definite natural areas (e.g. a depression surrounding a well, a mineral outcrop, etc.). On each étalon it is desirable to make not less than one description of an area of 100 m² (or four of 25 m²) and to dig a hole to the bed-rock or make a mineral bore-hole. Samples must be taken of the soil, the subsoil and underground water for general chemical analysis or for examination for necessary useful minerals.

In compiling lithological-geo-botanical maps and salinity maps one sometimes approaches the question of selecting étalons somewhat differently. Étalons are laid out in all, or at least in the most widespread, communities, with simultaneous construction of mineral workings (trenches, bore-holes) and taking of samples from them. In that case the investigator does not know beforehand the soil and subsoil conditions existing in the area, and he obtains data by analysis after the étalon is laid out; only then can he discover the indicational significance of the communities.

In the investigation of the étalons, much attention is given to examination of aerial photographs of the étalons and description of the characteristics of the appearance of the indicator communities (for further details on use of aerial methods in indicational investigations see below).

(ii) *Making Surveys for Indicational Purposes*

In the compilation of indicational maps all types of geo-botanical surveys are used except aero-geo-botanical surveys (although use of the latter is quite possible even in indicational surveys; in addition, the role of aerovisual surveys is so great there that the work often takes the nature of an aero-geo-botanical survey).

The most widely-used kind of indicational survey is a transect survey with use of aerial photographs or aerovisual observations.

The making of geo-botanical profiles is widely used in indicational surveys.

An indicational survey has no strongly-marked differences from the usual methods of geo-botanical survey.

We must remark, however, that there are two ways of making an indicational survey. In the first way the investigator, before beginning the survey work, investigates all étalons and makes an indicational chart, and he begins the survey with more or less firm knowledge of the indicational significance of each community.

With that arrangement of the work the geo-botanist, when delineating any community on the map, at the same time outlines the ecological conditions (geo-chemical, soil, hydro-geological, etc.) of the given area and combines areas with similar conditions under a common colour or hatching (retaining, however, the boundaries of complexes and their individual indexes). By the end of the season of field work the geo-botanist has a prepared indicational map, which requires only some very small corrections.

That method is complex and more difficult to put into effect; it is mostly used for hydro-indicational and exploration investigations.

The second method involves commencement by the investigator of compilation of a working geo-botanical map simultaneously with the beginning of the survey work, when the indicational significance of communities is still unknown to him. At the same time that he is compiling the map during the survey, the geo-botanist studies the étalons and collects material for different analyses, and only at the end of the field work (and sometimes even after leaving the field) is he able to construct the indicational chart. After that he must give an indicational interpretation to the working geo-botanical map. That interpretation consists in combining the areas of communities with similar indicational significance under a common colour or hatching, but retaining the geo-botanical boundaries and individual index for each community.

That method is generally used for compiling soil-salinity maps and lithological maps with geo-botanical data.

Indicational surveys are divided by their degree of detail (Viktorov, 1955) into reconnaissances, selective surveys, and continuous surveys. The aim of an indicational reconnaissance is the use of geo-botanical indicators not for continuous mapping of certain territory but for constructing a chart of the locations of certain definite objects—outcrops of certain strata, accumulations of underground water or distribution of mineral lodes.

In a selective survey the geo-botanist does survey work only on a few areas that are in some way of interest to the geologist or the soil-management officer (especially on plains or areas with little denudation).

In a continuous survey the whole of a given territory is investigated and an indicational map is made for it.

Reconnaissances are usually made by a small detachment or even by one geo-botanist with independent transport allotted to him. For indicational surveys it is necessary to make up a geo-botanical party of three or four geo-botanists. The number in the party is determined by the area and the scale of the work.

4. USE OF AERIAL METHODS IN INDICATIONAL GEO-BOTANICAL SURVEYS

Aerial methods are used in very many ways in indicational surveys. Geo-botanical indicational analysis is of particularly high importance.

The function of geo-botanical indicational analysis is to reveal, through the aerial photographic picture of the plant cover, the various environmental conditions in which the vegetation exists (soil, mineral strata, underground water, etc.).

The plant cover of bogs enables one to determine their hydrological conditions. The plant communities of the flooded peripheral depressed parts of raised bogs ("lagg" in the terminology of bog-management officers) have a darker and more uniform colour, and communities of the central, relatively higher part have a lighter and more patchy colour.

Outcrops of the underlying mineral layer in a background of bog are well identified by their vegetation. They are indicated by the presence of communities of deciduous tree species and luxuriant herbage. On aerial photographs these communities have the appearance of sharply-outlined forest "islands" in the bog. By these signs one can discern outcrops of bed-rock in boggy districts.

Cases are known where vegetation clearly shows the presence of karst phenomena hidden under the bog cover. Thus on the birch-moss fens of Ivanovskaya province underlain by carbonate strata, circular areas of treeless raised bog have developed at the locations of karst funnels where the carbonate floor lies at a great depth (Grebenshchikova, 1939).

We have given data above showing that the aerial photographic picture of a bog provides much material on the question of the origin of a bog massif (works of Ye. A. Galkina).

In the tundra zone indicational analysis may give considerable assistance in compiling maps of permafrost. Thus in Alaska sedge-shrub tundra has developed on peat bogs with permafrost not more than 1 m deep, and subalpine shrub tundra on sands and boulder clay with permafrost not nearer than 2.5 m (Benninghoff, 1953). The above types of tundra are well distinguished on aerial photographs. Therefore analysis of the vegetation enables one to establish both the boundaries of different soils (peats, clays, sands) and the boundaries of areas with different permafrost conditions.

Petrusevich (1954) gives, as an example of geo-botanical indicators of analysis, the suppression of tree growth and the unique undulating appearance presented by the distribution of shrub vegetation along the strips where water flows above permafrost, indicating the presence of permafrost at no great depth, in the northern part of the taiga zone.

In forested districts a change from one stand to another with a different dominant species often depends on lithological conditions. It is well known that pines are adapted to sands, spruce to clays, and a number of tree species to carbonate strata. Therefore by establishing the boundaries of different stands one may with great accuracy determine the limits of distribution of different mineral strata. Often belts of forest indicate with great accuracy the extent of different strata.

In indicational analysis it is necessary also to study the distribution of tree and herbage communities on aerial photographs. In places of irregular relief the analysis of these communities enables one to separate slopes with more mesophyllous conditions (forest areas) from relatively drier areas (herbaceous vegetation). Determination of the upper limits of distribution of vegetation belts enables one to distinguish on aerial photographs a number of areas differing in climatic conditions.

FIG. 14. Aerial photograph of *Artemisia arenaria* indicating the presence of lenses of fresh water in the sand.

Indicational analysis is used in the forests of the U.S.A. for soil investigations (Wieslander and Storie, 1953). In that case a map of the plant cover is first compiled from analysis of aerial photographs. Then on all the delineated areas bore-holes are sunk, so arranged that they are located near the boundary between these areas on different sides of it. Thus by these bore-holes one can determine to what extent the geo-botanical boundaries coincide with the boundaries of the varieties óf soil. Later all the geo-botanical boundaries that coincide fully with soil boundaries are transferred to a soil map. On those areas where the geo-botanical and soil boundaries do not coincide it is necessary to make a soil survey by the usual terrestrial methods. In work in California it was found that 87 per cent of the total length of the boundaries of different kinds of soil coincided with plant community boundaries.

In arid provinces geo-botanical analysis plays a very great role in determining moisture and salinity conditions. Here, in the first place, we must mention that on arid plains—steppes, semi-deserts and deserts —all depressions in the relief and the whole network of temporary and permanent watercourses become visible primarily because of the distribution of vegetation. Thus the relatively more moisture-loving mesophyllous and partly hygrophyllous plant communities distributed along the erosion network make it possible to discern on aerial photographs even the smallest erosion gullies.

The colour of the plant cover in steppe and desert conditions depends to a great degree on hydro-geological conditions. Therefore hydrogeological analysis is carried out there mainly from the plant cover (Viktorov, 1955; Vostokova 1955; *et al.*). Examination of aerial photographs taken in summer is particularly important. In summer all communities that were brought into existence by the moisture of meltwaters and atmospheric precipitation fade, and acquire a whitishgreyish tint on aerial photographs. A dark colour is retained, for the most part, by communities of phreatophytes, which are permanently connected with underground water and do not depend on seasonal fluctuations in moisture. Naturally these communities exist only in places where there are underground waters within the limits of penetration of the root system of phreatophytes and within the limits of possible vertical movement of water vapour in the soil (for semi-deserts 15–20 m, for deserts 40 m). Therefore in summer-taken aerial photographs areas with underground waters lying close beneath the surface are easily identified by the dark colour of phreatophyte communities (Fig. 14).

10

In wind-blown sands in arid provinces, indicational analysis also serves as a valuable aid in the search for underground water close to the surface, In wind-carved depressions in the sand there are often formed at slight depth lenses of fresh water, resulting partly from infiltration and partly from condensation. At the bottom or the edges of such depressions there usually develop fairly luxuriant growths of phreatophytes and psammophytes. These growths are clearly visible on aerial photographs as a dark ring or spot on the light background of the sand (Fig. 14). By these indicators one may make a hydro-geological analysis on sands (Demidova *et al.*, 1955).

Communities of moisture-loving plants in deserts and semi-deserts are clearly visible in summer in the form of light-green areas. Therefore summer aerovisual observations are of great positive value in the search for underground water (Viktorov, 1955).

Moisture-loving plants clearly indicate the presence in the arid zone of contacts of water-bearing and impervious strata, and also the lines of tectonic faults in cases where underground water is located not far from the surface along the latter (which occurs fairly often). In all such cases aerial photographs show dark straight or broken lines of varying width formed by strips of moisture-loving plants (see Viktorov, Vostokova and Voronkova, 1955; Vinogradov 1955). In identifying such lines, however, one must observe great care, as they may easily be confused with some growths that owe their origin to human activities (weeds along roads, windbreak belts in sandy areas, etc.).

In landlocked depressions without outlets in the arid zone vegetation is often concentrated in belts. The origin of these belts is connected with the fact that the hydro-geological and geochemical conditions of these depressions have a belt-formation. Their soils are generally less saline; or in saline complexes sulphates predominate, and in the centres of the depressions general mineralization of the soil occurs and chlorides predominate. Moreover, the peripheral belts are characterized by deeper-lying underground water, whereas in the centre the water is close to the surface. Therefore in the peripheral belts communities of glycophytes (salt-intolerant plants) or gypsophytes are found, and the vegetation as a whole has a more xerophilous character. In the centre of the basin the plant cover is formed of succulent halophytes and moisture-loving species. In an aerial photograph that difference in the plant cover appears in the form of a belted picture (usually lighter belts lie on the periphery and darker belts at the centre). Along the boundaries of these belts, by the analytical method, one can distinguish areas with different types of soil salinity and different depths of underground water.

At the present time geo-botanical indicators are also fairly widely used in the search for useful minerals: the presence of certain species of plants and certain plant communities, and also the occurrence of certain changes in the external appearance and structure of plants (gigantism, dwarfing, etc.).

Unfortunately the majority of geo-botanical indicators of useful minerals do not show up on aerial photographs (because of the very small size of the plant indicators, which can be observed only with the aid of a geo-botanical specialist). A number of instances are on record, however, where the indicational analysis is helpful in the search for useful minerals. We quote below some of these instances.

In dry regions (the Caspian depression and the deserts of Central Asia and Transcaucasia) it is observed that in soils containing an increased amount of petroleum bitumens the plants are marked by large size and great luxuriance and have a strong tendency towards second blooming and vegetation (i.e. they have two flowering and vegetative stages during a single season). In most cases that second cycle occurs in late autumn. Therefore all places on which luxuriant and dense vegetation is observed in aerial photographs taken in autumn are worthy of detailed ground examination, as also are areas where fresh greenery and a large number of blossoming plants are discerned by aerovisual observations in autumn. Close attention should be given to these indicators if the district being investigated has petroleum possibilities.

In the steppes of West Kazakhstan, when rock phosphate beds are close to the surface, groups of shrubs of the family Leguminosae (especially caragana, *Caragana frutex, C. grandiflora*) and less often of the family Rosaceae *(Spiraea crenifolia)* appear in the plant cover. These groups of shrubs are well distinguished against the steppe background and give a specific spotted picture, and also can easily be identified in aerovisual observations. Therefore the investigator should pay close attention to the appearance of shrubs on the steppes.

In sandy deserts (Kara-Kum, Kyzyl-Kum) beds of a dark lichen *Collema minor*, forming continuous dense carpets, indicate the presence of depression areas where extensive layers of gypsum lie within the strata of sand and form a continuous horizon not far below the surface. These lichen beds are called "kara-kharsangi". The same name refers also to areas covered by a dark moss, *Tortula desertorum*. The moss

10*

beds are distinguished from the lichen kara-kharsangi by the fact that the former develop on gypsum layers buried under sand, and the latter develop on sands somewhat compressed and enriched with salts and are not indicators of gypsum. On aerial photographs the lichen kara-kharsangi show up by their intense black colour, whereas the moss beds are considerably lighter.

In semi-deserts and in clayey and stony deserts a low-growing subshrub "biyurgun" *(Anabasis salsa, A. depressa)* is widely distributed, forming dense tussocks or bushes scarcely raised above the surface. A fact worthy of special attention is that, in cases where the bed-rock on which the biyurgun grows contains a considerable amount of iron compounds, the biyurgun shrubs take on a peculiar dark-raspberry or brownish-red colour in autumn, whereas on strata not containing iron they become orange or almost rose-coloured. In view of the mass distribution of biyurgun these autumn colourings of it are very noticeable in aerovisual observations.

In conclusion we must say that attention should be given to all areas where absence of tall plants is observed and the soil is covered only by lichens and mosses. Complete extirpation of tall plants usually takes place when the substratum contains excessive amounts of any compounds that have a very poisonous effect on plants. Such phenomena are observed on substrata containing platinum (South Africa) or sulphur (Kara-Kum). One should, however, keep in mind the fact that on very compact massive strata and also in high mountain districts the absence of tall plants and predominant development of lichens depends not on geo-chemical causes but on the density of the strata and on climatic conditions.

From the above examples it is seen that indicational geo-botanical analysis may serve as an auxiliary method in the most varied investigations in the fields of geology, hydro-geology, geomorphology, soil management, etc. The possibilities of its use are far from being exhausted.

CHAPTER VII

PLANNING AND ORGANIZING WORK AND REPORTING ON GEO-BOTANICAL SURVEYS

1. PLANNING GEO-BOTANICAL SURVEYS

THE drawing up of a plan is an extremely responsible part of the work on geo-botanical surveys.

An essential condition of successful planning is precise knowledge of the national-economic aims of the work, the approximate amount of funds allotted for carrying it out, and also the approximate scale and nature of the maps to be compiled as a result of the survey. Therefore it is desirable that a geo-botanist engaged in planning survey work should receive, before he begins to draw up the plan, brief information on all the subjects listed above (the basic outline of the plan).

Having received the basic outline of the plan, the geo-botanist should in the first place carry out a number of preliminary tasks, without which it would be impossible to draw up a plan. These tasks are as follows: (1) collecting information on natural conditions in the district to be studied, both from published data and from unpublished reports existing in various institutions (foundation material), (2) collecting information on geo-botanical surveys made previously in that district and their purposes, and on the scale and contents of maps that were compiled, and also directly familiarizing himself with those maps, (3) collecting information on the availability of topographic maps on various scales and on aerial photographic material covering the district of the work, (4) collecting a whole series of administrative, economic and medical reports on the given district (on means of communication, settlements, existence of aerodromes of the civil air service, possibilities of delivery of supplies and automobile fuel to the survey parties, special safety measures, etc.).

In collecting material on natural conditions in the district and also on geo-botanical surveys one must bear in mind the fact that a great amount of material on these subjects may be found in the following organizations: Botanical Institute, Soil Institute and Forest Institute of the U.S.S.R. Academy of Sciences, Fodder Institute, Peat Institute, biological and geographical faculties of universities, Ministry of Agriculture, Ministry of Forestry, botanical gardens of universities and of the Academy of Sciences, etc.

Information on the availability of topographical maps and aerial photographic material for the district may be obtained from the Chief Administration of Geodesy and Cartography (GUGK).

After obtaining all the above data the geo-botanist may begin to draw up the plan.

There is no single standard form of plan for geo-botanical surveys. In different organizations plans are drawn up in different forms. We may, however, mention some of the divisions that, in our opinion, may be used in drawing up any plan of geo-botanical work. These divisions and a brief statement of their contents are given below.

1. Introduction. Here is stated the national-economic significance of the work, and its aims and the methods of attaining them are sketched in the most general terms.

2. Outline of natural conditions in the district to be investigated. Here is given a fairly detailed outline of the physical geography of the district, with special attention being given to the soil and the plant cover. In the outline one should not only give a static picture of the plant cover but also provide a number of examples relating to the history of its development and its present dynamics.

3. History of investigation. This section gives a survey of expeditionary investigations in the district and pays special attention to a review of the nature, contents and scales of maps that have bean compiled. The survey of the history of investigation is usually presented by periods—in the division into periods it is important to pay special attention to the post-Revolution period, when the most planned and intense study of the natural resources of our country began; often also one distinguishes the period of investigations made in connection with migration measures, as in many cases these investigations provided rich and valuable material.

4. Method of working. In this section one should consider these questions: on what scale the map should be compiled, whether it should be a general geo-botanical map or whether it should belong

to any type of special geo-botanical maps (and, if so, which type), and also into what units the plant cover should be classified. Here one should also state what kind of geo-botanical survey should be used in the work, and give reasons for the choice of a particular kind of survey. One must state what density of transects is required and to what extent transects can be spread out if aerial photographs and aerovisual observations are used. It is also necessary to make clear to what extent, and on what scales, "keys" and profiles will be used in the survey. Special attention should be given to the technique of description: one must state how points for description are to be selected, what density of description-points should be used, by what method each of the defined outlines will be entered in the journals, and for what places more detailed descriptions will be given; one must list the indicators of plant cover that will be taken into account in the description and by what method the plant cover inventory will be made. One must also list all necessary supplementary tasks (cutting of samples, collection of soil samples) and state the order in which they will be done.

We must also point out that to compile a map on a certain scale it is necessary to carry out field survey work on a scale somewhat larger than that of the finished map. Thus, for example, to compile a map that will show the boundaries of groups of communities (i.e. on a scale of from 1 : 50,000 to 1 : 100,000), the mapping must be done with such precision that the areas of separate communities are delineated, and only later will these areas be combined. In other words, a geo-botanical map compiled in the field (a working geo-botanical map) by delineating upon it units of plant cover should be more detailed than the final version of the map.

The task is considerably lightened if there are standard departmental instructions for a given type of work. In that case, when describing the method of work one should dwell mainly only on those divergences from the standard investigation methods that are necessitated by natural or economic conditions in the district.

5. Organization of the work. In this section the order of organization and performance of the work is set forth. It is necessary to state the dates of beginning and ending the work, the number of detachments (or parties), their staff, the number and kind of transport vehicles provided for each detachment, the number of flying hours per detachment, and the number and scale of topographical maps and aerial photographs delivered to the detachments. It is necessary also to list all kinds of report material, both preliminary and final (reports, maps) and state

the dates when they will be submitted, and also the kinds of progress reports (quarterly, monthly, ten-day).

The locations of bases and sub-bases of the expedition must also be given and justified. If it is proposed to use radio for communication between the detachments and their base and between the detachments themselves, it is necessary to list the kinds of radio equipment to be used at the bases and by the parties and to provide a graphic radio-network diagram.

Serious attention should be given to problems of safety techniques (sometimes these problems are dealt with in a special section). Here one must list equipment and materials that must be provided to the detachments and workers of the expedition to avoid mishaps (general and individual water containers, protective spectacles in deserts, alpine equipment in high mountain districts, etc.). One must also attend to those elements of labour discipline, the observance of which is particularly necessary for safeguarding the lives and health of personnel (e.g. prohibition of travelling alone, observance of the regime for drinking, etc.).

In the same section a place should be found for all other organizational questions affecting the work of the expedition; e.g. if analysis of any samples (of soil or water) is proposed, the location of the laboratory, the principles and procedure of transportation of samples, the approximate dates of receipt of the results of analyses from the laboratory.

In this section of the plan a time-table of the work should be set out, with a statement of the dates of departure of detachments from the organization headquarters to the field base of the expedition, the dates of their setting out directly on field work, the time of return from the field to the base, the time allotted for preliminary office work, the dates of travel from the field base to the organization headquarters, the dates of final office work, etc.

An accounting section is appended to the plan containing all quantitative data to prove the soundness of the plan and an estimate containing all information of a financial or economic character. To compile the accounts and the estimate one must use consolidated departmental instructions and estimate reference books. There are no general norms and estimates for geo-botanical work.

It is desirable to append to the plan:

(1) a small-scale sketch of the district, with indication of the area to be surveyed;

(2) a chart of studies made in the district, with a statement of areas in it investigated by other organizations and also of areas on which geo-botanical surveys have already been made on any scale.

The above example of the drawing-up of a plan is only the most general outline, which may have many widely-different variations.

2. FIELD AND OFFICE WORK AND REPORTING

Work on a geo-botanical survey is divided into field and office work.

The process of direct study of the plant cover and natural conditions in a given district, accompanied by compilation of a field geo-botanical map, is field work. The period allotted to that work is called the field period.

The process of collecting published and background material and also the process of analysing the material collected during the field period and preparing various reports on the whole work comprise the office-work period. One must distinguish three kinds of office work—preparatory, preliminary, and final.

Preparatory office work precedes departure for the field. It consists basically in the collection of published and background material. Study of the most important material is generally done during the drawing-up of the plan, but one cannot usually succeed in familiarizing oneself with all the material during the planning period, and part of that work is transferred to the preparatory office-work period. As a result of that work it is desirable to make an annotated card-index—a catalogue of literature on the district of the work, conspectuses of all works containing data of substantial significance, and a consolidated list of plants found by different investigators in the territory of the given district.

During the same period a preliminary analysis of aerial photographs is made if it is expected to use it in the work.

Simultaneously with the carrying out of these research tasks economic preparations for the field work are made.

The date of departure for the field is very important. In deciding on it one must take into account seasonal phenomena affecting the passability of roads in the district under study, and fix the date of departure for the moment when the roads become completely usable. At the same time one must also take account of phenological phenomena, on which the successful outcome of the work often depends (thus, for example, a late departure for work on the pastures of Central Asia deprives the investigator of the opportunity of making an estimate of one of the important elements of the fodder crop—spring ephemerals).

On arriving at the place of work one should devote the necessary time to acquainting oneself with basic data from local organizations (if it has not been possible to assign an assistant to that task before the departure of the whole survey party). Organizations especially worthy of attention in that connection are land management branches, leskhozy, agricultural experimental stations, regional museums and hut laboratories. In the process of that work both the conspectuses and the annotated catalogues should be extended. These tasks are in essence also office work.

The nature of the work during the field period depends on the method selected for the geo-botanical survey.

One of the most important conditions for successful work during the field period, apart from its dependence on the type of survey, is properly-organized assembling of the observation data. That consists basically in: (1) clear writing of descriptions; (2) compilation of maps of factual material; (3) compiling a working geo-botanical map. There is no standard form of documentation for a geo-botanical survey. We must list some requirements, however, which it is necessary to observe in any kind of description.

(1) Each description should have its own number (the latter should not be duplicated by other surveyors, for which purpose the surveyors should apportion numbers among themselves beforehand) and also the date and exact address.

(2) Each description, however short, should contain information both on plant cover and on ecological conditions; otherwise it does not merit the name of geo-botanical description.

(3) All species of plants in herbaria taken from the area described should be marked in the description with a special symbol or note.

(4) A question mark should be placed against all specific names of whose correctness the investigator is uncertain.

(5) If the work is done from aerial photographs, the photograph on which a point described is located should be stated in the description.

(6) Specimens of plants that were not identified by the geobotanist and described under their correct names should be taken at once to a herbarium: the correct name of the plant is there written on a label, on which are also stated (besides the usual items on a label) the number of the description and the locality from which the plant was taken.

(7) It is desirable that the description should be in precise, clear handwriting, with an ordinary pencil, without erasures; when necessary, incorrect text should be scored through (but in such a way that it can still be read) but on no account should it be erased with a rubber. It is better to write on one side of the paper, using the other side for sketches.

(8) At the end of each description it is necessary to state what material has been retained for further study and to list the specimens of soil, rock strata, underground water and plants taken in connection with that description.

(9) Several departmental instructions and guides (Bykov, 1953) recommend making a list of separate delineated areas. In it are entered: (a) the number of each delineated area, (b) the name of the community dominant in the area, (c) the number of the description made in the area, (d) brief descriptions of the geomorphological, soil, and hydrogeological conditions, (e) a brief description of the plant cover, (f) the chief dominant species and their abundance. Depending on the aims of the survey, the list of areas may be supplemented by other data (for instance, in a description of pastures one should state for each area the season of use of that type of pasture, the fodder resources in it, etc.).

A very useful addition to the field documentation is the compilation of a so-called "map of factual material". On that map are entered all transects laid out in the district under study (subdividing them into ground and aerovisual transects), description points, bore-holes, points where samples of underground water were taken, location of "key" areas, areas covered by earlier surveys on a larger scale, etc. Thus that map shows material obtained as a result of investigations and makes it possible to judge in what detail the territory has been studied. The outlines of plant communities are not entered on the map of factual material. The map of factual material is compiled in the field, and transects and other data are entered on it in the course of the work.

A most important document of record in any geo-botanical survey is the working geo-botanical map, compiled in the field. It is compiled directly on the transects by sketching the outlines of plant communities within the limits of visibility (sometimes defining them more accurately by means of side trips). The greater part of the work on the map should be done on transects; in camp one may complete only some tasks connected with interpolation of data that were collected on different transects.

If the work is done with use of aerial photographs it is not necessary to enter the outlines on the map during the transects. The data may be transferred from the aerial photographs to the map in camp. In some organizations one is allowed to do the work on aerial photographs up to the end of the field period and to defer the transfer of outlines to the topographical map until the office-work period.

The working map (or the working aerial photographs) should have a legend. Compilation of the legend should be begun after the first reconnaissance study of the given district. The legend must be perfected during the course of the work.

Besides the three basic types of documents—descriptions, maps of factual material and working geo-botanical maps—there may be other, very different kinds of recording documents, depending on the nature of the work. The principal and the most widely used of these are the following: (1) journal of descriptions of soil samples, (2) journal for recording water samples, (3) record of results of harvesting sample plots, (4) herbarium notes.

The organization of work during the field period should include general familiarization with natural conditions in the district, direct survey work, the possibility of exchange of experience between different groups of surveyors, control over the quality of work and consideration of the results of the work before it is fully concluded. Based on that, we may suggest the following rough plan for carrying out work during the field period:

(1) Reconnaissance of the district under study (it is very desirable that this should be done by the aerovisual method).

(2) First stage of survey work (occupying approximately the first half of the period).

(3) Productive consultations by leaders of detachments and parties or a tour of all parties by the head of the survey in order to attain agreement of views by all the leaders on the basic laws of distribution of the plant cover.

(4) Second stage of survey work. During the period of its completion a number of control journeys are made by the head of the survey.

(5) Reception by the head of the work (or special commission) of field material: it is desirable that this should be done directly in the field, as then supplementary work is possible afterwards to remedy defects.

(6) Final productive consultation with detailed consideration of the merits and defects of the work.

Special attention should be given to the solution in field conditions of all controversial questions affecting scientific research problems, as solution of them in the office-work period is practically impossible. In particular, if in field conditions the work is done by several detachments, it is necessary on its conclusion to reach full agreement on the boundaries of all delineated areas passing from the territory of one surveyor into the territory of another, and also to ensure that the boundaries of the areas correspond with the results of surveys in earlier years.

The office-work period begins with preliminary office work, as a result of which a preliminary summing-up (sometimes accompanied by a map) is made. These tasks are sometimes performed at the field base of the expedition near the district of the work, and sometimes the expedition travels to some large centre, to its headquarters.

The office-work report should contain information on the aims, the district and the organization of the work, on those who carried it out, on the dates when the work (planning and actual) began and ended, on quantitative records of the work (number of descriptions, area surveyed, total number of km in transects, number of metres in bore-holes sunk, number of samples taken, etc.) and on the principal scientific results of the work. One should here give in a condensed and general form all the main conclusions that will later be presented in the final report in a more detailed form with supporting evidence. It is useful to give in the report a brief analysis of the reasons for various disagreements that hindered the work.

After the preliminary report is drawn up the office work proper begins. In the first stage of it one must: (1) obtain the results of all types of laboratory analysis (analysis of soils, water, plants, etc.), (2) identify all unknown plants, (3) examine all literature not previously studied. After that one may commence the final working-up of material. That consists in: (1) making precise and finally completing the outlines on the map and carefully checking the data on which the boundaries are based (this also includes supplementary analysis), (2) constructing the final legend from the comparison of data from descriptions and analyses, (3) critical scientific generalization of all material, comparison of personal observations and published data, and working out a general summary of the vegetation of the district under study.

Simultaneously with preparation of material for the report, work is done on compilation of the final version of the geo-botanical map. After the supplementary analysis has been completed and all outlines

11

have been perfected and brought into their final shape, the question of what units of plant cover are to be shown on the map must be settled. It has been stated above that smaller and more detailed units of plant cover are generally defined on the working geo-botanical map than are used on the final map. Therefore before the latter is compiled, the magnitude of the phyto-cenological units to be used on the map and the principles on which consolidation is to be made are determined.

If the map to be compiled is a general geo-botanical map, having no more detailed practical function to fulfil, the consolidation is done with use of the general features of the different phyto-cenological units, by means of which the smaller units are combined into larger ones. If it is a question of compiling a special geo-botanical map, the consolidation must take account of a number of practical considerations (fodder resources and seasonal use of pastures, forestry items on forest maps, etc.).

After determining the principles of consolidation and the factors involved, the areas delineated on the working map are combined into units of higher order corresponding to the scale of the final map.

At the same time conventional symbols should be worked out. Some data about conventional symbols used on other special maps are given in the respective chapters (see above).

It must be remarked that all the above tasks are performed during the same period and it is difficult to separate them. It is necessary more than once to pass from one kind of work to another. Particularly important here is wide exchange of views, as well as the frequent holding of scientific-productive conferences.

Only after the working-out of the material is completed can the drawing-up of the report be commenced. The plans of reports may vary greatly, depending on the aims of the surveys. We give below as an example a rough plan of the report on a geo-botanical survey. It includes the following main points:

Introduction (aim of the work and its national-economic significance).

Chapter I. Outline of the physical geography of the district studied and history of the study of it (zonal location, geological structure, climate, relief, soils, vegetation, fauna). Here one often gives also a brief history of the study of the district.

Chapter II. Organization and method of the work (information on the structure, number and personal composition of the detachment, dates of the work, transportation, provision of equipment and supplies); method of the work includes lay-out of transects, methods and density of observations, nature of use of aerial methods, and special methods of investigation called for by the specific character of the work. It must be remarked that the method and the organization of the work are often described separately in two different chapters.

Chapter III. Analysis of factual material. This is one of the most important chapters of the report. Here are listed and described the communities that are identified and their conditions of existence. Communities are usually described in the order in which they are arranged in the legend of the map. Since this chapter is essentially an extended commentary on the map, attention must be given to close correspondence of the contents of the chapter with the map and the legend. With a great volume of material one must allot two or three chapters to this subject, dividing them according to types of vegetation ("Forests", "Steppes", etc.).

Chapter IV. Basic laws in the structure of the plant cover. This chapter is a scientific-theoretical generalization of the factual material. Here one should critically examine the factual material and compare it with published data.

Chapter V. Productive results of the work. Here the economic results of the work are explained in the clearest way and made as comprehensible as possible for the general reader. Then follows a brief conclusion.

REFERENCES

CHAPTER I

Bykov, B. A. Geo-botany *(Geobotanika)*. Alma-Ata, 1953.
Sochava, V. B. Principles and tasks of geo-botanical cartography (Printsipy i zadachi geobotanicheskoi kartografii). Coll. Botanical problems. *(Voprosy botaniki.)* Izd. Akad. Nauk SSSR, Moscow-Leningrad, 1954.

CHAPTER II

Larin, I. V., Shiffers, Ye. V. and Byeidyeman, I. N. Mapping plant cover. (Kartirovaniye rastitel'nogo pokrova.) Short guide for geo-botanical investigations. *(Kratkoye rukovodstvo dlya geobotanicheskikh issledovaniyi.)* Moscow, 1952.
Method of field geo-botanical investigations *(Metodika polevykh geobotanicheskikh issledovanii)*. Izd. Akad. Nauk SSSR, Moscow-Leningrad, 1938.
Programmes for geo-botanical investigations *(Programmy dlya geobotanicheskikh issledovaniyi)*. Izd. Akad. Nauk SSSR, Leningrad, 1932.
Short guide for geo-botanical investigation in connection with windbreak planting and creation of a permanent food base in the south of the European part of the U.S.S.R. *(Kratkoye rukovodstvo dlya geobotanicheskikh issledovaniyi v svyazi s polezashchitnym lesorazvedeniyem ustoichivoi kormovoi bazy na yuge Yevropeiskoi chasti SSSR)*. Izd. Akad. Nauk SSSR, Moscow, 1952.

CHAPTER III

Anuchin, N. P. Forest Valuation *(Lesnaya taksatsiya)*. Goslesbumizdat. Moscow-Leningrad, 1952.
Samoilovich, G. G. Use of aviation and aerial photography in forestry *(Primeneniye aviatsii i aerofotos"emki v lesnom khozyaistve)*. Goslesbumizdat. Moscow-Leningrad, 1953.
Sukachev, V. N. Guide to investigation of types of forest *(Rukovodstvo k issledovaniyu tipov lesov)*. Third edition, Sel'khozgiz, Moscow-Leningrad, 1931.
Tsvetkov, M. Ya. Forest maps and the method of compiling them *(Lesnyye karty i metodika ikh sostavleniya)*. Izd. Akad. Nauk SSSR, Moscow-Leningrad, 1950.

CHAPTER IV

Anufriyev, G. I., Bogdanovskaya-Giyenef, I. D., Galkina, Ye. A. and Tsinzerling, Yu. D. Method of investigating bog vegetation (Metodika issledovaniya rastitel' nosti bolot). Method of field geo-botanical investigations *(Metodika polevykh geo-botanicheskikh issledovaniyi)*. Izd. Akad. Nauk SSSR, Moscow-Leningrad, 1938.
Galkina, Ye. A. Use of aerial surveys in bog management (Ispol'zovaniye aeros"emki v bolotovedeniyi). Bot. zh. **6**, 1953.
Instructions for investigating bogs in seeking routes for roads *(Instruktsiya po obsledovaniyu bolot pri izyskaniyakh dorozhnoi trassy)*, 1939.

NEISHTADT, M. I. On the question of detailed investigation of bogs for collective farms and state farms (K voprosu o detal'nom issledovaniyi bolot dlya kolkhozov i sov-khozov). *Sov. bot.*, **1**, 1937.

TYUREMNOV, S. M. Peat deposits and their investigation *(Torfyanyye mestorozhdeniya i ikh razvedka)*. Gosenergoizdat, Moscow-Leningrad, 1949

CHAPTER V

AMELIN, I. S. Pasture rotation in the karabul-breeding industry in Central Asia *(Past-vishcheoboroty v karakulevodstve Srednei Aziyi)*. Izd. Vses. nauchn.-issl. inst. karakule-vodstva, Samarkand, 1943.

ANDREYEV, V. N. Investigation of reindeer pastures on the tundra with the aid of air-craft (Obsledovaniye tundrovykh olen'ikh pastbishch s pomoshch'yu samoleta). *Trudy inst. polyarnogo zem.*, reindeer series, **1**, 1938.

ANDREYEV, V. N. Method of aerovisual investigation of reindeer pastures (Metodika vozdushno-glazomernogo obsledovaniya olen'ikh pastbishch). *Trudy nauch.-issl. inst. polyarnogo zem., zhivotnovodstva i prom. khoz.*, reindeer series, **12**, 1940.

DOKHMAN, G. I. Mapping of complexes (O kartirovanii kompleksov). *Uchen. zap. Moscow State University*, **36**, 1940.

CHAPTER VI

GAVEMAN, A. V. Aerial survey and investigation of natural resources *(Aeros"emka i issledovaniye prirodnykh resursov)*. Izd. Akad. Nauk SSR, Moscow-Leningrad, 1937.

LARIN, I. V. Classification of soils and agricultural lands by their plant cover *(Opredele-niye pochv i sel'skokhozyaistvennykh ugodii po rastitel'nomu pokrovu)* Sel'khozgiz, Mos-cow, 1953.

RAMENSKII, L. G. Introduction to complex soil-geo-botanical investigation of lands *(Vvedeniye v kompleksnoye pochvennogeobotanicheskoye issledovaniye zemel')*. Moscow 1938.

VIKTOROV, S. V. Use of the geo-botanical method in geological and hydro-geological investigations *(Ispol'zovaniye geobotanicheskogo metoda pri geologicheskikh i gidrogeologi-cheskikh issledovaniyakh)*. Izd. Akad. Nauk SSSR, Moscow, 1955.

ADDITIONAL REFERENCES

AGEYENKO, A. S. Aerial valuation of forests with use of small-scale aerial photographs (Aerotaksatsiya lesov s primeneniyem melkomasshtabnykh aerosnimkov). Report of discussion by Candidate in Science at the Leningrad S. M. Kirov Forest-technical Academy, 1954.

ALABYSHEV, V. V. Short programme for investigating bogs and peat beds as sources of sapropelites and similar deposits (Kratkaya programma po issledovaniyu bolot i torfyanikov kak mestorozhdyenii sapropelitov i rodstvennykh im otlozhenii). *Izv. Sapropel. komiteta*, **IV**, 1928.

ANDREYEV, V. N. Use of aerial methods for geo-botanical mapping and making inven-tories of fodder areas (Primeneniye aerometodov dlya geobotanicheskogo kartiro-vaniya i inventarizatsii kormovykh ploshchadyei). *Bot. zh.*, **6**. 1952.

ANDREYEV, V. N. Identification of different types of tundra from aerial photographs and their aerovisual characteristics due to frost-cracking (Deshifrirovaniye po aeros-nimkam razlichnykh tipov tundr i ikh aerovizual'naya kharakteristika po moroznoi treshchinovatosti). *Geogr. sb.* (Geogr. coll.), **7**. 1955.

APROLOV, V. A. Geological Mapping *(Geologicheskoye kartirovaniye)*. Gosgeolizdat, Moscow-Leningrad, 1952.

BARANOV, V. I. Use of symbols in geo-botanical maps (K simbolike geobotanicheskoi karty). *Izv. Perm. biol. nauch.-issled. inst.*, **8**. Nos. 6-8, 1933.

BENNINGHOFF, W. S. Ose of aerial photographs for terrain interpretation based on field mapping. *Photogr. Eng.*, 19, **3**. 1953.

BOGDANOV, P. D. Land management in reindeer pastures *(Zemleustroistvo olen'ikh pastbishch)*. Khabarovsk, 1954.

BUYALOV, N. I. and SHVYRYAYEVA, A. M. Geo-botanical methods of investigation in the search for boron compounds (Geobotanicheskiye metody issledovanii pri poiskakh bornogo syr'ya). *Trudy V. A. G. T.*, I, 1955.

CLEMENTS, F. *Plant indicators: the relation of plant communities to process and practice.* Carnegie Inst. Wash., Pub. 290, 1920.

DEMIDOVA, L. S., SHAVYRINA, A. V., KUZINA, Z. M , FADEYEVA, O I. and LEVIN, V. L. Experiment in use of the geo-botanical method in hydro-geological investigations on the Black Lands (Opyt ispol'zovaniya geobotanicheskogo metoda pri gidrogeologicheskikh issledovaniyakh na Chernykh Zemlyakh). *Trudy V. A. G. T.*, **1**. 1955.

DOKHMAN, G. I. On some classification units in complexes (O nekotorykh klassificatsionnykh yedinitsakh kompleksakh). *Zemlevedeniye*, **38**. 1936.

DOKHMAN, G. I. Vegetation of Mugodzhar. *(Rastitel'nost Mugodzhar.)* Geografgiz, Moscow, 1954.

DYUKAREV, N. P. Use of aerial photographs for investigating bogs and their agricultural significance (Ispol'zovaniye aerosnimkov dlya vyyavleniya bolot i ikh sel'skokhozyaistvennogo znacheniya). *Sb. Lesnaya aviatsiya* (Coll. Forest aviation), Leningrad, 1934.

DYUKAREV, N. P. Use of aerovisual survey material for discovering peat beds. (Ispol'zovaniye materialov vozdushno-glazomernoi s"emki pri vyyavlenii torfyanykh mestorozhdyenii). *Torfyanaya prom.*, **7**. 1948.

Fodder plants of natural hay-meadows and pastures in the U.S.S.R. *(Kormovyye rasteniye yestestvennykh senokosov i pastbishch SSSR)*. Edited by I. V. Larin, Izd. VASKhNIL, 1937.

GAYEL', A. G., DUBYANSKII, V. A., PETROV, M. P. and YAKUBOV, T. F. Programme for geo-botanical study of sands (Programma dlya geobotanicheskogo izucheniya peskov). Programmes for geo-botanical investigations *(Programmy dlya geobotanicheskikh issledovanii)*. Izd. Akad. Nauk SSSR, Leningrad, 1932.

GAYEL', A. G. and KOLIKOV, M. Problems of method in the complex investigation of sands (Voprosy metodiki kompleksnogo issledovaniya peskov). *Izv. Gos. geogr. obshch.*, 1, 1937.

GALKINA, YE. A. On the role of geo-botanical investigations in agricultural reclamation of bogs (O roli geobotanicheskikh issledovaniyi pri sel'skokhozyaistvennom osvoyeniyi bolot). *Sov. bot.*, **4**. 1936.

GALKINA, YE. A. Bog landscapes in the forest zone (Bolotnyye landshafty lesnoi zony). *Geogr. Sb.* (Geogr. coll.), **7**. 1955.

GREBENSHCHIKOVA, A. A. Instructions for use of conventional symbols on maps and profiles in investigations of peat bogs. (Instruksiyi po pol'zovaniyu uslovnymi znakami dlya kart i profilei pri issledovaniyi torfyanikov). *Trud. Vses. inst. torfa*, **4**. 1933.

GREBENSHCHIKOVA, A. A. On the problem of development of bogs in the karst funnels of Ivanovskaya province. (K voprosu a razvitii bolot v karstovykh voronkakh Ivanovskoi oblasti). *Sov. bot.*, **1**. 1939.

GROSSGEIM, A. A. Analysis of the flora of the Caucasus (Analiz flory Kavkaza). *Trud. Azerb. fil. Akad. Nauk. SSSR*, **1**. 1936.

IL'IN, I. A. Investigation of terrestrial waters. *(Issledovaniye vod sushi.)* Gidrometizdat, Leningrad, 1953.

Instructions for investigating bogs in seeking routes for roads *(Instruktsiya po obsledovaniyu bolot pri izyskaniyakh dorozhnoi trassy)*. Gushosdor NKVD SSSR, Dor. nauch.-issled. inst., Moscow, 1939.

KARPINSKII, A. Can living plants be indicators of the mineral strata and formations on which they are found, and are the places where they grow worthy of the special attention of the geologist? (Mogut li zhivyye rasteniya byt' ukazatelyami gornykh porod i formatsiyi, na kotorykh oni vstrechayutsya i zasluzhivayut li mestoprozyabaniya ikh osobogo vnimaniya geognosta?) *Sadovodstvo*, **3—4**. Moscow, 1841.

KARTSEV, A. A., TABASARANSKII, Z. A., SUBBOTA, M. I. and MOGILEVSKII, G. A. Geochemical methods of search for and research on oil and gas deposits *(Geokhimicheskive metody poiskov i razvedki neftyanykh i gazovykh mestorozhdyenii)*. Gostoptekhizdat, Moscow, 1954.

KAS'YANOVA, M. S. Aerovisual geo-botanical observations in semi-deserts and deserts. (Aerovizual'nyye geobotanicheskiye nablyudyeniya v polupustyne i pustyne). *Trud. VAGT*, **1**. 1955.

KOLOSOVA, A. V. Mapping as a method of study of the natural and technical characteristics of experimental plots (Kartirovaniye kak metod izucheniya prirodnoi i tekhnicheskoi obstanovki opytnykh delyanok). *Izv. Gos. lugov. inst.*, **4-5**. 1928a.

KOLOSOVA, A. V. Mapping experimental plots and estimating crops as a result of mapping(Kartirovaniye opytnykh delyanok i uchet urozhaya v svyazi s kartirovaniyem) Trud. Soveshch. lugovodov-opytnikov, 1928b.

KOLOSOVA, A. YE. and RAIZER, P. YA. Use of aeria photographs in forest valuation *(Izpol'zovaniye aerosnimkov pri taksatsiyi lesa)*. Goslesbumizdat, Moscow-Leningrad, 1953.

KOMAROV, N. F. Geo-botanical districts of Voronezh and Kursk provinces (Geobotanicheskiye raiony Voronezhskoi i Kurskoi oblastei). *Trud. BIN Akad. Nauk SSSR* ser. III, **4**. 1938.

KUNITSYN, A. G. On a method of quantitative estimates of the elements of a semi-desert complex (K voprosu o metode kolichestvennogo ucheta elementov polupustynnogo kompleksa). *Sov. bot.*, **5**. 1933.

KUNITSYN, A. G. On the use of material from aerial photographic surveys for compiling large-scale geo-botanical maps (K voprosu o metode kolichestvennogo ucheta elementov polupustynnogo kompleksa). *Sov. bot.*, **4**. 1934.

LARIN, I. V. Experiment in classifying soils, bed-rock, relief, agricultural lands and other elements of the landscape by the plant cover, in the central part of Ural region *(Opyt opredeleniya po rastitel'nomu okrovu pochv, materinskikh porod, rel'efa, sel'skokhozyaistvennykh ugodii i drugikh elementov landshafta srednei chasti Ural'skoi oblasti)*. Kzyl-Orda, 1926.

LARIN, I. V. Programme for geo-botanical study of pastures and haymeadows of the steppes, semi-deserts and deserts *(Programma dlya geobotanicheskogo izucheniya pastbishch i senokosov stepei, polupustyn' i pustyn')*. Izd. Akad. Nauk SSSR, Leningrad, 1932.

LEONT'EV, V. L. On the use of aerial photographic surveys and aerovisual observations of vegetation for reclamation of deserts (Ob ispol'zovanii aerofotos"emki i aerovizual'nykh obsledovanii rastitel'nosti pri osvoyenii pustyn). *Bot. zh.*, **6**. 1952.

LEPCHENKO, YA. F. Some ideas on the subject of a thorough and precise method of investigating bogs for the purpose of their agricultural utilization (Neskol'ko soobrazhenii po voprosu uglublennoi metodiki issledovaniya bolot v tselyakh sel'skokhozyaistvennogo ikh ispol'zovaniya). *Sov. botanika*, **5**. 1933.

LOMONOSOV, M. V. On ore bodies and lodes and mining them *(O rudnykh mestakh i zhilykh i priiske ikh)*. Gosgeolizdat, Moscow, 1949.

MALEV, P. I. Mapping the forests of the U.S.S.R. (Kartografirovaniye lesov SSSR). *Les. khoz.*, **3**. 1949.

MALYUGA D. P. On endemic plant diseases in districts of nickel ore deposits in the southern Urals (Ob endemicheskom zabolevanii rastenii v raionakh nikelevykh mestorozhdyenii Yuzhnogo Urala). Report at the conference on trace elements in the USSR (Ref. dokl. na konf. po mikroelementam SSSR). Moscow, 1950.

MOTOVILOV, G. P. Role of forest typology in forestry. *(Rol' lesnoi tipologii v lesnom khozyaistve.)* Moscow, 1955.

NESVETAILOVA, N. G. Geo-botanical investigations in the search for ore deposits. (Geobotanicheskiye issledovaniya pri poiskakh rudnykh mestorozhdyenii.) *Trud. VAGT,* **1**. 1955.

NECHAYEVA, N. T., MORDVINOV, N. A. and MOSOLOV, I. A. Pastures of Kara-Kum and their use *(Pastbishcha Kara-Kumov i ikh ispol'zovaniye)*. Ashkhabad, 1943.

OLENIN, A. S. Improving the quality of peat-research work for the peat industry (Povysit' kachestvo torforazvedochnykh rabot dlya torfyanoi promyshlennosti). *Torfyanaya prom.,* **6**. 1948.

OSOSKOV, P. A. Distribution of Lower Cretaceous iron-bearing strata in the region of the Zasursk forests (Rasprostraneniye nizhnemelovykh zhelezosodyerzhashchikh porod v oblasti Zasurskikh lesov. *Mat-ly k poznaniyu geol. stroyeniya Ros. imperii,* **1** 1899.

PEL'T, N. N. and CHIRVINSKII V. F. Methods of agriculture reclamation of Ust-Urt *(Puti sel'skokhozyaistvennogo osvoyeniya Ustyurta)*. Izd. Akad. Nauk SSSR, Moscow, 1956.

PETROV, M. P. Significance of aerial survey in study of the plant cover of deserts of the U.S.S.R. (Znacheniye aeros"emki v izuchenii rastitel'nogo pokrova pustyn' SSSR). *Sov. bot.,* **5**. 1936.

PETRUSEVICH, M. N. Geological exploration work on the basis of aerial methods *(Geologo-poiskovyye raboty na osnove aerometodov)*. Gosgeoltekhizdat, Moscow, 1954.

PRIKLONSKII, V. A. Vegetation and underground water (Rastitel'nost' i gruntovyye vody). *Sb. gidrogeologiya i inzhenernaya geologiya.* Coll. Hydro-geology and engineering geology), **1**. 1935.

PRONIN, A. K. Guide to interpretation of aerial photographs *(Rukovodstvo k deshifrirovaniyu lesnykh aerosnimkov)*. Goslestekhizdat, Moscow, 1936.

PROZOROVSKII, A. V. Method of Geo-botanical investigation of deserts and semi-deserts (Metodika geobotanicheskogo issledovaniya pustyn' i polupustyn). Method of field geobotanical investigations *(Metodika polevykh geobotanicheskikh issledovanii)*. Izd. Akad. Nauk SSSR, Moscow-Leningrad, 1938.

PROZOROVSKII, N. A. Short guide to geo-botany *(Kratkii uchebnik geobotaniki)*. Izd. MIIGAIK, Moscow, 1940.

RUMYANTSEV, S. N. Accuracy of survey of forest territory by the aerovisual method *(Tochnost' s"emki lesnoi territorii aerovizualnym metodom)*. Goslestekhizdat, Moscow, 1935.

SAMOILOVICH, G. G. On the theoretical bases of aerial valuation of forests (O teoreticheskikh osnovakh aerotaksatsii lesov). *Geogr. sb.* (Geogr. coll.), **7**. 1955.

SCHARFETTER, P. Die Kartographische Darstellung d. Pflanzengesellschaften. *Handbuch der biolog. Arbeitsmethoden,* **11**. Teil 5, Berlin, 1928.

SHAPOSHNIKOVA, L. A. Representation of forest on special forest maps (Izobrazheniye lesov na spetsial'nykh lesnykh kartakh). Thesis report by candidate in science, Moscow, 1954.

SHENNIKOV, A. P. Report on discussion in Botanical Institute of the U.S.S.R. Academy of Sciences (stenographic report). (Doklad na diskussii pri BIN AN SSSR.) *Trud. BIN Akad. Nauk SSSR,* **III**, 1938.

SHIFFERS, YE. V. On the devising of a single method for geo-botanical cartography in connection with the compilation of agricultural maps (Krazrabotke yedinoi metodiki geobotanicheskogo kartirovaniya v svyazi s sozdaniyem sel'khozkarty). *Sov bot.,* **3**. 1934.

SHIFFERS, YE. V. Method of geo-botanical cartography *(Metodika geobotanicheskogo kartirovaniya)*. Izd. Akad. Nauk SSSR, Moscow-Leningrad, 1938.

SMIRNOV, L. A. Method of field determination of the numerical proportions of elements in complexes of plant cover (Metod polevogo opredyeleniya chislennykh sootnoshenii elementov kompleksov rastitel'nogo pokrova). *Sov. bot.*, **2.** 1934.

SOKOLOV, S. YA. Report on discussion in Botanical Institute of the U.S.S.R. Academy of Sciences (stenographic report). (Doklad na diskussii pri BIN AN SSSR). *Trud. BIN Akad. Nauk SSSR*, **III**, 1938.

TEMNOYEV, N. I. and SHIROKOVSKAYA, V. A. Checking data of aerovisual geo-botanical observations by the comparison method (Proverka dannykh aerovizual'nogo geobotanicheskogo obsledovaniya metodom slicheniya). *Bot. zh.*, **1**, 1955.

TRET'YAKOV, N. YE., GORSKII, P. V. and SAMOILOVICH, G. G. Valuator's companion *(Sputnik taksatora)*. Goslesbumizdat, Moscow-Leningrad, 1952.

TSATSENKIN, I. A. Experiment in complex geo-botanical and soil mapping of pastures and hay-meadows in the Cis-Caspian districts with use of aerial photographs (Opyt kompleksnogo geobotanicheskogo i pochvennogo kartirovaniya pastbishch i senokosov v raionakh Prikaspiya s ispol'zovaniyem aèrofotosnimkov). *Bot. zh.*, **3.** 1952.

TSATSENKIN, I. A. Experiment in organizing work on geo-botanical mapping of pastures by transects in an automobile (Opyt organizatsii rabot po marshrutnomu geobotanicheskomu kartirovaniyu pastbishch na avtomobile). *Biol. MOIP*, 54, **1.**1949.

TYURIN, A. V. Forest Valuation *(Taksatsiya lesa)*. Goslestekhizdat, Moscow, 1945.

VIKTOROV, S. V. Bog landscapes as indicators of the characteristics of bog waters of the Volkhov valley (Bolonyye landshafty kak indikatory svoistv bolotnykh vod doliny reki Volkhova). *Trud. Bot. sada, book 6 (Uchen. zap. Moscow State University*, No. 129), 1948.

VIKTOROV, S. V., VOSTOKOVA, YE. A. and VORONKOVA, L. F. Use of Geo-botanical indicators to discover tectonic faults (Ispol'zovaniye geobotanicheskikh priznakov dlya obnaruzheniya tektonicheskikh narushenii). *Trud. VAGT*, **1.** 1955.

VINOGRADOV, B. V. Examples of links of vegetation and soil with the most recent tectonics (Primery svyazi rastitel'nosti i pochv s noveishei tektonikoi). *Bot. zh.*, **6.** 1955.

VLASTOVA, N. V. Instructions for description of plant cover (Instruktsiya po opisaniyu rastitel'nogo pokrova). *Trud. Vses. inst. torfa*, **5.** 1933.

VOSTOKOVA, YE. A. Use of the geo-botanical method in hydro-geological investigations (Primeneniye geobotanicheskogo metoda pri gidrogeologicheskikh issledovaniyakh). *Trud. VAGT*, **1.** 1955.

VOSTOKOVA, YE. A. and ZHDANOVA, G. I. Use of geo-botanical indicators in aerial geological mapping in West Kazakhstan (Ispol'zovaniye geobotanicheskikh priznakov pri aerogeologicheskom kartirovanii v Zap. Kazakhstane). *Trud. VAGT*, **1**, 1955,

VYSOTSKII, G. N. On maps of types of plant habitats (O karte tipov mestoproizrastaniya). *Sb. Sovremen. voprosy russk. sel-khoz.* (Coll. Modern problems of Russian agriculture). Moscow, 1904.

VYSOTSKII, G. N. On phyto-topological maps, methods of compiling them and their practical significance (O fito-topologicheskikh kartakh, sposobakh ikh sostavleniya i ikh prakticheskom znachenii). *Pochvovedeniye*, 11, 2. 1909.

VYSOTSKII, N. K. Some geo-botanical observations in the northern Urals (Neskol'ko geobotanicheskikh nablyudyenii na Sev. Urale). *Pochvovedyeniye*, 6, 2. 1904.

VYSHIVKIN, D. D. Methods of compiling maps of soil salinity from geo-botanical data. (Metodika sostavleniya kart zasoleniya gruntov po geobotanicheskim dannym). *Trud. VAGT.*, **1.** 1955.

WOESLANDER, A. E. and STORIE, R. E. Vegetational approach to soil surveys on wildland areas. *Proc. Soil Sc. Soc. Am.* 17, **2.** 1953.

ZDANCHUK, V. A. and ARTAMONOVA, A. I. On the problem of methods of determining the proportions of areas of plant associations in a complex steppe (K voprosu o metodakh opredyeleniya sootnoshenii ploshchadyei rastitel'nykh assotsiatsii v kompleksnoi stepi). *Sov. bot.*, **1**. 1937.

ZHILKIN, B. D. Experiment in study of types of forest in the White Russian SSR *(Opyt izucheniya tipov lesa BSSR)*. Izd. nauch.-tekh. obshch. sl. i les. khoz., Minsk, 1957.

INDEX

20. P. Dasgupta and G. H. Heal, "Resource Depletion, Research and Development and the Social Rate of Discount," Paper presented at Resources for the Future Conference on Energy Planning and the Social Rate of Discount, March 1977.
21. K. J. Arrow and A. C. Fisher, "Preservation, Uncertainty, and Irreversibility," *Quarterly Journal of Economics* vol. 88 (May 1974) pp. 312–319.
22. C. Henry, "Option Values in the Economics of Irreplaceable Assets," *The Review of Economic Studies,* Symposium on the Economics of Exhaustible Resources, 1974.
23. G. C. Rausser, "Technological Change, Production, and Investment in Natural Resource Industries," *American Economic Review* vol. 64 (December 1974) pp. 1049–1059.
24. J. Stiglitz, "Growth with Exhaustible Natural Resources: The Competitive Economy," *The Review of Economic Studies,* Symposium on the Economics of Exhaustible Resources, 1974.
25. M. I. Kamien and N. L. Schwartz, "A Note on Resource Usage and Market Structure," *Journal of Economic Theory* vol. 15 (June 1977) pp. 394–397.
26. M. I. Kamien and N. L. Schwartz, "The Optimal Resource Capital Ratio and Market Structure," Discussion Paper No. 233 (Evanston, Ill., Center for Mathematical Studies in Economics and Management Science, Northwestern University, August 1976).
27. J. R. Moroney, "Are Natural Resources Capital Using? A Microanalytic Approach," *Southern Economic Journal* vol. 43 (January 1977) pp. 1203–1217.
28. F. M. Fisher, "The Existence of Aggregate Production Functions," *Econometrica* vol. 37 (October 1969) pp. 553–577.
29. L. Johansen, *Production Functions* (Amsterdam, North-Holland, 1972).
30. K. Sato, *Production Functions and Aggregation* (Amsterdam, North-Holland, 1975).
31. H. S. Houthakker, "The Pareto Distribution and the Cobb–Douglas Production Function in Activity Analysis," *Review of Economic Studies* vol. 23 (1955–56) pp. 27–31.
32. D. Levhari, "A Note on Houthakker's Aggregate Production Function in a Multifirm Industry," *Econometrica* vol. 36 (January 1968) pp. 151–154.
33. F. M. Fisher, R. M. Solow, and J. M. Kearl, "Aggregate Production Functions: Some CES Experiments," *Review of Economic Studies* vol. 44 (June 1977) pp. 305–320.
34. J. Stiglitz, "Growth with Exhaustible Natural Resources: Efficient and Optimal Growth Paths," *The Review of Economic Studies,* Symposium on the Economics of Exhaustible Resources, 1974.
35. R. Cummings and W. D. Schulze, "Ramsey, Resources, and the Conservation of Mass-Energy." Paper presented at Conference on Natural Resource Pricing, Trail Lake, Wyoming, August 1977.

36. D. B. Brooks, "Mineral Supply as a Stock," in W. A. Vogely, ed., *Economics of the Mineral Industries* (3rd. ed., New York, American Institute of Mining, Metallurgical and Petroleum Engineers, 1976).

37. V. E. McKelvey, "Relation of Reserves of the Elements to their Crustal Abundance," *American Journal of Science* vol. 258-A (1960).

38. R. L. Erickson, "Crustal Abundance of Elements and Mineral Reserves and Resources," D. A. Brobst and W. P. Pratt, eds., in *United States Mineral Resources,* Professional Paper 820 (Washington, D.C., U.S. Geological Survey, 1973).

39. R. T. Page, *Conservation and Economic Efficiency* (Baltimore, Johns Hopkins University Press for Resources for the Future, 1977).

40. F. P. Ramsey, "A Mathematical Theory of Saving," *Economic Journal* vol. 38 (December 1928) pp. 543–559.

41. J. Rawls, *A Theory of Justice* (Cambridge, Mass., Harvard University Press, 1971).

42. T. Sandler and V. Kerry Smith, "Intertemporal and Intergenerational Pareto Efficiency," *Journal of Environmental Economics and Management* vol. 2 (February 1976) pp. 151–159.

43. T. Sandler and V. Kerry Smith, "Intertemporal and Intergenerational Pareto Efficiency Revisited," *Journal of Environmental Economics and Management* vol. 4 (September 1977) pp. 252–257.

44. N. Rosenberg, *Technology and American Economic Growth* (New York, Harper & Row, 1972).

45. A. V. Kneese and W. D. Schulze, "Environment, Health and Economics —The Case of Cancer," *American Economic Review, Proceedings* vol. 67 (February 1977) pp. 326–332.

46. W. Vickrey, "Economic Criteria for Optimum Rates of Depletion," in Mason Gaffney, ed., *Extractive Resources and Taxation* (Madison, University of Wisconsin Press, 1967).

47. G. Heal, "The Long-Run Movement of the Prices of Exhaustible Resources." Paper presented at International Economic Association Conference on Economic Growth and Resources, Tokyo, Japan, September 1977.

48. W. J. Baumol, "Macroeconomics of Unbalanced Growth: The Anatomy of Urban Crisis," *American Economic Review* vol. 57 (June 1967) pp. 415–426.

49. R. W. Jones, "The Structure of Simple General Equilibrium Models," *Journal of Political Economy* vol. 73 (December 1965) pp. 557–572.

50. V. Kerry Smith, "A Note on Baumol's Unbalanced Growth Model," *Public Finance* vol. 30 (1975) pp. 127–130.

51. R. N. Batra, *Studies in the Pure Theory of International Trade* (New York, St. Martins, 1973).

52. G. M. Brannon, "Existing Tax Differentials and Subsidies Relating to the Energy Industries," in G. M. Brannon, ed., *Studies in Energy Tax Policy* (Cambridge, Mass., Ballinger, 1975).

53. V. Kerry Smith, "Measuring Natural Resource Scarcity: Theory and Practice," *Journal of Environmental Economics and Management* vol. 5 (May 1978) pp. 150–171.

54. R. Manthy, *Natural Resource Commodities 1870–1973: Prices, Output, Consumption, and Employment* (Baltimore, Johns Hopkins University Press for Resources for the Future, 1978).

55. N. Potter and F. T. Christy, Jr., *Trends in Natural Resource Commodities* (1870–1957) (Baltimore, Johns Hopkins University Press for Resources for the Future, 1962).

56. N. Wiener, *The Human Use of Human Beings* (New York, Doubleday, 1954).

2

A Neoclassical Analysis of the Economics
of Natural Resources

J. E. Stiglitz

I
Introduction

The oscillations in the general views on the prospects for the future, alternating between the despair of imminent and inevitable doom and the euphoria of an impending new millenium, have a remarkable regularity about them, perhaps matching that of the long business cycle. The nineteenth century concern about the implications of the second law of thermodynamics, as represented, for instance, in the work of Henry Adams, has its twentieth century counterpart in Georgescu-Roegen, and Malthus's worry about food scarcity has its twentieth century counterpart in Meadows and Forrester. There are those who would suggest that the nineteenth century preachers of inevitable progress have been replaced by the modern neoclassical economist who, if he does not believe that we are on the verge of the new millenium, finds it difficult to take seriously the prognostications of imminent doom.

What are we to make of these continuing controversies? How could what appears to be essentially the same controversy continue for so long (not always, of course, with the same intensity)? Those who forecast imminent disaster in the nineteenth century were clearly wrong. Why were they wrong? Were they wrong only in the time predicted for disaster but correct in their long-run analysis?

There are, I think, two reasons for the failure to resolve these disputes. The first is that the issues have not been posed in such a way as to admit an unambiguous answer. The second is that, when properly posed, it becomes clear that some of the more important issues cannot be answered on the basis of presently available evidence.

This paper attempts to pose what I consider the appropriate ques-

The author is indebted to V. Kerry Smith for his helpful comments on an earlier draft.

tions and to suggest what kind of evidence might resolve them. There are, of course, important policy issues in which one's position inevitably depends on the answers to these unresolved questions. What is one to do until these are obtained? Some preliminary thoughts on this question constitute the third objective of this paper.[1] However, there are a few distinctions which will help clarify the scope of my subject.

First, it is obvious that <u>continued exponential growth is impossible,</u> if only because eventually, at a strictly positive growth rate, the mass of people would exceed the mass of the earth. I am not concerned here with such very long-run problems. (Similarly, I am not concerned with long-run problems arising from the laws of thermodynamics.) I am concerned here with the more immediate future.

Second, <u>it is important to distinguish between natural resources which can be treated as *private goods,*</u> such as coal, oil, and iron, <u>and those which are basically *public goods,*[2]</u> such as air and water. Whether public intervention is required in the allocation of the former is at least a moot question about which we shall have much to say later; but in the case of the public goods, appropriate allocation inevitably will require some type of government action. There is a third category of natural resources— those which are normally publicly managed but which are really private goods, as for example, forests. A clear distinction has to be made between these resources and true public goods.

Although it is often clear whether the good is a public good, a private good, or a publicly provided private good, there are some ambiguous cases. The fish in a lake are often thought of as a public good although fish caught by one individual may reduce the amount available to others, and property rights for fishing in a lake could be given to an individual. The appropriate method of organizing the allocation of such goods is one of the more important issues in the economics of natural resources.

Third, I have not yet defined what I mean by natural resources. Presumably a natural resource is any commodity or factor which is provided by nature and not produced, or producible, by man. Although such a definition is not very precise, it will suffice for our purposes. (Most of what we think of as natural resources, such as oil, require human activity

---

[1] I was asked by RFF to present a survey of the neoclassical view of the problem of the scarcity of natural resources. I have chosen to provide an "interpretive review" rather than an exhaustive review of the literature; for the latter, see Peterson and Fisher [1].

[2] The distinction I have in mind is based on the traditional definition of public goods: those involving difficulties in appropriability and those in which the marginal cost of an extra person enjoying the benefits of the good is zero. Thus coal can be marketed just like any other produced good and if one person burns a unit of coal, it is not available for use by any other individual. It would be hard to charge for the use of air.

to convert them into a useful form and indeed to extract them from the ground. Moreover, the supply of many natural resources, say fish, can be affected by human activity.) It will, however, be useful to consider some polar cases. These are *exhaustible natural resources,* the supply of which is fixed and cannot be augmented; *renewable natural resources* such as fish, the supply of which can be increased (renewed) after utilization; *inexhaustible but nonaugmentable resources,* for example, land; and *recyclable resources*.

In fact, many cases do not fall into these neat categories; land—at least arable land—can be augmented as well as depleted. A resource which was perfectly recyclable would essentially be inexhaustible but nonaugmentable, while so long as some of the resource cannot be recovered for reuse, a recyclable resource is like an exhaustible natural resource.

We used to think of air as an inexhaustible resource. Clean air, we now recognize, is a resource which can be exhausted, but in most cases it should be viewed as a renewable natural resource: by taking appropriate action, a dirty atmosphere can be changed into a clean one if there is sufficient time.

I am primarily concerned here with the first category of natural resources, that is, exhaustible, nonrenewable, natural resources, since they are considered to pose the most serious problem. Much of what I shall have to say is, however, applicable with appropriate modifications to the other categories as well.

The paper is divided into eight sections. Section II identifies the major issues; sections III–VI are concerned with each of the major issues in turn; section VII is concerned with a brief discussion of two important recent policy issues, and our concluding remarks are contained in section VIII.

II
The Issues

There are several distinct issues which have become confused in many of the popular discussions of resource availability. This section is intended to help identify and distinguish them.

Viability.   Is it possible to have sustained economic growth? This is concerned not with the question of whether it is likely that we face imminent doom if we do not take remedial action soon (the forecasting issue), but with whether doom is *inevitable*. Is there anything we can do? This is one of the questions to which neoclassical economics has provided a clear answer. There are conditions under which growth cannot be sustained and conditions under which it can. In section III we identify these conditions.

Forecasting. Forecasting is concerned with predicting what the world will be like in twenty-five, fifty, or a hundred years. One might be interested in a forecast to satisfy one's curiosity by gazing into a crystal ball. But information is valuable mainly to the extent that it leads to alteration in behavior, and usually the forecasters have some policy prescription in mind. Thus their forecasts have a qualification, "unless a certain prescribed course of action is taken." Forecasting usually entails an extrapolation of past events into the future; this extrapolation requires certain, usually quite strong assumptions, and a great deal of the disagreement concerning predictions is concerned with precisely those assumptions. We talk about these assumptions at greater length in section IV.

There are two distinctive issues on which the forecasts of the future are supposed to provide us with some information. (1) The more popular versions focus on some cataclysm; the economy, in any form similar to that which we presently know, is not viable. "We shall be unable to sustain current energy consumption rates." "The temperature of the earth will increase by $x°$ and New York City will be under water." "We shall suffocate from . . . poisoning." (2) The more mundane versions are concerned with estimating the magnitude of the increase in natural resource prices and gauging the effect of this increase on our standard of living.

Efficiency. The question of whether we are wasting our resources is quite separate from the question of whether doom is imminent or inevitable. We might not be facing imminent doom, yet we could still be misusing our resources. Much of the popular literature seems to take the position that doom is not inevitable but because of wastage of resources, it is nevertheless likely to occur, perhaps soon, and it is in this sense that the three issues are closely linked.

There are a number of reasons that the economy might not allocate natural resources efficiently, some arising out of peculiarities of the private market, and some arising from particular government actions. These are discussed in section V.

Intertemporal Equity. The economy could be efficient, resources might be being used efficiently, but still, because of the rate at which we use our resources, our descendants will be poorer. There is a tradeoff between our consumption and that of our descendants, and the market solution may be inequitable. We shall have a few words to say on this in section VI.

III
The Viability Issue: Is Sustained Growth Possible in the Presence of Exhaustible Natural Resources?

Any analysis of the economics of natural resources should, I think, begin with the question of why the scarcity of natural resources is different from the scarcity of any other factor of production (or any commodity, for that matter). The layman's response to this question would probably be that if we run out of corn we can produce more corn. With natural resources there is simply nothing we can do. This, of course, is not a completely satisfactory answer.

For there to be a meaningful natural resource problem, several conditions need to be satisfied:

1. A resource must be in limited supply relative to current usage rates; thus, if there are several hundred years' worth of reserves[3] of some natural resource, there is, at most, a very long-run problem.

2. It must be nonrenewable and nonrecyclable. Natural resources (such as metals) do not disappear after they are used; rather, they become available for reuse. Only that part which is not renewable—or more precisely, that part, for which the cost of renewing to a marketable state will exceed the market prices—is exhausted in economic terms. The net utilization rate of natural resources may thus be considerably less than the gross.

3. It must be essential, that is, it must be required for production (or consumption).

4. There cannot exist substitutes for it; for example, capital cannot be substituted for it in production.

5. It must be impossible to improve the efficiency with which the resource is utilized beyond some point; for there to be an immediate problem, we must be near that point. Technical change which increases the productivity of a resource is referred to as "resource-augmenting technical progress," since its effect is equivalent to an increase in the stock of the resource.

[3] I have used the term "reserves" in the casual way that it is usually used; it is important to observe, however, that the natural economic definition of reserves is not that conventionally employed, for example, by geologists. Since the amount of a natural resource which can be extracted depends on the expenditure on extraction, reserves is an economic, not a geological concept. The appropriate definition entails an analysis of how much can be extracted, not at current market prices, but at market prices that will prevail as the supply becomes smaller; there is some presumption that this may be significantly larger than that implied by the conventional definitions.

6. It must be impossible to develop a substitute for the given resource.

Several of the recent articles on the economics of natural resources have attempted to make more precise the conditions under which it is possible to sustain a constant per capita consumption [2–4]. Most of these conditions are fairly intuitive.

The assumption that the natural resource is essential implies that the isoquants (between the natural resource and the other produced factors of production) never hit the axis of the produced factor. (See figures 2-1 to 2-7 where the other factor of production is taken to be capital. In figure 2-1 natural resources are essential; in figure 2-2 natural resources are not essential.) Note that what is crucial for the question of whether the natural resource is essential is not any property of the production (isoquant) function when there is a large input of natural resources. If the isoquant has relatively little curvature (i.e., is flat, as in figure 2-3) we might be tempted to extrapolate the curve and to infer that the natural resource is nonessential, but the curvature could easily be changed as the resource input becomes small, so that although at present it is easy to substitute, say capital, for resources, eventually it becomes quite difficult. Conversely, it may be quite difficult to substitute now (the isoquant can still be quite curved) but when the resources become sufficiently scarce, we may be able to switch to a completely different technology, for which the substitution is relatively easy, and the isoquant does hit the axis (figure 2-4).

The concept that economists usually use for measuring the ease of substitution is the "elasticity of substitution," which gives the percentage change in the input ratio (say, of natural resources to capital) which would be engendered by a percentage change in the relative price of capital to natural resources.[4] If a 1 percent change in relative prices does not give rise to a change in factor inputs (figure 2-5), the elasticity of substitution is zero; if we discontinue using the factor whose price has risen, we say that the elasticity is infinite. The central case where a 1 percent change in factor prices gives rise to a 1 percent change in factor inputs is called the Cobb–Douglas production function.[5] If the elasticity of substitution between natural resources and capital and/or labor is

---

[4] The production function $Q = \phi([aK^\rho + (1-a)R^\rho]^{1/\rho}, L)$ where Q is output; K is the stock of capital; R is the flow of natural resources used in production; L is the labor supply has a constant elasticity of substitution between K and R: $\partial Q/\partial K = \phi[aK^\rho + (1-a)R^\rho]^{1/\rho-1}aK^{\rho-1}$; $\partial Q/\partial R = \phi[aK^\rho + (1-a)R^\rho]^{1/\rho-1}(1-a)R^{\rho-1}$

$$-1/\sigma \equiv \text{elasticity of substitution} = \frac{d \ln [(\partial Q/\partial K)/(\partial Q/\partial R)]}{d \ln K/R} = \frac{1}{(\rho-1)}.$$

[5] The Cobb–Douglas production function can be written: $Q = K^{\alpha_1}R^{\alpha_2}L^{\alpha_3}$, $\alpha_1 + \alpha_2 + \alpha_3 = 1$. With a constant population, a sustained per capita consumption is possible if $\alpha_1 > \alpha_2$.

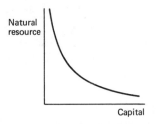

Figure 2-1. Natural resource essential.

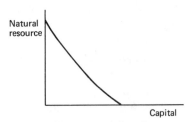

Figure 2-2. Natural resource not essential.

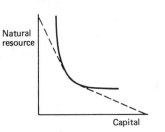

Figure 2-3. Local high elasticity: resource essential.

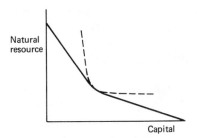

Figure 2-4. Local low elasticity: resource inessential.

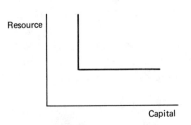

Figure 2-5. Zero elasticity of substitution.

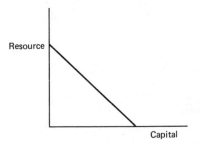

Figure 2-6. Infinite elasticity of substitution.

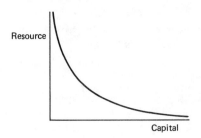

Figure 2-7. Unity elasticity of substitution.

constant, then a sustained constant per capita consumption is feasible if (1) the elasticity is greater than unity, or (2) if the elasticity is unity and if the share of capital exceeds that of natural resources.

If the elasticity of substitution is not constant, what is crucial is what happens to the elasticity asymptotically as resource input goes to zero. In these cases the produced input is sufficiently substitutable for the natural resource that the decrease in supply of the natural resource can be compensated for by an increased supply of capital. Of the two cases, the Cobb–Douglas case is clearly the most interesting for there natural resources are essential in the sense that some input of the natural resource is required for production (the isoquants never do hit the axes). But a small input of natural resource can be compensated for by a sufficiently large input of capital, and whether that is feasible for the economy depends simply on the relative shares of the two.

The conditions under which technical change makes sustained per capita consumption viable are also easily interpretable. The development of a produced substitute can be interpreted as changing the isoquant so that in fact it does hit the natural resource axis. The other condition is that there be a strictly positive rate of resource-augmenting technical progress.[6] If the input of the natural resource were to decline at the rate of the resource-augmenting technical progress—clearly a feasible policy —the effective input would be constant, and with a constant population a constant per capita level of consumption would thus be viable.

IV
The Forecasting Issue

The way we have posed the problem makes it easy to see what is required if we are to forecast the future: we need to know to what extent it will be possible to substitute produced goods for natural resources and we need to know the likelihood of technical changes which will lead either to the development of substitutes or to an increase in the efficiency with which we use what resources we have.

This problem can be approached in several different ways. The "engineering approach" examines the set of presently available techniques and attempts to assess the difficulties associated with developing new technologies. There seems to be an "informed consensus" that within the next 100 years technologies for the production of essentially a boundless supply of energy at "reasonable cost" (for example, solar energy)

---

[6] A production function with factor-augmenting technical progress may be written:
$$Q = F(K, R, L, t) \equiv F[\mu(t)K, \gamma(t)R, \lambda(t)L].$$
One unit of resource at t is a perfect substitute for $1/\gamma(t)$ units at time zero.

will become available. On other issues, for example, whether the atmosphere will be affected by certain technological developments, there seems to be less of a consensus. The economist, I suspect, has relatively little to say on these technological issues. The economist's approach is, in some sense, much cruder. He attempts to look at the past and to extrapolate from that into the future. It is not, however, obvious what the appropriate method of extrapolation is. The crucial question is what is to be taken as a constant. For instance, is the average *rate* of growth of the input of oil and the *stock* of presently discovered oil to be taken as given? If so, we are probably indeed in trouble. Or is the rate of increase of discovered resources to be taken as given, in which case prospects are not quite so bleak. And if the rate of growth is to be calculated, over what period should we make the calculation? How is one to choose among these alternative hypotheses and calculations?

Economists approach this problem by formulating a model which is sufficiently general to encompass the entire range of competing hypotheses as special cases and then subjecting the model to empirical testing. In principle then, we should be able to ascertain, at least by extrapolating from past experience, which hypothesis is more reasonable.

If this were as easily done as said, there would be far fewer disputes. Three problems are repeatedly encountered. (1) The data may not be able to distinguish among hypotheses; that is, two alternative hypotheses could be equally consistent with past observations, yet have very different implications for the future. (2) Most tests involve some kind of parameterization; thus, the actual test performed is not of the hypotheses in their most general form. (3) The structure of the economy may have changed, making "testing" of alternative hypotheses on the basis of past data inappropriate.

Let me illustrate these points with the issue at hand. We identified in our earlier discussion two parameters determining the future viability of the economy: the elasticity of substitution and the rate of technical progress augmenting natural resources. I focus my attention here on attempts to measure the former. The question, as we noted earlier, is whether the elasticity of substitution between natural resources and, say, capital, is greater or less than unity (again, recall that what is crucial is the limiting elasticity as the input of natural resources goes to zero). Note that no simulation exercise will ever resolve the question of the correct value of a parameter such as the elasticity of substitution. Moreover, if we know the value of the elasticity, analytical methods can completely answer the question of whether the economy is viable in the long run; we do not need to resort to simulation. What simulation can do—if we have a reasonable model with reasonable estimates of the parameters—is to give us some feel for how long the long run is (for example, if there is a "long-run natural resource problem," is it likely to make itself evident in 50 or 500 years?). Simulation may also enable us to identify the crucial parameters but, here as elsewhere, direct analytical methods are likely to be less ambiguous.

The easiest way of obtaining an estimate of the elasticity of substitution entails introducing one further assumption: that of competitivity, that the prices of (returns to) factors of production equal the value of the marginal productivity of the factor. With this additional assumption, if the elasticity of substitution were much less than unity, then we should expect the share of various natural resources in national income to have changed dramatically; those which have become relatively scarce should have a rapidly increasing relative share, those for whom unexpectedly large supplies have been found (and hence, whose scarcity had previously been overestimated) should have a falling share. In fact, at least in the aggregate, such dramatic shifts do not for the most part seem to have occurred if we take as our period of calculation the past 100 years; obviously if we look only at the past few years we could obtain quite different results. In the one case—land—where there has been a marked change in the share over the past several hundred years, it has been in the wrong direction. The share of land, for instance, in the past was as high as 50 percent; today it is much less in spite of a much larger ratio of population to land.

Resource optimists might argue that the share, say of land, has declined either because the elasticity of substitution is not low and/or because the effective supply of natural resources (land), taking account of technical change, has increased.

Resource pessimists might argue against these results in a number of different ways. (1) The competitive assumption on which the analysis was based might not be true, but for them to argue that the elasticity is low, they must argue further that the degree of monopoly in natural resources has changed in a significant way. (2) The future may not be like the past: it is at this point then that recourse has to be made to the "engineering approach" discussed earlier. (3) The particular parameterization implicit in the above calculation that the elasticity of substitution is constant is not correct: for example, they might argue that as resources become scarcer, the elasticity declines.

I am not aware of any convincing test of this hypothesis; my own guess is that the data are consistent with the hypothesis of a constant elasticity of substitution, but that if some parameterizations involving nonconstant elasticities were employed, nonzero point estimates of the rate of change of the elasticity would be observed. I am not sure whether the point estimates would side with the pessimists or optimists, but the value might well vary according to the parameterization adopted. My own suspicion is that the standard errors would be large enough to allow pessimists and optimists to continue arguing their case.

No matter how the test turned out, either side could argue against the result on the grounds that the analysis had been carried on at too high a level of aggregation. A real test, it might be argued, entails an analysis at a much more disaggregated level, taking into account different productivities of different firms within the industry, elasticities of substitution within each sector, and intersector elasticities of demand. Thus, for instance, changes in the distribution of firms within a sector (say, the difference between best practice and average practice) would result in the aggregate elasticity of substitution appearing not to be constant, although the "best practice" production function does have a constant elasticity.[7] Similarly, even if the production of neither commodity A nor commodity B allows the substitution of capital for natural resources, if commodity A uses less of the resource relative to capital than does commodity B, by substituting commodity A for commodity B, we can reduce our utilization of natural resources. Thus, estimating the full potential for substituting other factors for natural resources requires an understanding of all the possible patterns of substitution available in consumption and production.

Once we recognize possible methods of substituting produced for nonproduced goods, a further kind of technological adaptation becomes possible: tastes may change to reflect the changing environment. Although there is a widespread feeling that tastes are "endogenous," that they respond to changing circumstances, the extent to which changed patterns of consumption reflect a rational response to changing prices (the changed patterns of consumption reflect the changes in the best method of obtaining the "basic wants" but the underlying utility function

---

[7] For a more extended discussion of the relationship between micro and macro production function see K. Sato [5, 6].

Many of the attempts to estimate the elasticity of substitution are based on cross-sectional data, rather than the heuristic time series approach that we have employed above. There are a number of problems involved in using these cross-sectional estimates as a basis of predicting the long-run elasticity of substitution; this is not the place for an extended discussion of these econometric problems except to note one that has not received sufficient attention in the literature. Consider the traditional method of estimating constant elasticity functions, originally introduced by Arrow and coauthors [7], entailing regressing marginal product (wage) on average product. Assume that labor is not homogeneous and one cannot observe how many "efficiency units" are associated with any particular individual. Then, if some firms hired mostly efficient workers and paid them a high wage, and if some firms hired mostly inefficient workers and paid them a low wage, it would appear as if there were a positive elasticity of substitution, even though the elasticity might have been zero.

remains unchanged) rather than a change in basic attitudes and preferences remains a moot question.

Where does this leave us? The kinds of tools economists have used in the past are not likely to resolve this issue for those who are firmly committed to one side or the other in this debate. Yet it seems that what economic theory does remind us of is "that there is more than one way to skin a cat."/If the resource pessimists are correct that we are going to be facing a serious resource problem in the immediate future, they must convincingly show that (1) within each sector the elasticity of substitution is low and the demand elasticities are also low, so that as resources become scarcer we do not, or cannot, substitute less resource-intensive commodities for more resource-intensive commodities; (2) the prospects of adapting tastes to the new set of economic circumstances are poor; and (3) the prospects are bleak for technical changes that would enable us better to use what resources we have.

The more mundane forecasting problem of estimating the likely impact of increasing scarcity of natural resources on our standard of living not only requires a knowledge of some of the same critical parameters, but also entails information concerning a few other parameters.

Elasticity of Demand. If the elasticity of demand for natural resources is high (either because there are readily available substitutes in production or because there are readily available substitutes in consumption which are less resource intensive), then increasing scarcity will not be a serious problem. Note that while for the question of viability we needed to know what happened to the elasticity as the resource input became arbitrarily small, here we only need to know the elasticity associated with levels of input not too different from those at present—a far easier question.

Costs of Extraction. There is, however, an argument that to assess the impact of increasing scarcity in the short run we need not know the demand elasticity; in competitive markets prices will be rising in such a way as to make net royalties (price minus cost of extraction) rise at the rate of interest.[8] The level of prices and the patterns of consumption are affected by the nature of the demand curve, but not changes in the price level.[9] Thus, to forecast real price movements all we need to do is fore-

---

[8] Consider a competitive firm. It must decide whether to extract a unit of oil today, receiving net $p_t - c_t$ where p is the price and c_t is the extraction cost; or to extract it tomorrow, receiving net $p_{t+1} - c_{t+1}$ whose present value is $(p_{t+1} - c_{t+1})/(1 + r_t)$ where r is the rate of interest. In equilibrium, it must be indifferent, that is, $(p_{t+1} - c_{t+1})/(1 + r_t) = p_t - c_t$ or in continuous time $(\dot{p} - \dot{c})/[p(t) - c(t)] = r(t)$.

[9] Of course, changes in the consumer surplus, that is, welfare, associated with given changes in the price will depend on the elasticity of demand, so that the impact of a given increase in prices will be greater the lower the demand elasticity.

cast real interest rates and movements in real costs of extraction. The former are not likely to vary much in the immediate future (if anything, the increased scarcity of natural resources will lower the real return on capital and the rate of increase in prices). Thus, predicting future price movements comes down to predicting movements in the cost of extraction. There are two offsetting effects here. On the one hand it is in general optimal to first extract natural resources from deposits with lower extraction costs; as these are used up, extraction costs increase. Now, if natural resources were not scarce so that the price were determined by the extraction costs (as for a conventionally produced commodity), then this would raise the price. But for a natural resource, the increased extraction cost actually leads to a lower *rate* of increase of prices.[10] The second effect, which in the past has dominated, is that technological change has lowered the cost of extraction.[11] The lowering of the cost of extraction enables royalties to rise, even with a constant consumer price. As a consequence, in the recent past, there has been no significant increase in the real costs of extraction for many commodities, and a decline for several. If this trend continues, then it is not likely that an increase in resource scarcity will significantly lower standards of living.

New Deposits. The third factor which is important in determining the likely movements of prices in the short run is discoveries of new deposits. To the extent that such discoveries are anticipated (in a probabilistic sense), they should have no effect on price movements; but to the extent that the actual discoveries are greater or less than anticipated, prices will rise or fall (or rise at a faster or lower rate than they otherwise would have). Since by definition it is only the "unanticipated" discoveries which affect the price path, there is no way that we can say anything about the direction of these effects (similarly with respect to the discovery of substitutes for natural resources).

Finally, it should be noted that exhaustible resources constitute a small fraction of national income so that even a significant rise in price will have only a small effect on standards of living. (This is not to say that there might not be costly adjustments associated with significant price rises.)

---

[10] $\dot{p}/p = (1 - c/p)r$ so an increase in c lowers $\dot{p}/p$. This argument assumes that c is not changing over time.   cf p 24

[11] One ought really to include in the costs of extraction the total costs associated with discovery, bringing the resource from below ground to above ground, refining, and delivering the resource to the user. The "consumer price" may be lowered because of a reduction in any of these costs. Note that much of the technological change has resulted from better methods of extracting the mineral of interest from the ore. Some technological change may be indistinguishable from "returns to scale": as the economy grows, it may be possible or economical to have larger mines and refineries.

In short, it is not likely that resource shortages will lead to a significant lowering of standards of living in the immediate future. The arguments are reinforced if one believes that there are incentives within the market for estimating resource scarcities (as we shall argue in the next section), so that prices reflect the judgments of those participating in the market concerning the scarcity of resources. To argue that we will face, in the near future, a significant lowering of the standard of living requires arguing that the market systematically underestimates future demands and overestimates available supplies. A fuller analysis than we have been able to present here would recognize more explicitly that there is uncertainty associated with forecasts of demand and supply; it would then calculate the consequences, say, of underestimating demand by one standard deviation and overestimating supply by one standard deviation. If demand elasticities are low, such errors may be associated with large welfare losses. The market, however, presumably at least partially takes these risk considerations into account. The extent to which it does this is discussed more fully in the next section.

V
The Efficiency Issue

There is, admittedly, something satisfying about knowing whether the economy, as we know it, will come to an end in fifty years or so, or not. But there are those who seem to feel that establishing the fact that the economy faces dire problems with respect to natural resources has obvious implications for the role of the government. On the contrary, I would argue that the existence of a natural resource problem has no immediate implications: it is neither a necessary nor a sufficient condition for governmental intervention in the markets for natural resources. The market could be doing as well as could be done, and the economy could still be facing a doomsday; and the market could be doing a quite bad job of resource allocation, and yet there might be no doomsday in store.

This section is concerned with the *efficiency* issue as opposed to the equity issue, which we treat in the next section. Efficiency has a very precise definition: Is it possible to increase the consumption (welfare) of any individual (consumption at any date) without decreasing it at any other? If it is, we are clearly wasting resources. Efficiency is not, of course, the only objective of economic policy; we are also concerned with the intertemporal distribution of income. A pattern of growth which left our grandchildren with few resources might be efficient, yet very undesirable.

The object of this section is to analyze the efficiency with which the market allocates resources; the role of the government in resource markets (as in other markets) is customarily justified in terms of some kind of market failure. We consider here the major possible sources of market failure.

In the discussion below we show that there are a number of reasons to expect that the market allocation of natural resources might not be efficient; some of the effects lead to excessively rapid rates of resource utilization, others lead to excessive conservation; in still other cases we are able to show only that the market may not be efficient but are, in general, unable to argue whether the market is too profligate or too conservation minded. The conclusion of the analysis is that there is no overriding case that we are using our resources too rapidly, but that there are a number of actions which the government could take which would probably lead to a more efficient utilization of our natural resources.

We first show that the problems associated with monopoly are probably less important than for other commodities, while the problems associated with imperfect risk and futures markets, and costly information, are perhaps more important. The most convincing case for government intervention is in the area of support for research and development.

The government has, of course, intervened extensively in the market for natural resources; these interventions have probably been the most important source of inefficiency in the allocation of resources, and although one perhaps should not infer from this that future interventions would be equally as unsuccessful, there is little reason to believe that the efficiency with which the government allocates resources would be drastically better in the future than it has been in the past (we do not present any argument for why there should be systematic inefficiencies associated with governmental regulation; these have been discussed elsewhere in the literature). We now turn to a detailed discussion of each of the major sources of market and nonmarket failure.

Monopoly. In the wake of the oil embargo there developed a widespread belief that the noncompetitive nature of the oil industry raised prices and led to resource inefficiencies. For conventional *commodities,* monopoly results in the raising of prices and a decrease in consumption. For natural resources the effect is less clear, for if fewer natural resources are consumed today, there will be more to consume in the future; thus, raising the price today means that the price will be lower at some date in the future.

The fundamental principle defining efficient intertemporal allocation of resources is that the present discounted value of the (net) marginal product[12] must be the same at all dates, that is, the value of the marginal product rises at the rate of interest. This is ensured in a competitive economy by having the price rise at the rate of interest. A monopolist will equate the present value of *marginal revenue* at all dates, so marginal revenues rise at this rate of interest.[13] Thus, if price is proportional to marginal revenue, that is, for a constant (over time as well as for different levels of consumption) elasticity demand function, the *monopoly and competitive allocation are identical*. If the elasticity increases over time, as one might expect with development of substitutes, or if there are positive extraction costs, then the monopolist adopts an excessively *conservationist* policy.[14]

Absence of Futures Markets. The presumption that the market allocates resources efficiently follows from the more general result that, under certain conditions, a competitive economy provides efficient (Pareto optimal) allocation of resources. One of the conditions is that there be a full set of markets, including markets for trading into the future and trading different risks. These are obviously absent and their absence may have important implications.

Before discussing these, there is one fallacious argument which does need to be disposed of: it is sometimes argued that because our children

---

[12] Net of extraction costs. For simplicity we assume here that extraction costs are negligible.

[13] These basic principles of the intertemporal allocation of resources were originally discussed by Hotelling. They are just the application to this problem of the fundamental principles of efficient resource allocation. A unit of, say, oil must have the same *value* in all its uses. Among its alternative uses are its consumption today versus its consumption next period. Postponing consumption by a unit lowers output this period by the marginal product of oil today MP_{t+1}; it raises it by the marginal product of oil next period MP_{t+1}, but a unit of output next period is worth less than a unit of output today, if the rate of interest is positive. We require: $MP_t = (MP_{t+1})/(1 + r)$ where r is the rate of interest.

[14] These results are discussed in greater length in Stiglitz [8]. They apply only for the case of an elasticity of demand exceeding unity (which it must be at the point at which the monopolist is operating since otherwise revenues could be raised by lowering output). Gilbert [9] has analyzed models in which the elasticity is less than unity, but there is a limit price, that is, a price above which a substitute is introduced or developed. Gilbert [9], Salant [10], Stiglitz [11], and Cremer and Weitzman [12] have analyzed the behavior of a single large producer facing a competitive fringe. They have employed different models, entailing slightly different solution concepts; Salant has analyzed a Nash equilibrium, while Gilbert and Stiglitz have used a Stackleberg equilibrium with the monopolist acting as the leader; the monopolist knows the response of the competitive fringe to his actions. Gilbert has shown that the behavior of the large producer depends critically on whether the competitive fringe is supply constrained. If it is, it can be shown that as the supply of the competitive fringe is increased, the supply of the large producer will be increased. Newbery [13] has shown how the argument of Stiglitz [11] for random taxation can be reinterpreted in this context as establishing that under certain conditions it is optimal for a monopolist facing a limit price to randomize his prices.

and grandchildren are not present today, the market will systematically underrate their importance; that it will be reluctant to undertake investment decisions lasting longer than the lifetime of the typical investor (for example, planting and harvesting hardwood trees). (One guise in which this argument sometimes appears is that the social rate of time preference ought to be lower than the market rate of interest.) This overlooks the fact that the investor can sell the asset (for example, the hardwood forest) to another investor (say, in the next generation) to obtain his return; the forest does not have to be felled for him to get a return on his investment.

The consequence of the absence of futures and risk markets is that investors have to *guess* about future prices and have to absorb the risks associated with the uncertainty. Thus, whether the market pursues an excessively conservationist or excessively profligate consumption policy depends on whether there are systematic errors in the forecasts of future prices (demands); but even if it turned out that in some past period there were systematic errors, that does not imply that there is a need for government intervention, or indeed that government intervention is desirable. There are strong incentives within the market for discovering systematic errors—incentives which are, in general, lacking within a bureaucratic framework. Because the rewards obtained within the private sector depend on the accuracy of their forecasts, speculators and firms will strive to obtain better forecasts; and when they fail they bear the brunt of the costs. This is not so with a government allocation.

Moreover, when individuals differ in their judgments—as they are likely to—the market provides a systematic way of aggregating their beliefs, although it may be objected that the beliefs of the wealthy carry more weight than those without financial resources. On the other hand, little is known about how a bureaucracy would aggregate their beliefs.

Although it does seem to me that these considerations strongly suggest that the basic responsibility for the intertemporal allocation of our resources remains with the market, the absence of futures markets does result in at least three distinct problems for which remedial action by the government might be desirable.

The first is the case of the individual who believes that the market is underestimating the magnitude of resource scarcity. This person purchases the resource (or claims on the resource), holding it until the date (which he believes will surely come) when the scarcity is recognized. At that date the price rises and he will have made a capital gain. In effect he transfers resources that would have been consumed today to some date in the future, capturing the difference in (present) prices as his return. But if the shortage is not recognized within his lifetime, then there will be no way in which he can capture the returns; thus the individual has no incentive to enter the market.

Similarly, if an individual believes that the market overestimates future demand (underestimates supply), he would engage in a long-term contract for future delivery; he believes that eventually the market will recognize that prices are too high, so that prices will fall and he will make as his profit the difference between the contracted price and the lower spot price then prevailing. There are two difficulties with this. First, the long-term contracts required may not (generally do not) exist. (There is an apparent asymmetry in the market associated with holding positive and negative quantities of an asset.) Second, in order to capture the returns, the error in market forecasts has to be recognized within the individual's lifetime.

In fact, in the case where the market is excessively conservationist, the error might never be reflected in market price. The price of the natural resources may be rising at the rate of interest so that over the short run there is an efficient allocation of natural resources, but the initial price may be too low or too high. In the former case it can be shown that in finite time with a Cobb–Douglas production function the price will become infinite, but if the initial price is too high, nothing will happen except that we will never use up all our resources; thus short-run perfect foresight (short-run efficiency) can be consistent with an excessively profligate consumption policy for a finite time, but it can be consistent with an excessively conservationist policy forever [15].[15]

These considerations do, I think, provide a convincing argument that the market allocation may not be efficient, but it is not clear whether there is a bias for or against conservation.

Second, the efficient intertemporal allocation of resources requires the acquisition of information concerning future demands and supplies. Although the fundamental theorem of welfare economics establishes the Pareto optimality of the market allocation of resources with a given information structure, there is no theorem establishing its optimality when information has to be acquired. On the contrary, it can be established that the market may not be Pareto optimal [9, 16]; there may be excessive expenditures on information (arising from unnecessary duplication, as when different individuals attempt to acquire the same piece of information, for example, about the value of some lease) or there may be too

---

[15] Indeed, the problems associated with excessively high rates of capital accumulation (savings) which were the center of so much of the discussion in the pure theory of growth in the 1960s (see, e.g. [14]) are resolved by the presence of natural resources: there can never be a problem of oversaving in capital since with very low rates of interest, lower than the rate of growth, resources will be exhausted in finite time; but there can be a problem of oversaving of resources [15].

little expenditure because information is partially a public good. In particular, if the market prices adjust to reflect information, then individuals who do not do the research themselves may, by observing the market prices, obtain the information indirectly (thus part of the total benefits of obtaining information accrue to individuals other than those who purchase it directly) [17].

Third, many natural resource markets seem to be characterized by excessive instability, and this instability may in part be a result of the absence of future markets. There are strong a priori reasons to believe that adjustment processes for natural resources may not work well; we showed earlier that equilibrium in the market requires the expected rate of change of (net) price to be equal to the rate of interest. If for some reason price rises slightly faster than the rate of interest (for example, because some individuals believe that there is an impending resource scarcity and hold back supplies), then that has two effects: those who base their expectations of future price movements on past movements will extrapolate the high rate of price increase into the future, and thus expect the price to rise faster than the rate of interest; they will then hold back their supplies as well, leading to further increases in price in a destabilizing way.[16] Second, the reduced supplies will lower the rate of interest if resources and capital are complements in production (as one would normally expect); thus the gap between the expected rate of price increase and the rate of interest is again increased. (For a fuller discussion, see Stiglitz [15].)

These considerations suggest that there may be a role for the government in indicative planning in helping to forecast future demands and supplies, but it should be emphasized that this role is far different from one of actually allocating the resources themselves.

Absence of Risk Markets.   The absence of risk markets means that those who hold stocks of natural resources may not be able to insure themselves against the risks of a price fall because of the discovery of a substitute or of a new supply of the resource.

The effect of this is actually very hard to analyze. There is a simple intuitive argument: viewing the holding of a resource (not extracting it) as a risky investment, an increase in uncertainty makes it less attractive, thus increasing the rate of consumption.

But this misses the fact that the risk depends on the stock (the amount by which the price falls when a substitute is discovered depends

---

[16] Note that the instability arises from individuals having to forecast future prices; futures markets, were they to exist, might equilibrate the process. The expectations formation process may, under not unreasonable conditions, be very destabilizing.

on the stock available at that date) and that what is critical for the inter-temporal allocation of the resource is how the risk varies over time.

In one simple model in which the probability of discovery of a substitute is constant per unit time and there is risk neutrality [with respect to income but not with respect to consumption of oil, i.e., the indirect utility function is of the form $V(p, Y) = V(p)Y$], for large stocks of the natural resource, uncertainty leads to greater conservationism, whereas for small stocks, it leads to a more profligate policy.[17] In another model where the stock of the resource is unknown and the only information that is acquired over time is that one had at least as much as one had consumed, it has been shown that uncertainty always leads to more conservation [18].

Uncertainty undoubtedly has an effect on intertemporal allocation, but for some purposes this is not as important as the question of what policy implications this has. For policy purposes it is inappropriate to compare an allocation of one market structure with an allocation which would emerge from another, except if the policy to be considered is a change in the market structure; the risks associated with uncertain future supplies and demands borne by private individuals in imperfect risk markets are real "costs"; and the fact that under some idealized world in which these risks are not borne by these individuals the intertemporal allocation of oil would be different is of interest, but of no direct policy import. An appropriate question to ask, for instance, is whether a Pareto optimal improvement could be made within our market structure by taxing or subsidizing the return to holding oil; or to put it another way, to ask whether the intertemporal allocation of natural resources arising from a stock market provides a "constrained" Pareto optimum. The answer, in general, is no, but the magnitude and direction of bias depend on a number of factors, for example, on differences in attitudes to risk in the economy [11]. A full analysis of this problem is presently under way. Until this is completed, it is difficult to ascertain how important this potential inefficiency of the market is.

Common Resource Problems. As we noted earlier, there are several distinct categories of natural resources; most of this paper is concerned with private exhaustible natural resources. Many of our most

[17] One might have thought that the effect of uncertainty is to raise the effective interest rate, thereby increasing the rate at which the price of a natural resource increases, hence leading to a lower price (more consumption) today. Although there is an effect going in this direction, there is another effect, which may be called the precautionary effect. Because one does not know when the substitute will arrive, one must hold back a supply of the resource as a precaution against the contingency that it does not arrive until some date far in the future.

important natural resources are, however, "public"—such as atmosphere—and for these the presumption that the market provides an efficient allocation of resources is reversed; only under the most unusual circumstances would one expect the market solution to be efficient. Individuals and firms will not, for instance, take into account the effect of their activities in lowering the quality of the air.

Most of these resources are "renewable": a stock of fish can be maintained, provided fish aren't consumed too rapidly; a "reasonable" quality of air may be maintained so long as the flow of pollutants is not too high. We are concerned here, however, only with three aspects of the problem: whether this will lead to an "exhaustion" of our natural resources and, even if it does not lead to exhaustion, whether it will lead to a significant lowering of the standard of living of succeeding generations, and whether there are any simple remedies for these problems.

There are some cases where the failure to charge for "common resources" has led to near exhaustion of a renewable natural resource: for example, whales, and there is evidence that if governments had not taken action, the air in certain cities would have become so polluted as to be almost unbreathable.

Most of the resources with which we are concerned here are renewable resources; hence there is a sustained level of per capita consumption which can be maintained with these resources with a constant population. Whether a sustained per capita level of consumption can be maintained with a growing population depends on exactly the same kinds of parameters we discussed in previous sections, for example, the substitutability between the given natural resource (now viewed as a constant flow) and other factors of production, the development of new substitutes, and the continuation of technical progress that augments resources.

There are, however, strong reasons to believe that with common resource problems the rate of extraction will be too rapid. Consider, for instance, a pool of oil which is available to anyone who wishes to take from it (or who purchases some land over the pool). Clearly, the intertemporal tradeoff of the individual is considerably different from when the resource is completely privately owned. For now the individual does not ask what will he get if he sells a unit today or tomorrow. He observes that if he does not extract it today, someone else will, and there will be no oil available for him to extract tomorrow. Thus market equilibrium will be associated with excessively rapid rates of extraction.

There are a variety of remedies for these problems. For many common resource problems a simple solution is to put the entire pool under a single management (for example, unitization of the oil pools, or giving a monopoly for fishing within a lake; obviously where there is more than one governmental jurisdiction involved, as for fishing in international waters, arriving at a solution will be more difficult). For other resources, such as "atmosphere," either governmental regulation or taxation is required. The relative merits of alternative methods are too broad to be discussed here.

Nonmarket Failures.   The market failures discussed above appear to be the major ones. There are, in addition, a number of sources of nonmarket failure, of government interventions leading to inefficiencies both in the rate and pattern of extraction. These inefficiencies are perhaps even more important than those discussed above because they result in what appears to be shortages, when in fact they would not exist were it not for the government's actions; this is particularly true of the regulatory practices described below.

Taxation.   There are several provisions of the tax code which may have an important effect on the allocation of natural resources.

Depletion Allowances. The impact of a depletion allowance at a constant rate may be less than is generally thought; if extraction costs were zero and the sector were competitive, it would have no effect. The reason for this is simple: the depletion allowance only changes the pattern of resource extraction to the extent that it changes the intertemporal tradeoffs between extracting today and extracting tomorrow. A depletion allowance increases receipts today but it increases receipts tomorrow by exactly the same percentage, and hence has no effect on intertemporal tradeoffs. If extraction costs were positive and constant, they would lead to faster extraction (than in the absence of the depletion allowance).[18] If the sector were monopolized, it would also lead to a faster rate of extraction if the monopoly was excessively conservation minded (as it would be with positive extraction costs and a declining elasticity of demand), offsetting the effects of the monopoly. If the monopoly were excessively profligate, the depletion allowance would lead to a still faster rate of consumption.

Although the effects of a constant depletion allowance may be smaller than is widely assumed, the effects of the gradual removal of the depletion allowance are larger than is widely assumed; if a depletion allowance is to be removed, it should be removed as quickly as possible. For again, the gradual removal of the depletion allowance means that it

---

[18] See Stiglitz [16]. Let the depletion rate be d. Assume extraction costs are constant, then equilibrium with the depletion allowance requires $[(1 + d)\dot{p}]/[(1 + d)p - c] = r$ or $\dot{p}/p = r(1 - [c/p(1 + d)])$ from which it is clear that the depletion allowance raises the rate of price increase and hence must lower the price initially.

is more profitable to extract now than later, and this encourages depletion.

Other provisions of the depletion allowance probably have serious implications for the structure of the industry; what implications this has for economic efficiency is not clear. For instance, any provision which assigns a depletion allowance for some categories of firms and not for others ought to result in most of the extraction being conducted by those who receive the depletion allowance. Limiting the amount of the depletion allowance as a percentage of profits, unless computed on a well-by-well or mine-by-mine basis, will also affect the structure of the industry.

Although the depletion allowance would have no effect on the pattern of extraction from known reserves with zero extraction costs, it does affect the incentive for discovering oil. The total stock of oil which is likely to be discovered is greater, and because of that, present prices are lower and consumption rates higher. Similarly, if there is a positive extraction cost, oil, which it would never pay to extract without a depletion allowance, will be extracted. But, apart from considerations of monopoly, the cost of discovery and extracting this oil will exceed its benefits, and so such a policy is undesirable.

If the removal of the depletion allowance has not been anticipated, the immediate effect of the removal will be to raise the price of oil, both because of the slower rate of extraction and the smaller stock of oil that will eventually be extracted. These effects may be disguised at present because the short-run effect of a gradual removal of the depletion allowance is to increase the supply of oil.

Immediate Write-Off of Drilling Expenses. With immediate write-off of capital expenditures, the corporation tax can be viewed as a pure profits tax, and is thus nondistortionary.[19] But since other sectors are not so treated, there is a relative distortion; investment in oil exploration is encouraged relative to other kinds of investment. There is no justification for this favorable treatment.

Inability to Write Off Immediately Expenditure on Lease (or Land) Acquisition. For expenditures other than drilling, the oil sector is treated like any other sector. But this symmetric treatment does induce a distortion in the rate of extraction relative to what it would be in the absence of taxation. Consider a firm which purchases land under which there is oil. After the oil has been extracted, the land will be worth less. The firm can take a capital loss on the reduction in land value, and thus reduce its tax liability. The present value of the tax write-off is increased by accelerating extraction. It would probably be desirable to allow imme-

---

[19] Without interest deductibility of debt. Immediate write-off with interest deductibility would appear to act like a capital subsidy.

diate write-off of these expenditures. In order to discourage excessive allocation of resources to this sector relative to others, other taxes would have to be imposed.

Special Treatment of Capital Gains. Since the return to holding oil is the increase in its price, if this increase in price is subjected to capital gains taxation, the return to holding oil will exceed the return to holding conventional assets, and there will be excessive conservation. This effect could be significant because the difference in rates is large. Since the sale of oil is treated as ordinary income, this distortion requires that firms that do the exploration hold on to the land until the date of extraction. They then sell their land; the purchaser extracts the oil, the income from the oil being perfectly offset by the reduction in the value of the land.

Of the various provisions discussed above, several have been introduced to offset the tax-induced biases of the general tax structure (or so proponents of the provision argue). The depletion allowance is justified as a simple alternative to depreciation, but the present tax code essentially allows triple depletion; immediate write-off of drilling expenses, depletion allowances, and write-off of the loss in value of leases or land after extraction is completed. Other proponents of these provisions admit that it constitutes favorable treatment but argue that the, favorable treatment is required to offset the distortionary effects of the corporation tax structure, which unduly penalizes risky and capital-intensive sectors. Elsewhere it has been argued that the sector is not more risky than other sectors, that the corporation tax does not discourage (but rather encourages) risk taking, that it does not penalize capital-intensive industries, and that there are second-best arguments for taxing the oil industry at a higher rate than other industries because the share of rents in that sector is larger.

Leasing Policy. The terms on which the government leases oil probably have a significant effect, not so much on the total rate of extraction as on the pattern of extraction. Efficiency requires that oil be taken from tracts of land with low extraction costs before it is taken from tracts with high extraction costs. (Similarly, tracts with low exploration costs should be explored before tracts with high exploration costs.) One of the provisos in government leases is the so-called diligence clause, requiring some development of the tract within five years. It pays the firm to extract at the end of five years so long as price exceeds extraction costs; but in the absence of the clause it would pay the firm to postpone extraction on tracts with high extraction costs.

Moreover, in models of competitive bidding it can be shown that the return in excess of extraction costs is a function of the number of bidders; this, it can be shown, leads to too little expenditure on exploration in areas in which there are a large number of "informed" firms, that is, firms who have extensive information about the tract; and it induces firms to nominate for leasing and explore fringe areas where there are likely to be few bidders and high exploration costs. This is inefficient.

In addition to these inefficiencies, there is an inefficiency arising from excessive and, from a social point of view, misdirected prebidding exploration, the object of which is not to discover oil but to ascertain how much should be bid for the lease. This has a private but not a social return. (It leads, for instance, to inefficiencies in the location of wells; for example, locating wells at boundaries of tracts to find out about neighboring tracts.)

It is not easy to devise more efficient policies. Recent proposals for developing pools as a single unit avoid the obvious inefficiencies arising when there are several tracts within a pool owned by different firms (the usual common-pool problem, where each firm fails to take account of its effect on the extraction of others; this normally leads to excessively rapid rates of depletion). The royalty bidding experiments showed that firms would bid very high royalty rates, but the consequence was that the well would be abandoned if the extraction costs as a percentage of price plus the royalty rate exceeded unity. Since these would be tracts with high extraction costs from which extraction should be postponed, provided they could eventually be leased again, this is not as great a disadvantage as it might seem.

Regulatory Policies.   The government has engaged in both long-term and short-term attempts at price regulation. In the case of natural gas, the government has attempted to keep the price low; in the case of oil, following the embargo, they have attempted to keep it from rising to its scarcity value. Both policies have serious effects. Because the price was not allowed to rise with the rate of interest, there was an incentive to extract as quickly as possible. Because the price was kept at a very low level, consumers had little incentive to conserve on natural resources.

The effects of price regulation in the oil embargo are not as apparent. The immediate effects were the usual inefficiencies associated with prices which are fixed below a market-clearing level, for example, lines at gas stations. It might be thought that because the supply was inelastic, there would be no effects on the total rate of consumption; although this is true in the short run, it is not in the long run. If firms and individuals come to believe that when there is an event such as an oil embargo prices will be kept below their market-clearing level, they will not have the incentive to take the efficient precautionary policies; firms will extract too much oil today (since they obtain a return on holding a precautionary stock that is less than its social value) and individuals will adopt technologies of consumption involving less flexibility than is socially optimal.[20]

VI
The Intertemporal Equity Issue

One of the major issues underlying the debate concerning natural resources is whether, with present policies, our descendants will be left in an impoverished state, without natural resources. What is of concern here is an equity issue—the welfare of our descendants versus the welfare of the present generation. There are two important observations to be made in this respect.

First, one should not view equity in a narrow sense of simply looking at the division of natural resources between present and future generations; the present generation may give future generations fewer natural resources (this is inevitable in the case of exhaustible natural resources), but it will give future generations a higher level of technology and more capital. One has to look at the relative welfare of the different generations and there is a strong presumption that future generations may be better off than the present generation. On grounds of equity it might be argued that we should consume even more now (including more natural resources).

Second, the appropriate instrument to use for obtaining more equitable distribution of welfare (if one believes that the present distribution is not equitable) are general instruments, for example, monetary policy directed at changing the market rate of interest. These do not lead to an inefficient allocation of resources. (Obviously, prior to using such general instruments, policies directed at correcting inefficiencies in the allocation of resources, as discussed in the previous section, have to be adopted.)

There has been an extensive recent literature concerned with the optimal pattern of consumption of natural resources. Although the models employed in this literature are obviously overly simple, they do give us a method of obtaining a rough check on whether the present allocation,

---

[20] Indeed, recent regulatory policies have punished those who have adopted flexible technologies: electricity generating plants which were convertible to coal were required to do so, forcing those who had adopted the flexible technology to pay more for their fuel than those who had not.

with all its market distortions, is different in a significant way from an optimal allocation. We solve for the optimal rate of extraction, using the utilitarian criterion, that is,

$$\max \int U(c)e^{-\delta t}e^{nt}\, dt$$

where $U(c)$ is the utility associated with a per capita consumption flow of c, n is the rate of growth of population, and δ the rate of discount, subject to the national income constraint,

$$C + \dot{K} = F(K, R, L, t) = K^{\alpha_1}R^{\alpha_2}L^{\alpha_3}\, e^{\lambda t}$$

(where F is a constant return to scale production function, which we have specialized as the Cobb–Douglas production function, with λ being the rate of technical progress; K is aggregate capital; L is labor; R is resource flow; and C is aggregate consumption), and to the resource constraint

$$\int R(t)\, dt = S$$

where S is the stock of the resource today.

The exact nature of the optimal consumption path (which, unlike the case without resources, may not be monotonic) depends on the elasticity of marginal utility, the rate of time preference, the rate of population growth, and the rate of technical change.[21] If the utility function is logarithmic $U = \ln c$, then it can be shown that the optimal rate of extraction is just equal to the pure rate of time discount minus the rate of population growth $(R/S) = \delta - n$. If $\delta - n$ is a number around 3 percent, this means that we should use up 3 percent of our remaining stocks each year, that is, at *current* rates of consumption, we have approximately thirty-three years' supply left, a number which is certainly smaller than our stock of energy-producing materials.

VII
Two Policy Issues

In the preceding two sections we discussed several policy issues in the context of whether a sustained level of per capita consumption growth is feasible and whether there are systematic misallocations of natural resources arising from market failure. In this section I wish to look at two further policy questions which have received widespread discussion.

[21] The general formula is that, asymptotically: $R/S = ([\delta(1 - \alpha_1) - \nu\lambda])/(1 - \alpha_1 - \alpha_2\nu) - n$ where ν is the elasticity of utility [4].

Operation Independence. A careful analysis of the costs associated with attaining energy independence (autarchy) would likely lead to a realization of the undesirability of that policy. Here, I wish to draw attention to two aspects of the debate.

The first question that ought to be posed is whether there is any reason to believe that the market has taken insufficient precautions for the contingencies of an embargo or a large price rise. The fact that individual economic agents have not "fully" insured against these contingencies is to be expected, given the high cost of such insurance. Our previous analysis suggested that in the absence of government regulatory policies (which do not allow the price to rise when scarcity values rise), there is no particular reason to believe that the market will make insufficient provision for these contingencies.[22]

Second, with respect to measures designed to obtain greater independence through increasing domestic supply, there is really a question of the intertemporal allocation of dependency; increased extraction today may reduce the costs of an embargo today, but would increase it in the future. Indeed, the argument of nondependency was one of the main ones used in support of the oil quotas in the 50s and 60s; this led to a higher level of consumption of our domestic supply, leaving us now with less domestic oil than we would have had then. (Thus, although we were better "protected" then we are less well protected now.)

R and D Policy. It has recently been suggested that some kind of price guarantee is required in order to elicit the appropriate levels of investment in R and D. The patent system is probably not an effective instrument in encouraging investment in R and D for energy (or natural resource) substitutes; the immediate effect of a discovery is to lower the price of the natural resource,[23] hence there is likely to be a long delay

[22] Obviously, if the market's assessments of the probabilities of an embargo or price rise are wrong, then it will take incorrect precautionary actions. If it underestimates these probabilities, then it will take insufficient precautionary actions. This can be corrected (assuming that the bureaucracy has reason to believe that it has better information about the probabilities, and that releasing this information to the market will not affect the market allocation, presumably because they refused to believe the bureaucrats) but tariff policy may not be an effective instrument. If individuals have point estimates of the price next period and production is not capacity constrained, then they always wish either to extract everything this period, everything next period, or are indifferent. Hence, with elastic foreign supplies, tariffs cannot control the intertemporal domestic supply allocation (although they do control domestic consumption). However, quotas will work.

[23] In a recent unpublished paper, Steinmuller [19] has reinterpreted the introduction of coal in Britain: it is not that the exhaustion of the forests led to the introduction of coal, but rather that less expensive methods of extracting coal made wood uneconomic as a fuel; although coal extraction was cheaper than planting and cutting a forest, it was not cheaper than cutting a forest; hence the immediate effect was to exhaust the forests and it was only later that it became economic to extract coal.

between invention and innovation. In addition, the lowering of the price is a social benefit which (apart from engaging in speculative activity) the inventor cannot capture. Although this does suggest that some kind of government price support program might be desirable, the price support should take the form of long-run contracts rather than a price support for the market as a whole.

VIII
Concluding Remarks

In this paper we have taken the view that natural resources are basically no different from other factors of production. There are presently extensive possibilities of substitution between resources and other factors (capital) and, with further research, there are likely to be further ways of substituting other factors for natural resources and making what resources we use go further. There is not a persuasive case that we face a problem from the exhaustion of our resources in the short or medium run, and although there are undoubtedly market failures leading to inefficiencies in resource allocation, there is no reason to believe they are worse here than elsewhere. Indeed, in the case of the effects of monopoly there is reason to believe that they are significantly less. In addition, a number of sources of inefficiency arising out of government intervention have been identified.

Although this is the conclusion that I, and I think many other economists would come to, I should emphasize that many of the points raised are moot. Although the economics of resource allocation in a static environment without uncertainty are well understood, there are many gaps in our understandings of dynamic economies with imperfect information, imperfect risk markets and imperfect futures markets, and these limitations are probably more important here than for conventional commodities. Further, at a number of points we have had to make empirical judgments (for example, about the value of the elasticity of substitution) about which there clearly can be disagreement. Perhaps more important than reaching agreement on the answer is reaching agreement on how we might resolve our disagreements. It is my hope that in this paper I have presented a framework within which this may be done.

References

1. F. M. Peterson and A. C. Fisher, "The Exploitation of Renewable and Nonrenewable Natural Resources," *Economic Journal* vol. 87 (December 1977) pp. 681–721.

2. P. Dasgupta and G. M. Heal, "The Optimal Depletion of Exhaustible Resources," *Review of Economic Studies,* Symposium on the Economics of Exhaustible Resources, 1974, pp. 3–28.

3. R. M. Solow, "The Economics of Resources or the Resources of Economics," *American Economic Review* Papers and Proceedings (May 1974) pp. 1–14.

4. J. E. Stiglitz, "Growth with Exhaustible Natural Resources: Efficient and Optimal Growth Paths," *Review of Economic Studies,* Symposium on the Economics of Exhaustible Resources, 1974, pp. 123–138.

5. K. Sato, "Micro and Macro Constant Elasticity of Substitution Production Functions in a Multi-firm Industry," *Journal of Economic Theory* vol. 1 (1969).

6. K. Sato, *Production Functions and Aggregation* (Amsterdam, North-Holland, 1975).

7. K. Arrow, H. Chenery, B. Minhas, and R. M. Solow, "Capital Labor Substitution and Economic Efficiency," *Review of Economics and Statistics* vol. 43 (1961) pp. 225–250.

8. J. E. Stiglitz, "Monopoly and the Rate of Extraction of Exhaustible Resources," *American Economic Review* vol. 66 (1976) pp. 655–661.

9. R. Gilbert, "Imperfect Competition and the Allocation of Oil," Working Paper No. 87, Department of Economics, University of California at Berkeley, 1976.

10. S. Salant, "Nash-Cournot Equilibrium for an Exhaustible Resource Like Oil," Federal Reserve Board, mimeo, 1975.

11. J. E. Stiglitz, "Utilitarianism and Horizontal Equity: The Case for Random Taxation," Institute for Mathematical Studies in the Social Sciences, Report, Stanford University, 1976.

12. J. Cremer and M. Weitzman, "OPEC and the Monopoly Price of World Oil," *European Economic Review* vol. 8, no. 2 (August 1976) pp. 155–164.

13. D. Newbery, "Feasible Price Stability May Not be Desirable," Institute for Mathematical Studies in the Social Sciences, Working Paper 68, Stanford University, April 1976.

14. P. Diamond, "National Debt in a Neoclassical Growth Model," *American Economic Review* vol. 55 (December 1965) pp. 1126–1150.

15. J. E. Stiglitz, "Growth with Exhaustible Resources: The Competitive Economy," *Review of Economic Studies,* Symposium on the Economics of Resources, 1974, pp. 139–152.

16. J. E. Stiglitz, "Information and Economic Analysis," unpublished monograph.

17. S. J. Grossman and J. E. Stiglitz, "Information and Competitive Price Systems," *American Economic Review* vol. 66, no. 2 (May 1976).

18. R. Gilbert, "Resource Depletion Under Uncertainty," Department of Economics, Stanford University, mimeo, 1975.

19. W. E. Steinmuller, "The Seventeenth Century Energy Crisis: a Critique of the Timber Famine Theory," unpublished paper, Department of Economics, Stanford University, July, 1976.

Bibliography

Barnett, H. J., and C. Morse. *Scarcity and Growth: The Economics of Resource Availability* (Baltimore, Johns Hopkins University Press for Resources for the Future, 1963).

Dasgupta, P. "Some Recent Theoretical Explorations in the Economics of Exhaustible Resources," in H. W. Gottinger, ed., *Systems Approaches and Environmental Problems* (Göttingen, Vandenhoek and Ruprecht, 1974) pp. 193–214.

———— and J. E. Stiglitz. "Uncertainty and the Rate of Extraction under Alternative Institutional Arrangements," Department of Economics, Stanford University, mimeo, 1975.

Herfindahl, O. C. "Depletion and Economic Theory," in Mason Gaffney, ed., *Extractive Resources and Taxation* (Madison, University of Wisconsin Press, 1964).

Hotelling, H. "The Economics of Exhaustible Resources," *Journal of Political Economy* vol. 39 (1931) pp. 137–175.

Nordhaus, W. "The Allocation of Energy Resources," *Brookings Papers on Economic Activity* no. 3 (Washington, D.C., Brookings Institution, 1973).

Pindyck, R. S. "Gains to Producers from the Cartelization of Exhaustible Resources," World Oil Project Working Paper, Massachusetts Institute of Technology, 1976.

Salant, S. W. "No End to the Age of Zinc: The Length of the Optimal Program when Depletion Affects Extraction Costs," International Finance Discussion Paper 73, Board of Governors, Federal Reserve System, 1976.

Solow, R. M. "Intergenerational Equity and Exhaustible Resources," *Review of Economic Studies,* Symposium on the Economics of Exhaustible Resources, 1974, pp. 29–45.

Stiglitz, J. E. "Tax Policy and the Oil Industry," report prepared for the Energy Policy Project sponsored by the Ford Foundation, partly published as chapter 3, "The Efficiency of Market Prices in Long Run Allocations in the Oil Industry," in G. Brannan, ed., "Studies in Energy Tax Policy" (Cambridge, Mass., Ballinger, 1975), pp. 55–100.

————, P. Dasgupta, R. Gilbert, G. Heal, and D. Newbery. "An Economic Analysis of the Conservation of Natural Resources," Federal Energy Administration Report (forthcoming).

Sweeney, J. "Economics of Depletable Resources: Market Forces and Intertemporal Bias," Department of Engineering Economics, Stanford University, mimeo, 1974.

3

Entropy, Growth, and the Political Economy of Scarcity

Herman E. Daly

Debts are subject to the laws of mathematics rather than physics. Unlike wealth, which is subject to the laws of thermodynamics, debts do not rot with old age and are not consumed in the process of living. On the contrary, they grow at so much per cent per annum, by the well known laws of simple and compound interest . . . as a result of this confusion between wealth and debt we are invited to contemplate a millenium where people live on the interest of their mutual indebtedness.

Frederick Soddy (*Wealth, Virtual Wealth, and Debt* pp. 68, 89)

I
Introduction

Chemistry has outgrown alchemy, and astronomy has emerged from the chrysalis of astrology, but the moral science of political economy has degenerated into the amoral game of politic economics. Political economy was concerned with scarcity and the resolution of the social conflicts engendered by scarcity. Politic economics tries to buy off social conflict by abolishing scarcity—by promising more things for more people, with less for no one, forever and ever—all vouchsafed by the amazing grace of compound interest. It is not politic economics to point out, as the Nobel laureate chemist and heretical economist Frederick Soddy [1] did in the above quote, that compound interest is the law of

This paper was presented at the RFF Conference on Natural Resource Scarcity on October 19, 1976 in Washington, D.C. I wish to acknowledge the benefit of comments received at that time from N. Georgescu-Roegen, B. Hannon, C. Morse, T. Page, and V. Kerry Smith. I have also benefited from comments by my colleagues, W. Culbertson, S. Farber, D. Johnson, and A. Toevs. Of course none of the above are to be held responsible for the views expressed, or for any errors committed.

debt, and that wealth is subject to the law of entropy, the law of moth, rust, accident, and decay. It is not politic to remember with John Ruskin:

the great, palpable, inevitable fact—the root and rule of all economy—that what one person has, another cannot have; and that every atom of substance, of whatever kind, used or consumed, is so much human life spent; which if it issue in the saving present life or the gaining more, is well spent, but if not is either so much life prevented, or so much slain. [2, p. 96]

Or as Ruskin more succinctly put it, "there is no wealth but life." Nor is it considered politic economics to take seriously the demonstration of the same insight by Georgescu-Roegen who has made us aware that

the maximum of life quantity requires the minimum rate of natural resources depletion. By using these resources too quickly, man throws away that part of solar energy that will still be reaching the earth for a long time after he has departed. And everything that man has done in the last two hundred years or so puts him in the position of a fantastic spendthrift. There can be no doubt about it: any use of natural resources for the satisfaction of nonvital needs means a smaller quantity of life in the future. If we understand well the problem, the best use of our iron resources is to produce plows or harrows as they are needed, not Rolls Royces, not even agricultural tractors. [3, p. 21]

Significantly, the contribution of Georgescu-Roegen is not so much as mentioned in the *Journal of Economic Literature's* 1976 survey of the literature of environmental economics [4]. The first sentence of that survey beautifully illustrates the environmental hubris of growth economics: "Man has probably always worried about his environment because he *was once* totally dependent on it" (emphasis supplied). Contrary to the implication, man's dependence on the environment is still quite total, and is overwhelmingly likely to remain so. Nevertheless, Robert Solow [5, p. 11] assures us that, thanks to "the productivity of natural resources increasing more or less exponentially over time," it is to be expected that, "the world can, in effect, get along without natural resources." In view of such statements it is evidently impossible to insist too strongly that, in Soddy's words:

life derives the whole of its physical energy or power, not from anything self-contained in living matter, and still less from an external diety, but solely from the inanimate world. It is dependent for all the necessities of its physical continuance primarily upon the principles of the steam-engine. The principles and ethics of human convention must not run counter to those of thermo-dynamics. [6, p. 9]

Lack of respect for the principles of the steam engine also underlies the basic message of the influential book *Scarcity and Growth* [7]. We are told that, "nature imposes particular scarcities, not an inescapable general scarcity" (p. 11). We are also asked to believe that:

Advances in fundamental science have made it possible to take advantage of the uniformity of matter/energy—a uniformity that makes it feasible, without preassignable limit, to escape the quantitative constraints imposed by the character of the earth's crust. . . . Science, by making the resource base more homogeneous, erases the restrictions once thought to reside in the lack of homogeneity. In a neo-Ricardian world, it seems, the particular resources with which one starts increasingly become a matter of indifference. The reservation of particular resources for later use, therefore, may contribute little to the welfare of future generations. [p. 11]

Unfortunately for the politic economics of growth, it is not the uniformity of matter-energy that makes for usefulness, but precisely the opposite. If all materials and all energy were uniformly distributed in thermodynamic equilibrium, the resulting "homogeneous resource base" would be no resource at all. It is nonuniformity, differences in concentration and temperature, that make for usefulness. The mere fact that all matter-energy may ultimately consist of the same basic building blocks is of little significance if it is the *potential for ordering those blocks* that is ultimately scarce, as the entropy law tells us is the case. Only a Maxwell's Sorting Demon could turn a lukewarm soup of electrons, protons, neutrons, quarks and whatnot, into a resource. And the entropy law tells us that Maxwell's Demon does not exist. In other words, nature really *does* impose "an inescapable general scarcity," and it is a serious delusion to believe otherwise.

The differences cited above could hardly be more fundamental. It seems necessary therefore to start at the very beginning if we are to root out the faddish politic economics of growth and replant the traditional political economy of scarcity. The standard textbooks have long defined economics as "the study of the allocation of scarce means among competing ends." A reconsideration of ends and means will provide our starting point. Modern economics' excessive devotion to growth will be explained in terms of an incomplete view of the total ends-means spectrum. The arguments of two main traditions of criticism will be discussed —the "scarce means arguments" and the "competing higher ends arguments." The concepts of entropy, scarcity, and growth are brought into relationship with the ends-means spectrum, and it is argued that a holistic view of the spectrum leads away from growth mania and toward something like John Stuart Mill's [8] vision of a "stationary state" (here called a steady-state economy, or SSE for short). The basic concepts used to elaborate this alternate paradigm are set forth, drawing on the work of Mill, Irving Fisher [9], Kenneth Boulding [10] and Nicholas

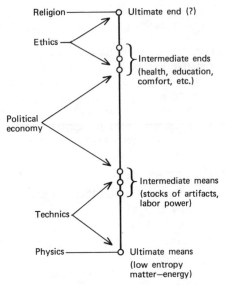

Figure 3-1. Ends-means spectrum.

Georgescu-Roegen [3]. Policies for a noncatastrophic transition from a growth economy to a SSE are suggested, including a prescriptive institutional model for the social rationing of low entropy.

II
The Ends–Means Spectrum

In the largest sense, man's ultimate economic problem is to use means wisely in the service of the Ultimate End. Stated so generally, it is not hard to understand our tendency to divide up the single, unified problem into a number of smaller subproblems, as indicated in figure 3-1. This is a good procedure as long as we do not forget about other parts of the spectrum in our zeal to solve the problem of one segment.

At the top of the spectrum is the Ultimate End—that which is intrinsically good and does not derive its goodness from any instrumental relation to some higher good. At the bottom is ultimate means, the useful stuff of the world, low entropy matter-energy, which man can only use up and cannot create or replenish, and the net production of which cannot possibly be the end of any human activity. Each intermediate category in the spectrum is an end with respect to lower categories and a means with respect to higher categories. Below the Ultimate End we have a hierarchy of intermediate ends which are in a sense means in the service of the Ultimate End. Intermediate ends are ranked with reference to the

Ultimate End. The mere fact that we speak of priorities among our goals presumes a first place, an ordering principle, an Ultimate End. We may not be able to define it very well, but logically we are forced to recognize its existence. Above ultimate means are intermediate means (physical stocks) which can be viewed as ends directly served by the use of ultimate means (the entropic flow of matter-energy, the "throughput").

On the left of the spectrum line are listed the traditional disciplines of study that correspond to each segment. The central, intermediate, position of economics is highly significant. In looking only at the middle range, economics has naturally not dealt with ultimates or absolutes and has falsely assumed that the middle range pluralities, relativities, and substitutabilities among competing ends and scarce means were representative of the whole spectrum. Absolute limits are absent from the economists' paradigm because absolutes are encountered only at the poles of the spectrum, which have been excluded from the focus of attention. Even ethics and technics exist for the economist only at the very periphery of professional awareness.

In terms of this diagram, economic growth implies the creation of ever more intermediate means (stocks) to satisfy ever more intermediate ends.[1] Orthodox growth economics, as we have seen, recognizes that particular resources are limited, but does not recognize any general scarcity of all resources. The orthodox dogma is that technology can always substitute new resources for old, without limit. Ultimate means are not considered scarce. Intermediate means are scarce, it is argued, only because our capacity to transform ultimate means has not yet evolved very far. Growth economists also recognize that any single intermediate end or want can be satisfied for any given individual. But new wants keep emerging (and new people as well), so the aggregate of all intermediate ends is held to be insatiable, or infinite in number, if not in intensity. The growth economist's vision is one of continuous growth in intermediate means (unconstrained by any scarcity of ultimate means) in order to satisfy ever more intermediate ends (unconstrained by any impositions from the Ultimate End). Infinite means plus infinite ends equals growth forever.

A consideration of the two poles of the spectrum, however, gives us a very different perspective. It forces us to raise two questions: (1) What, precisely, are our ultimate means, and are they limited in ways that cannot be overcome by technology? (2) What is the nature of the Ultimate End, and is it such that, beyond a certain point, further accumulation of intermediate means (bodies and artifacts) not only fails to serve the

---

[1] Qualitative change in physical stocks is "development." Growth refers to quantitative change. The distinction will be developed in section V.

Ultimate End, but actually renders a disservice? It will be argued below that the answer to both sets of questions is "yes." The absolute scarcity of ultimate means limits the *possibility* of growth. The competition from other ends, which contribute more heavily at the margin toward the Ultimate End, limits the *desirability* of growth. Moreover, the interaction of desirability and possibility provides the *economic* limit to growth, which is the most stringent, and should be the governing limit.

Paradoxically, growth economics has been both too materialistic and not materialistic enough. In ignoring the ultimate means and the laws of thermodynamics it has been insufficiently materialistic. In ignoring the Ultimate End and ethics it has been too materialistic. There are impressive intellectual traditions that criticize standard growth economics from each of these two perspectives. Table 3-1 gives a brief outline, with some of the representative members of each tradition.

The classification into ends-based (moral) and means-based (biophysical) critics of growth is in terms of emphasis and starting point only. Many writers to a considerable extent belong to both traditions. This is to be expected because the two traditions are not really so logically independent as may at first appear. For example, many moral issues regarding distributive justice and intergenerational equity hardly arise if one believes that continual economic growth is biophysically possible. Likewise, if one's arena of moral concern excludes the poor, future generations, and subhuman life, then many biophysical constraints are no longer of interest. To crack the nut of growth mania, it is not enough to hammer from above with moral arguments because there is sufficient "give" underneath supplied by optimistic biophysical assumptions. Hammering only from below with biophysical arguments leaves too much room for elastic morality to absorb the blow. (The interest rate automatically looks after the future, growth itself is the Ultimate End, or as close as we can come to it, man's manifest destiny is to colonize space— the earth is a mere "dandelion gone to seed," etc.) Growth chestnuts have to be placed on the unyielding anvil of biophysical realities, and then crushed with the hammer of moral argument. The entropy law and ecology provide the biophysical anvil. Concern for future generations, subhuman life, and inequities in current distribution of wealth provide the moral hammer.

Man is both a material creature in absolute dependence upon his physical environment, and a rational being who has purposes and strives to become better. These two aspects must be consistent with each other. Improvement presupposes survival, and survival in an entropic and evolving world is impossible without continual striving for improvement. Biophysically based conclusions about economic growth, or any other

Table 3-1. Intellectual Traditions of Growth Criticism

Biophysically or Means Based		Ethically or Ends Based	
Physical or bio-economists	Frederick Soddy Kenneth Boulding N. Georgescu-Roegen John Ise A. J. Lotka	John Ruskin Thomas Carlyle Henry Thoreau William Morris	Early critics of industrialism
	J. Culbertson R. Wilkinson	G. K. Chesterton H. Belloc	Distributism
Ecologists	Rachel Carson Paul Ehrlich Garrett Hardin Barry Commoner *Blueprint for Survival* Eugene Odum	Narodniki American agrarians Kropotkin Tolstoy Gandhi	Rural agrarian critics of industrialism
Systems ecologists	Howard Odum Kenneth Watt	J. S. Mill E. F. Schumacher E. J. Mishan D. Goulet	Humanist economists
Geologists	M. K. Hubbert Earl Cook	H. Daly	
	Harrison Brown Preston Cloud	Lewis Mumford Ivan Illich Jacques Ellul	Critics of technological society
Systems engineers	Jay Forrester Dennis Meadows	Theodore Roszak	
	Bruce Hannon Mesarovic and Pestel 1930s Technocracy, Inc.	Thomas Derr John Cobb Frederick Elder	Emerging theology of ecology
Conservationists	G. P. Marsh William Vogt David Brower Denis Hayes	William Ophuls Richard Falk L. K. Caldwell	Political science of survival
Demographers	K. Davis N. Keyfitz		
Physicists	A. Lovins D. Abrahamson J. Holdren H. Bent		

Note: See bibliography for references to representative work of each author.

subject, should be in accord with morally based conclusions. If there is a discrepancy it must indicate a flawed understanding of the natural world or a warped set of values. That ends-based and means-based arguments should converge in their rejection of growth mania is both comforting and not unexpected. Let us consider each line of argument, beginning with the means-based, biophysical arguments.

III
Means-Based Arguments

From a basic branch of physics, thermodynamics, we learn that for man's purposes the ultimate usable stuff of the universe is low entropy matter-energy.[2] What is low entropy? In terms of materials, low entropy means structure, organization, concentration, order. Dispersed, randomly scattered molecules of any material are useless (high entropy). In terms of energy, low entropy means capacity to do work, or concentrated, relatively high-temperature energy. Energy dispersed in equilibrium temperature with the general environment is useless (high entropy).

We have two sources of low entropy: terrestrial stocks of concentrated minerals, and the solar flow of radiant energy. The terrestrial source (minerals in the earth's crust) is obviously limited in total amount, though the rate at which we use it up is largely a matter of choice. The solar source is practically unlimited in total amount, but strictly limited in the rate at which it reaches the earth. Both sources of ultimate means are limited—one in total amount, the other in rate of arrival. These means are finite. Furthermore, there is an enormous disproportion in the total amounts of the two sources: if all the world's fossil fuels could be burned up, they would provide the energy equivalent of only a few weeks of sunlight. The sun is expected to last for another five or six billion years.

This raises a cosmically embarrassing economic question: If the solar source is so vastly more abundant, why have we over the past 150 years shifted the physical base of our economy from overwhelming dependence on solar energy and renewable resources, to overwhelming dependence on nonrenewable terrestrial minerals? An important part of the answer is that terrestrial stocks can, for a while at least, be used at a rate of man's own choosing, that is, rapidly. The use of solar energy and renewable resources is limited by the fixed solar flux, and the rhythms of growth of plants and animals, which in turn provide a natural constraint on economic growth. But growth can be speeded beyond this constraint, for a time at least, by consuming geological capital—by using up the reserves of terrestrial low entropy. If the object is high growth rates now, then it can be most easily attained by using up terrestrial sources rapidly. Such growth permits us to achieve population and per capita consumption levels that are beyond the capacity of renewable resources alone to support—thereby creating a strong vested interest in the continuing consumption of geological capital.

[2] The following paragraphs draw heavily on the pioneering work of Nicholas Georgescu-Roegen [3, 11].

The difficulty is twofold. First, we will eventually run out of accessible terrestrial sources. Second, even if we never ran out we would still face problems of ecological breakdown caused by a growing throughput of matter-energy. Even if technology were able to double the incident flow of solar energy (by far the cleanest source), the millions of years of past evolutionary adaptation to the usual rate would make a doubling of that rate totally catastrophic. The whole biosphere has evolved as a complex system around the fixed point of a given solar flux. Modern man is the only species that has broken the solar income budget. The fact that man has supplemented his fixed solar income by rapidly consuming terrestrial capital has thrown him out of balance with the rest of the biosphere. As stocks of artifacts and people have grown, the throughput necessary for their maintenance has had to grow also, implying more depletion and more pollution. *Natural biogeochemical cycles become overloaded. Not only has the throughput grown quantitatively, but its qualitative nature has changed. Exotic substances are produced and thrown wholesale in the biosphere—substances with which the world has had no adaptive evolutionary experience, and which are consequently nearly always disruptive (e.g., DDT and plutonium).

But are we not giving insufficient credit to technology in claiming that ultimate means are limited? Is not technology itself a limitless resource? No, it is not. All technologies, nature's as well as man's, run on an entropy gradient, that is, the total entropy of all outputs taken together is always greater than the total entropy of all inputs taken together. No organism can eat its own outputs and live, and no engine can run on its own exhaust. If the outputs of a process were of lower entropy than the inputs, once *all* inputs and outputs were accounted for, we would have a process that violates the second law of thermodynamics, and so far no such process has ever been observed. Technology itself depends on the ultimate means of low entropy. If low entropy sources are not unlimited, then neither is technology. If the technological optimist really believes in "exponentially growing resource productivity" and in a world that can "get along without natural resources," then he should not object to quantitative restrictions on the resource throughput, as will be urged in section VI. If resource productivity can really approach infinity, then that is reason for using fewer resources, not more!

It is especially ironic to be told by growth advocates that technology is freeing man from dependence on resources [7, p. 11]. It has in fact done the opposite. Modern technology has made us *more* dependent on the *scarcer* of the two sources of ultimate means. It has also made us more dependent on each other, on remote experts, and more vulnerable to systemic breakdowns and sabotage by small groups. In view of the

These limits to population have been given.

Malthus — food/fiber

Meadows et al — mineral resource base

Daly — pollution absorption capacity

popular belief in the omnipotence of technology, it is even more ironic to recall that the most basic laws of science are statements of impossibility: it is impossible to create or destroy matter-energy; it is impossible to have perpetual motion; it is impossible to exceed the speed of light; it is impossible to measure anything without in some way interfering with the thing being measured, etc. The remarkable success of physical science has been in no small measure due to its intelligent recognition of impossibilities and its refusal to attempt them. Paradoxically this success has, in the popular mind, been taken as "proof" that nothing is impossible!

The entropy law tells us that when technology increases order in one part of the universe, it must produce an even greater amount of disorder somewhere else. If that "somewhere else" is the sun (as it is for nature's technology and for man's traditional preindustrial technology), then we need not worry. If "somewhere else" is here on earth, as it is for technologies based on terrestrial mineral deposits, then we had better pay close attention. The throughput flow maintains or increases the order within the human economy, but at the cost of creating greater disorder in the rest of the natural world, as a result of depletion and pollution. There are limits to how much disorder can be produced in the rest of the biosphere and still allow it to function well enough to continue supporting the human subsystem. There is a limit to how much of the ecosphere can be converted into technosphere.

Although technology cannot overcome these basic limits, it could achieve a much better accommodation to them, and could work more in harmony with nature's technology than it has in the past. There are enormous possibilities for artful technological finesse and elegant frugality [12]. But arbitrarily cheap energy has given the edge to brute force, and has driven really clever technology off the market. An improved technological accommodation to limits, while certainly possible and desirable, is not likely to be forthcoming in a growth context, in an economy that would rather maximize throughput than reduce it. Such improvement is much more likely within the framework of an SSE, where profits would be made from development, not growth, as will be elaborated later.

IV
Ends-Based Arguments

The temper of the modern age resists any discussion of the Ultimate End. Teleology and purpose, the dominant concepts of an earlier time, were banished from the mechanistic, reductionistic, positivistic mode of thought that came to be identified with the most recent phase of the evolution of science. Economics followed suit by reducing ethics to the level of personal tastes. No questions are asked about whether individual priorities are right or wrong, or even about how they are formed. The same goes for collective priorities. Whatever happens to interest the mass public is assumed to be in the public interest.

Our modern refusal to reason about the Ultimate End merely assures the incoherence of our priorities, both individually and collectively. It leads to the tragedy of Herman Melville's Captain Ahab, whose means were all rational, but whose purpose was insane. The apparent purpose of growth economics is to seek to satisfy infinite wants by means of infinite production. This is about as wise as chasing a white whale, and the high rationality of the means employed cannot be used to justify the insanity of purpose. Rational means simply make insane purposes all the more dangerous. Among our presumed "infinite" wants is there not the desire to be free from the tyranny of infinite wants? Is there not a desire for finite wants, for only good wants? If the assumption of infinite wants includes the desire for finite wants (and how could it be excluded except as a moral commandment that "thou shalt want more"?), then we have a kind of liar's paradox—one of our "infinite" wants is the want for finite wants! And even if wants were infinite, it does not follow that infinite production, even if possible, would be capable of satisfying more than a finite subset of our "infinite" wants. Some logical cracks thus appear in one of growth mania's cornerstones.

What is the Ultimate End? The question is logically unavoidable. But only a minimum answer to such a maximum question is likely to command much consensus. As a minimum answer let me suggest that whatever the Ultimate End is, it presupposes a respect for and continuation of creation and the evolutionary process through which God has bestowed upon us the gift of self-conscious life. Whatever values are put in first place, their further realization requires the continuation of life— the survival of the biosphere and its evolving processes. It may be a noble act to sacrifice the remaining years of one's own life to a higher cause. But to sacrifice, or even to risk sacrificing, most of creation to some "higher cause" is surely fanaticism. This minimum answer begs many important questions. What direction should survival and evolution take? To what extent should evolution be influenced by man and to what extent should it be left spontaneous? For now, however, the only point is that survival must rank very high in the ends-means hierarchy, and consequently any type of growth that requires the creation of means that threaten survival should be forbidden. The nuclear-powered "plutonium economy" is a prime example of the kind of growth that must be halted. The long-run survival costs of extravagant luxury (Rolls-Royces rather than plows), must also be allowed to temper our enthusiasm for growth. No one doubts that the basic needs of the present must take precedence over the basic needs of the future. But should not the trivial wants of the present yield at some point to the basic needs of the future?

But what about other kinds of growth? Are *all* kinds of physical growth subject to desirability limits? Is there such a thing as *enough* in the material realm, and is enough better than "more than enough"? Is "more than enough" inimical to survival? Certainly all organic needs can be satisfied and to go beyond enough is usually harmful. Satisficing[3] should play a larger role in economic theory, and maximizing a correspondingly smaller role. The only want that seems insatiable is the want for distinction, the desire to be in some way superior to one's neighbors. Even the want for distinction need not cause problems except when the main avenue of distinction in society is to have a larger income than the next fellow and to consume more. The only way for everyone to earn more is to have aggregate growth. But that is precisely the rub. If everyone earns more, then where is the distinction? It is possible for everyone's *absolute* income to increase, but not for everyone's *relative* income to increase. To the extent that it is higher relative income that is important, growth becomes impotent. As British economist E. J. Mishan put it:

> In an affluent society, people's satisfactions, as Thorstein Veblen observed, depend not only on the innate or perceived utility of the goods they buy, but also on the status value of such goods. Thus to a person in a high income society, it is not only his absolute income that counts but also his relative income, his position in the structure of relative incomes. In its extreme form—and as affluence rises we draw closer to it—only relative income matters. A man would then prefer a 5 per cent reduction in his own income accompanied by a 10 per cent reduction in the incomes of others to a 25 per cent increase in both his income and the incomes of others.
>
> The more this attitude prevails—and the ethos of our society actively promotes it— the more futile is the objective of economic growth for society as a whole. For it is obvious that over time everyone cannot become relatively better off. [13, p. 30]

Aggregate growth can no more satisfy the relative wants of distinction than the arms race can increase security. When society has reached a level of affluence such that at the margin the relative wants of distinction are dominant, then aggregate growth becomes either futile, or the source of increasing inequality. At some point growth becomes undesirable, even if still possible.

The effective limit to growth, however, is neither desirability nor

---

[3] Satisificing, as used here, means to seek enough rather than the most. The concept of enough is difficult to define, but even more difficult to deny.

possibility, but the interaction of the two, that is, the *economic* limit. It is not necessary that the marginal benefits of growth should fall all the way to zero, nor that the marginal costs of growth should rise to infinity, but only that the two should become equal. As growth continues we know that marginal benefits fall, and marginal costs rise and at some point they will become equal. We do not satisfy our ends in any random order, but strive always to satisfy our most pressing needs first. Likewise, we do not use our low entropy means in any order, but exploit the highest grade and most accessible resources first. This elementary rule of sensible behavior underlies both the law of diminishing marginal benefit and the law of increasing marginal costs, which are the very keystones of economic theory, and which apply to aggregate output as well as to individual commodities. The fact that growth-induced disruptions of ecosystem services cannot be arrayed to occur in increasing order of severity is a major obstacle to economic calculation, and leads one away from maximizing and toward "satisficing" strategies.

Once one has convinced one's self that absolute scarcity is real, and that growth should be a means to some end rather than an end in itself, then the next question is: What is a feasible and desirable alternative and how could it be attained? How can we move away from the politic economics of growth and toward a political economy of scarcity? The next section presents the alternative of a steady-state economy, and the following section offers some policies for making the transition.

V
The Concept of a Steady-State Economy

The steady-state economy (SSE) is defined by four characteristics:

1. a constant population of human bodies,
2. a constant population or stock of artifacts (exosomatic capital or extensions of human bodies),
3. the levels at which the two populations are held constant are sufficient for a good life and sustainable for a long future,
4. the rate of throughput of matter-energy by which the two stocks are maintained is reduced to the lowest feasible level. For the population this means that birth rates are equal to death rates at low levels so that life expectancy is high. For artifacts it means that production equals depreciation at low levels so that artifacts are long lasting, and depletion and pollution are kept low.

Only two things are held constant—the stock of human bodies, and the total stock or inventory of artifacts. Technology, information, wisdom, goodness, genetic characteristics, distribution of wealth and income, product mix, etc., are *not* held constant. In the very long run of course nothing can remain constant, so our concept of an SSE must be a medium run concept in which stocks are constant over decades or generations, not millenia or eons.

Three magnitudes are basic to the concept of an SSE:

1. *Stock* is the total inventory of producers' goods, consumers' goods, and human bodies. It corresponds to Irving Fisher's [9] definition of capital, and may be thought of as the set of all physical things capable of satisfying human wants and subject to ownership.

2. *Service* is the satisfaction experienced when wants are satisfied, or "psychic income" in Fisher's [9] sense. Service is yielded by the stock. The quantity and quality of the stock determine the intensity of service. There is no unit for measuring service, so it may be stretching words a bit to call it a "magnitude." Nevertheless, we all experience service or satisfaction and recognize differing intensities of the experience. Service is yielded over a period of time and thus appears to be a flow magnitude. But unlike flows, service cannot be accumulated. It is probably more accurate to think of service as a "psychic flux" [3, 11].

3. *Throughput* is the entropic physical flow of matter-energy from nature's sources, through the human economy, and back to nature's sinks, and is necessary for maintenance and renewal of the constant stocks [3, 10, 14].

The relationship among these three magnitudes can best be understood in terms of the following simple identity [15].

$$\frac{\text{service}}{\text{throughput}} \equiv \frac{\text{service}}{\text{stock}} \times \frac{\text{stock}}{\text{throughput}}$$

The final benefit of all economic activity is service. The original useful stuff required for yielding service, and which cannot be produced by man, but only used up, is low-entropy matter-energy, that is, the throughput. But throughput is not itself capable of directly yielding service. It must first be accumulated into a stock of artifacts. It is the stock that directly yields service. We can ride to town in only one of the existing stock of automobiles. We cannot ride to town on the annual flow of automotive maintenance expenditures, nor on the flow of newly mined iron ore destined to be embodied in a new chassis, nor on the flow of worn rusting hulks in junkyards. Stocks may be thought of as throughput that has been accumulated and "frozen" in structured forms capable of satisfying human wants. Eventually the frozen structures are "melted" by entropy, and what flowed into the accumulated stocks from nature then flows back to nature in equal quantity, but in entropically degraded quality. Stocks are intermediate magnitudes that belong at the center of analysis, and provide a clean separation between the cost flow and the benefit flux. On the one hand stocks yield service, on the other hand stocks require throughput for maintenance. Service yielded is benefit; throughput required is cost.

The identification of cost with throughput should not be interpreted as implying a "throughput or entropy theory of value." There are other costs, notably the disutility of labor, and the accumulation time required to build up stocks. In the steady state we can forget about accumulation time since stocks are only being maintained, not accumulated. The disutility of labor can be netted out against the services of the stock to obtain net psychic income or net service. In the steady state, then, the value of net service is imputed to the stocks that render the service, which is in turn imputed to the throughput that maintains the stocks. It is in this sense that throughput is identified with cost. The opportunity cost of the throughput that maintains artifact A is the service sacrificed by not using that throughput to maintain more of artifact B. The throughput is a physical cost which is evaluated according to opportunity cost principles. However, the opportunity cost of the throughput must be evaluated not only in terms of alternative artifact services forgone (which the market does), but also in terms of natural ecosystem services forgone as a result of the depletion and pollution caused by the through-put (which escapes market valuation). Depletion reduces the service of availability of the resource to future people who cannot bid in present markets, and pollution reduces the ability of the ecosystem to perform its life support services. The true opportunity cost of an increment in throughput is the greater of the two classes: artifact service sacrificed and ecosystem services sacrificed. Thus throughput is better thought of as a cost-inducing physical flow rather than identified with cost itself, which by definition must always be a sacrificed benefit, not a physical magnitude. In like manner the stock is a benefit-yielding physical magnitude and should not be identified with benefit or service itself.

We can arrive at the same basic result by following Irving Fisher's reasoning. Fisher [9] argued that every intermediate transaction involves both a receipt and an expenditure of identical magnitude which cancel out in aggregating the total income of the community. But once the final user has obtained the asset, there is no further exchange and cancelling of accounts among individuals. The service yielded by the asset to the final consumer is the "uncancelled fringe" of psychic income, the final uncancelled benefit left over after all intermediate transactions have cancelled out. Subtracting the psychic disservices of labor, Fisher arrived at *net psychic income,* the final net benefit of all economic activity. It is highly interesting that Fisher did not identify any original, uncancelled, real cost against which the final value of net psychic income should be balanced. Here we must supplement Fisher's vision with the more recent visions and analyses of Boulding [10] and Georgescu-Roegen [3, 11], concerning the physical basis of cost. As everyone recognizes, the stock of capital wears out and has to be replaced. This continual maintenance and replacement is an unavoidable cost inflicted by entropy. Fisher treated it as cancelling out in the aggregate: house repair is income to the account of the carpenter and an identical outgo to the account of the house. But Fisher did not trace the chain all the way back to any "uncancelled fringe" at the beginning which would correspond to uncancelled final costs in the same way that net psychic income corresponds to uncancelled final benefits. If we do this, we come to the unpaid contribution from nature: the provision of useful low-entropy matter-energy inputs, and the absorption of high-entropy waste matter-energy outputs. These contributions from nature have no costs of production, only a cost of extraction or disposal, which is paid and enters the cancelling stream of accounts. But we do not pump any money down into a well as we pump oil out nor do we dump dollars into the sea along with our chemical and radioactive wastes. If service is an "uncancelled fringe," then so is throughput. In other words, if we consolidate the accounts of all firms and households, everything cancels out except service and throughput.

In the SSE a different behavior mode is adopted with respect to each of the three basic magnitudes. (1) *Stock* is to be *"satisficed,"* that is, maintained at a level that is sufficient for an abundant life for the present generation, and ecologically sustainable for a long (but not infinite) future. (2) *Service* is to be *maximized,* given the constant stock. (3) *Throughput* is to be *minimized,* given the constant stock. In terms of the two ratios on the right hand side of the identity, this means that the ratio service/stock is to be maximized by maximizing the numerator, with denominator constant, while the ratio stock/throughput is maximized by minimizing the denominator with numerator constant. These two ratios measure two kinds of efficiency: service efficiency and maintenance efficiency.

Service efficiency (service/stock) depends on allocative efficiency (does the stock consist of artifacts that people most want, and are they allocated to the most important uses), and on distributive efficiency (is the distribution of the stock among alternative people such that the trivial wants of some people do not take precedence over the basic needs of others). Standard economics has much of value to say about allocative efficiency, but treats distribution under the heading of social justice rather than efficiency, thus putting it on the sidelines of disciplinary concern. Although neoclassical economists carefully distinguish allocation from distribution in static analysis, they seem not to insist on any analogous distinction between intertemporal allocation (one person allocating over different stages of his lifetime) and intertemporal distribution (distribution between different people, that is, present people and future people). Intertemporal distribution is a question of ethics, not a function of the interest rate. The notion of optimal allocation over time must be confined to a single lifetime, unless we are willing to let ethics and distributional issues into the definition of optimum. Neoclassical economics seems inconsistent, or at least ambiguous on this point.

Maintenance efficiency (stock/throughput) depends on durability (how long an individual artifact lasts), and on replaceability (how easily the artifact can be replaced when it finally does wear out). Maintenance efficiency measures the number of units of time over which a population of artifacts yields its service, while service efficiency measures the intensity of that service per unit of time. Maintenance efficiency is limited by the entropy law (nothing lasts forever, everything wears out). Service efficiency may conceivably increase for a very long time, since the growing "magnitude," service, is nonphysical. There may, however, be physical limits to the capacity of human beings to experience service. But the definition of the SSE is in terms of physical stocks and throughput, and is not affected by whether or not service could increase indefinitely.

Conceptually it is easier to think of stock as the operational policy variable to be directly controlled. Practically, however, as will be seen below, it would be easier to control or limit throughput directly, and allow the stock to reach the maximum level sustainable by the fixed throughput. This presents no problems.

The above concepts allow us to make an important distinction between growth and development. *Growth* refers to an increase in service that results from an increase in stock and throughput, with the two efficiency ratios constant. *Development* refers to an increase in the efficiency ratios, with stock constant (or alternatively, an increase in service with throughput constant). Using these definitions, we may say that a SSE develops but does not grow, just as the planet earth, of which it is a subsystem, develops without growing.

How do these concepts relate to GNP, the more conventional index of "growth"? GNP makes no distinction among the three basic magnitudes. It simply adds up value estimates of some services (the service of those assets that are rented rather than purchased, including human bodies, and omitting the services of all owned assets not rented during the current year, with the exception of owner-occupied houses), plus the value of the throughput flow (maintenance and replacement expenditures required to maintain the total stock intact), plus the value of current additions to stock (net investment). What sense does it make to add up benefits, costs, and change in inventory? Services of the natural ecosystem are not counted, and more important, services sacrificed are not subtracted. In fact, defensive attempts to repair the loss of ecosystem services are added to GNP. The concept of an SSE is independent of GNP, and what happens to GNP in the SSE simply does not matter. The best thing to do with GNP is to forget it. The next best thing is to try to replace it with two separate social accounts, one measuring the value of service (benefit), and the other measuring the value of throughput (cost). In this way costs and benefits could be compared, although this aggregate macro level comparison is not at all essential, since regardless of how it turns out, the behavior modes remain the same with respect to each of the three basic magnitudes. If we really could get operational cost and benefit accounts, then we might optimize the level of stocks by letting it grow to the point where the marginal cost of an addition to stock just equals the marginal benefit. But that is so far beyond our ability to measure that for a long time satisficing will remain a better strategy than optimizing. Aggregate economic indexes should be treated with caution, since there are always some kinds of stupid behavior that would raise the index, and thus become "justified."

Neither the concept nor the reality of an SSE is new. John Stuart Mill [8] discussed the concept in his famous chapter "on the stationary state." Historically, man has lived for 99 percent of his tenure on earth in conditions very closely approximating a steady state. Economic growth is essentially a phenomenon of the past 200 years, and only in the past fifty years has it become the dominant goal of nations. Growth is an aberration, not the norm. Development can continue without growth, and is in fact more likely under an SSE than a growth economy.

Even "cornucopians" like Weinberg and Goeller [16] evidently consider an SSE to be a precondition for achieving their Age of Substitutability, in which "society will settle into a steady state of substitution and recycling . . . assuming, of course, a stable population." But why postpone the SSE to some hypothetical future age? Why not seek to come to terms with the SSE now, before we use up the remaining easily available resources that could help in making the transition? Why continue to fan the fires of growth up to the point where the flame's appetite is so voracious that even maintaining it in a steady state would require technologies and social institutions that are so demanding and unforgiving as to reduce the quality of life to that of a regimented community of social insects?

VI
Policies for a Steady-State Economy

How can we achieve an SSE without enormous disruption? The difficult part is mustering the moral resources and political will to do it. The technical problems are small by comparison. People often overestimate the technical problems because they mistakenly identify an SSE with a failed growth economy. A situation of nongrowth can come about in two ways: as a result of the success of steady-state policies or the failure of growth policies. Nongrowth resulting from the failure to grow is chaotic beyond repair. This is precisely why we need an SSE—because it is so much better than a failed growth economy.

In an effort to stimulate discussion on policies for attaining an SSE, I have suggested three institutions [17] which seem to me to provide the necessary social control with a minimum sacrifice of individual freedom. They build on the existing bases of private property and the price system, and are thus fundamentally conservative, though they will appear radical to some. The kinds of institutions needed follow straight from the definition of an SSE: "constant stocks of people and artifacts maintained at chosen levels that are sufficient for a good life and sustainable for a long future, by the lowest feasible rate of throughput." We need an institution for limiting population, one for limiting stocks of artifacts, and one for limiting inequality in the distribution of artifacts among the population.

Let us leave population issues to one side. Of all the population control schemes now being debated, I prefer the *transferrable birth license plan,* first advocated by Kenneth Boulding (Boulding [18]; Daly [17]; Heer [19]), but for purposes of this discussion will invite the reader to substitute his own favorite population control scheme, if he does not like that one.

A constant aggregate stock of artifacts will result from holding the throughput flow constant by means of a *depletion quota auction,* to be discussed below. Since aggregate growth can no longer be appealed to as the "solution" to poverty, we must face the distribution issue directly by setting up a *distributist institution* which would limit the range of inequality to some justifiable and functional degree. This could be accomplished by setting a minimum income limit, maximum income and wealth limits for individuals and families, and a maximum size for corporations. The maximum and minimum would define a range within which inequality is legitimate and beyond which it is not. The exact numbers are of secondary importance, but just suppose a minimum of $7,000 and a maximum of $70,000 on family income. The idea of a minimum income is familiar, but the notion of a maximum is not, because in the growth paradigm it is not necessary. But in the steady-state paradigm the total stock is constant and this implicitly sets a maximum on individual wealth and income. Some limits on inequality are essential, though we may debate just how much inequality is legitimate.

The key institution would be the *depletion quota auction* by which the annual amount extracted of each basic resource would be set, and through which the quota rights would be auctioned by the government in conveniently divisible units. The resource market would become two-tiered. First, the government, as monopolist, would auction the limited quota rights to many resource buyers, who, having purchased their quota rights, would enter the second tier of the market where they would confront many resource producers in a competitive market. Buyers would pay the resource producers the market price and surrender the requisite quota rights to the producer at the time of purchase. The firms in the extractive industry would be audited to make sure that sales balanced with quota certificates collected.

Figure 3-2 illustrates more clearly how things would work.

DD' is the market demand curve for the resource in question, and SS' is the industry supply curve. A depletion quota in the aggregate amount Q is imposed, shown by the vertical line QQ'. The total price paid per unit of the resource (unit price paid to resource producer plus unit price of the quota right paid to the government) is OC. Of the total price OC the amount OB is the price paid to resource producers, and BC is the price paid to the government for the quota right. Of the total amount paid, $OQAC$, the amount $OSEQ$ is cost, reflecting necessary sup-

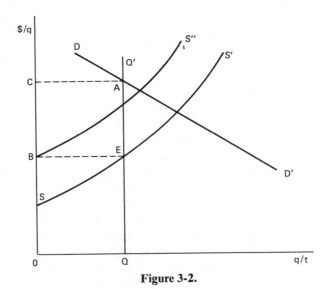

Figure 3-2.

ply price (extraction costs). The remainder, *SEAC,* is surplus or rent. Rent is defined as payment in excess of supply price. Of the total rent area, the amount *BES* is differential rent and accrues to the resource producers as profit. The remainder, the amount *CAEB,* is pure scarcity rent and accrues to the government. As a monopolist in the sale of quota rights (the first tier of the resource market which controls entry into the second tier), the government is able to extract the full amount of pure scarcity rent that results from the restricted quantity.

Let us review what is achieved by the depletion quota auction. First, the throughput of basic resources is physically limited, and with it the rate of depletion and pollution associated with those resource flows. Allocation of the fixed aggregate resource flow among competing uses and firms is done by the market. The price of the resource increases, inducing greater efficiency of use, both in production and in consumption. Resource-saving technical improvement is induced, and so is recycling. Dependence is gradually shifted away from scarce terrestrial sources and toward the abundant solar source of low entropy. The monopoly profits resulting from the higher resource prices are captured by the government, while resource producers earn normal competitive profits. The government revenues could be used to finance the minimum income part of the distributist institution. Efficiency is served by high resource prices, equity is served by redistributing the proceeds of the higher prices to the poor, and by a maximum limit on incomes of the rich. Rent is the optimal source of revenue for the government, and though one must stop short of proclaiming the realization of Henry George's dream of a single tax on rent, the depletion quota auction carries us about as far in that direction as is practical. Although ownership of resources remains in private hands, resource owners do suffer a capital loss when production is cut and their earnings are forced to the purely competitive level by the quota auction. Compensation for this one-time windfall loss could be given to the affected resource owners in the interest of fairness.

What criteria are there for setting the "proper" aggregate quota amounts for each resource? For renewable resources there is the fairly operational criterion of maximum sustainable yield. For nonrenewables there is, of course, no sustainable yield. But economist John Ise [20] suggested fifty years ago that, as a rule of thumb, nonrenewables should be priced equal to or more than their nearest renewable substitute. Thus virgin timber should be priced at least as much per board foot as replanted timber; petroleum should be priced at its Btu equivalent in terms of sugar or wood alcohol, assuming that is in fact the closest renewable substitute. For nonrenewables with no reasonably close renewable substitute, the matter is simply a question of how fast we should use it up, that is, an ethical weighing of the needs of present versus future people. One further criterion might be added: even if a resource is in no danger of depletion, its use may produce considerable pollution (e.g., coal), and depletion quotas may be imposed with the objective of limiting pollution, the other end of the throughput pipeline.

Over time, the supply curve for nonrenewable resources would shift upward as the more accessible sources become depleted, and previously marginal mines and wells have to be used. In the diagram, the higher supply curve is represented by BS'', which may be thought of as the "unused" segment of the original supply curve, ES', shifted in parallel fashion to the left until it touches the vertical axis. Assuming the same demand curve and quota, it is clear that the rising cost of production (area under the supply curve) will eventually eliminate the pure scarcity rent, leaving only differential rent. Quotas slow down the upward shift of the supply curve, relative to what it would have been with faster depletion, but of course cannot arrest the inevitable process. Probably the quota would have to be reduced as the supply curve shifted up in order to pass along the higher price signals to users, and to maintain some scarcity rent for public revenue.

For renewable resources with the quota set at maximum sustainable yield, there would be no upward shift in the supply curve. However, the demand curve for renewables would shift up as nonrenewable resource usage became restricted and more expensive. The quota on renewables would keep them from being exploited beyond their sustainable capacity, would ration access to the sustainable amount, and would divert the windfall profits into the public treasury. In sum, the depletion quota auction is an instrument for helping us make the transition from a nonrenewable to a renewable resource base in a gradual, efficient, and fair manner.

The combination of these three institutions presents a nice reconciliation of equity and efficiency, and provides the ecologically necessary macro control with the least sacrifice of micro freedom and variability. The market is relied upon to allocate resources and distribute incomes within imposed ecological and ethical boundaries. The market is not allowed to set its own boundaries, but is free within the boundaries imposed. The boundaries can be tightened with any degree of gradualism desired. It is necessary to set the boundaries externally. It is absurd to expect that market equilibria will automatically coincide with ecological or demographic equilibria, or with a reasonably just distribution of wealth and income. The very notions of "equilibrium" in economics and ecology are antithetical. In macroeconomics "equilibrium" refers not to physical magnitudes at all, but to a balance of desires between savers and investors. Macroeconomic equilibrium implies, under current conventions, a positive flow of net investment to offset positive savings. Net investment implies increasing stocks and a growing throughput, that is, a biophysical *dis*equilibrium. If a balance of desires between savers and investors is insufficient to ensure even full employment at a stable price level, as the Keynesians argue, then how much more remote is the likelihood that it will ensure ecological and demographic equilibria! Physical boundaries guaranteeing reasonable ecological equilibrium must be imposed on the market in quantitative terms. The orthodox economist's claim that economic and ecological equilibria would coincide, if only all external costs were internalized, is on a par with Archimedes' claim that he could move the earth if only he had a fulcrum and a long enough lever. A clever illustration of an abstract principle is not the same as an operational policy measure.

How do these proposals differ from the orthodox economists' prescription of "internalizing externalities via pollution taxes"? Pollution taxes are price controls on the output end of the throughput, while depletion quotas are quantitative controls on the input end. Depletion is spatially far more concentrated than pollution, and consequently much easier to monitor. Quantity rather than price should be the control variable because prices cannot limit aggregate throughput. Higher relative prices on resources would induce substitution and bring the resource content per unit of output down to some minimum. But prices cannot limit the number of units of output produced, and therefore cannot limit the total volume of resource throughput. Aggregate income is always sufficient to purchase the growing aggregate supply, regardless of prices. To paraphrase Say's law, "A growing supply creates its own growing demand." Taxes, by raising relative prices of basic resources, could provide a one-shot reduction in aggregate throughput by reducing throughput per dollar's worth of output to some feasible minimum, but the number of "dollar's worth" units of output could keep growing, unless the government ran an ever-growing budget surplus. Finally, it is quantity that affects the biosphere, not price. It is safer to set ecological limits in terms of fixed quantities, and let errors and unexpected events work themselves out in price changes, than to set prices and let errors and omissions cause quantity changes.

The "internalization of externalities" is a good strategy for fine tuning the allocation of resources by making relative prices better measures of relative social marginal costs. But it does not enable the market to set its own absolute physical boundaries within the larger ecosystem. To give an analogy: proper allocation arranges the weight in a boat optimally, so as to maximize the load that can be carried. But there is still an absolute limit to how much weight a boat can carry, even if optimally arranged. The price system can spread the weight evenly, but unless supplemented by an external absolute limit, it will just keep on spreading the increasing weight evenly until the evenly loaded boat sinks. No doubt the boat would sink evenly, *ceteris paribus, but* that is less comforting to the average citizen than to the neoclassical economist.

Two distinct questions must be asked about these proposed institutions for achieving an SSE. First, would they work if people accepted the need for an SSE and, say, voted these institutions into effect? Second, would people ever accept the goal of an SSE? I have argued that the answer to the first question is "yes." Although the answer to the second question would surely be "no" if a vote were held today, that is because the growth paradigm is still dominant. With time, the concepts and arguments sketched out here and the two critical traditions identified will look more appealing and will themselves be sharpened as the real facts of life push the growth paradigm into ever greater anomalies, contradictions, and practical failures.

References

1. Frederick Soddy, *Wealth, Virtual Wealth, and Debt* (London, Allen and Unwin, 1926).
2. John Ruskin, *Unto This Last: Four Essays on the First Principles of Political Economy,* edited by Lloyd J. Hubenka (Lincoln, University of Nebraska Press, 1967).
3. Nicholas Georgescu-Roegen, *The Entropy Law and the Economic Process* (Cambridge, Mass., Harvard University Press, 1971).
4. Anthony C. Fisher and Frederick M. Peterson, "The Environment in Economics: A Survey," *Journal of Economic Literature* vol. XIV, no. 1 (March 1976) pp. 1–33.
5. Robert Solow, "The Economics of Resources or the Resources of Economics," *American Economic Review* vol. LXIV (May 1974) pp. 1–14.
6. Frederick Soddy, *Cartesian Economics: The Bearing of Physical Science upon State Stewardship* (London, Hendersons, 1922).
7. Harold Barnett and Chandler Morse, *Scarcity and Growth: The Economics of Natural Resource Availability* (Baltimore, Johns Hopkins University Press for Resources for the Future, 1963).
8. John Stuart Mill, *Principles of Political Economy* (New York, Appleton-Century-Crofts, 1881).
9. Irving Fisher, *The Nature of Capital and Income* (London, Macmillan, 1906).
10. Kenneth Boulding, "The Economics of the Coming Spaceship Earth," in Henry Jarrett, ed., *Environmental Quality in a Growing Economy* (Balti-

more, Johns Hopkins University Press for Resources for the Future, 1966).

11. Nicholas Georgescu-Roegen, *Analytical Economics* (Cambridge, Mass., Harvard University Press, 1966).

12. Amory Lovins, "Energy Strategy: The Road Not Taken?", *Foreign Affairs* vol. LV (October 1976) pp. 65–96.

13. E. J. Mishan, "Growth and Anti-Growth: What Are the Issues?", *Challenge* (May/June 1973).

14. Herman E. Daly, "On Economics as a Life Science," *Journal of Political Economy* vol. LXXVI (May/June 1968) pp. 392–406.

15. Herman E. Daly, "The Economics of the Steady State," *American Economic Review* vol. LXIV (May 1974) pp. 15–21.

16. Alvin M. Weinberg and H. E. Goeller, "The Age of Substitutability," *Science* (February 20, 1976) pp. 683–688.

17. Herman E. Daly, ed., *Toward a Steady-State Economy* (San Francisco, W. H. Freeman, 1973). See reading number seven.

18. Kenneth Boulding, *The Meaning of the Twentieth Century* (New York, Harper and Row, 1964).

19. David Heer, "Marketable Licenses for Babies: Boulding's Proposal Revisited," *Social Biology* (Spring 1975).

20. John Ise, "The Theory of Value as Applied to Natural Resources," *American Economic Review* vol. XV (June 1925) pp. 284–291.

Bibliography

Abrahamson, Dean E. *The Energy Crisis: Some Policy Alternatives* (Los Alamos Scientific Laboratory of the University of California, 1972).

Belloc, Hilaire. *The Servile State* (Boston, LeRoy Phillips, 1912).

Bent, Henry A. "Haste Makes Waste: Pollution and Entropy," *Chemistry* vol. 44 (October 1971) pp. 6–15.

―――. *The Second Law: An Introduction to Classical and Statistical Thermodynamics* (New York, Oxford University Press, 1965).

Boulding, Kenneth E. "Environment and Economics," in William W. Murdoch, ed., *Environment* (Stamford, Conn., Sinauer Associates, 1971).

―――. "The Economics of the Coming Spaceship Earth," in Henry Jarrett, ed., *Environmental Quality in a Growing Economy* (Baltimore, Johns Hopkins University Press for Resources for the Future, 1966).

Brower, David R. *The de facto Wilderness: What is its Place?* (San Francisco, Sierra Club, 1962).

Brown, Harrison S. *Population: Perspective* (San Francisco, Freeman, 1971).

―――, ed. *Are Our Descendants Doomed?* (New York, Viking Press, 1972).

Brown, Lester R. *In the Human Interest: A Strategy to Stabilize World Population* (New York, W. W. Norton, 1974).

―――. "The Environmental Consequences of Man's Quest for Food," in Peter Albertson and Margery Barnett, eds., *Managing the Planet* (Englewood Cliffs, N.J., Prentice-Hall, 1972).

Caldwell, Lynton Keith. *Man and His Environment: Policy and Administration* (New York, Harper and Row, 1975).

———. *In Defense of Earth: International Protection of the Biosphere* (Bloomington, Ind., Indiana University Press, 1972).

Carlyle, Thomas. *Past and Present* (London, J. M. Dent, 1947).

Carson, Rachel L. *Silent Spring* (Boston, Houghton Mifflin, 1962).

Chesterton, G. K. *The Outline of Sanity* (London, Library Press).

Cloud, Preston. "Mineral Resources in Fact and Fancy," in William W. Murdoch, ed., *Environment: Resources, Pollution and Society* (Stamford, Conn., Sineaur Associates, 1971).

———, ed. *Resources and Man* (San Francisco, Freeman, 1969).

Cobb, John. "Ecology, Ethics, and Theology," in H. E. Daly, ed., *Toward a Steady-State Economy* (San Francisco, Freeman, 1973) pp. 307–332.

Commoner, Barry. *The Closing Circle: Nature, Man and Technology* (New York, Knopf, 1974).

———. *Environment* (New York, Knopf, 1971).

———. "Technology and the Natural Environment," *Architectural Forum* vol. 130 (1969) pp. 68–73.

Cook, Earl. "Energy Sources for the Future," *The Futurist* vol. 6 (1972) pp. 142–150.

Culbertson, John M. *Economic Development: An Ecological Approach* (New York, Knopf, 1971).

Daly, Herman E. *Steady-State Economics: The Economics of Biophysical Equilibrium and Moral Growth* (San Francisco, Freeman, 1977).

Davis, Kingsley. "Population," *Scientific American* vol. 209 (1963) pp. 62–71.

———. "Colin Clark and the Benefits of an Increase in Population," *Scientific American* vol. 218 (1968) pp. 133–138.

———. "The Urbanization of the Human Population," *Scientific American* vol. 213 (1965) pp. 40–53.

Derr, Thomas S. *Ecology and Human Need* (Philadelphia, Westminister, 1975).

Ehrlich, Paul R. *The Population Bomb* (New York, Ballantine Books, 1968).

——— and Anne H. Ehrlich. *Population, Resources Environment: Issues in Human Ecology* (San Francisco, Freeman, 1970).

——— and John Holdren. "Impact of Population Growth," *Science* vol. 171 (1971) pp. 1212–1217.

Elder, Frederick. *Crisis in Eden: A Religious Study of Man and Environment* (Nashville, Abingdon Press, 1970). Argues for an environmental theology against those who would exclude nature from theological concerns.

Ellul, Jacques. *The Technological Society.* Translated by John Wilkinson (New York, Vintage Books, 1967).

———. "Technique, Institutions, and Awareness," *American Behavioral Scientist* vol. 2 (1968) pp. 38–42.

Faulk, Richard. *This Endangered Planet: Prospects and Proposals for Human Survival* (New York, Random House, 1971).

Forrester, Jay. "Counterintuitive Behavior of Social Systems," *Technology Review* vol. 73 (January 1971) pp. 52–68.

———. *World Dynamics* (Cambridge, Mass., Wright-Allen, 1971).

Georgescu-Roegen, Nicholas. *The Entropy Law and the Economic Process* (Cambridge, Mass., Harvard University Press, 1971).

Goulet, Denis. *The Cruel Choice: A New Concept in the Theory of Development* (Cambridge, Mass., Atheneum, 1971).

———. "Voluntary Austerity: The Necessary Art," *Christian Century* vol. 83 (June 1966) pp. 748–752.

Hannon, Bruce. "Energy, Growth, and Altruism," (Mimeographed) (Center for Advanced Computation, University of Illinois, 1975).

Hardin, Garrett. "The Tragedy of the Commons," *Science* vol. 162 (1968) pp. 1243–1248. Reprinted in H. E. Daly, ed., *Toward a Steady-State Economy* (San Francisco, Freeman, 1973) pp. 133–149.

———. *Exploring New Ethics for Survival: The Voyage of the Spaceship Beagle* (New York, Viking, 1972).

Hayes, Denis. *Energy: The Case for Conservation,* Worldwatch Paper No. 4 (Washington, D.C., Worldwatch Institute, 1976).

Holdren, John, and P. Herrera. *Energy* (New York, Sierra Club, 1971).

Hubbert, Marion K. *U.S. Energy Resources, a Review as of 1972* (Washington, GPO, 1974).

———. "Energy Resources," in William W. Murdoch, ed., *Environment: Resources, Pollution, and Society* (Stamford, Conn., Sinauer Associates, 1971).

Illich, Ivan. *Energy and Equity* (New York, Harper and Row, 1974).

———. *Tools for Conviviality* (New York, Harper and Row, 1973).

Ise, John. "Theory of Value as Applied to Natural Resources," *American Economic Review* vol. XV (June 1925) pp. 284–291.

———. *Our National Park Policy: A Critical History* (Baltimore, Johns Hopkins Press for Resources for the Future, 1961).

———. *The United States Oil Policy* (New Haven, Conn., Yale University Press, 1926).

Keyfitz, Nathan. *Introduction to Mathematics of Population* (Reading, Mass., Addison-Wesley, 1968).

———. "World Resources and the World Middle Class," *Scientific American* vol. 235 no. 1 (July 1976) pp. 28–35.

Lotka, Alfred J. *Elements of Physical Biology* (Baltimore, Williams & Wilkins, 1925).

———. "The Law of Evolution as a Maximal Principle," *Human Biology* vol. XVIII (1945) pp. 180–191.

———. "Related Branches of Society," *Proceedings of the American Philosophical Society* vol. 90 (1951) pp. 601–626.

Lovins, Amory B. "Energy Strategy: The Road Not Taken," *Foreign Affairs* vol. 55 (1976) pp. 65–97.

Malthus, Thomas Robert. *Population: The First Essay* (London, MacMillan, 1926).

Marsh, George Perkins. *The Earth as Modified by Human Action* (New York, Arno, 1970).

Meadows, Dennis. "The Predicament of Mankind," *The Futurist* vol. 5 (1971) pp. 137–144.

Meadows, Donella, Dennis L. Meadows, Jørgen Randers, and William W. Behrens, III. *The Limits to Growth*, A Report for the Club of Rome's Project on the Predicament of Mankind (New York, Universe Books, 1972).

Mesarovic, Mihajlo, and Edward Pestel. *Mankind at the Turning Point* (New York, Dutton, 1975).

Mill, John Stuart. *Principles of Political Economy, with Some of Their Applications to Social Philosophy* (London, Longmans, 1929).

Mishan, E. J. *The Costs of Economic Growth* (London, Staples, 1967).

———. *Technology and Growth: The Price We Pay* (New York, Praeger, 1970).

Mumford, Lewis. *Techniques and Civilization* (New York, Harcourt, Brace & World, 1934).

Odum, Eugene. *Fundamentals of Ecology* (Philadelphia, Saunders, 1971).

———. "The Strategy of Ecosystem Development," *Science* vol. 164 (1969) pp. 262–270.

Odum, Howard T. *Environment, Power, and Society* (New York, Wiley–Interscience, 1970).

———. "Energy, Ecology, and Economics," *AMBIO* vol. 2, no. 6 (1973).

——— and Elisabeth C. Odum. *Energy Basis for Man and Nature* (New York, McGraw-Hill, 1976).

Ophuls, William. "Leviathan or Oblivion?" in H. E. Daly, ed., *Toward a Steady-State Economy* (San Francisco, Freeman, 1973) pp. 215–231.

Roszak, Theodore. *Where the Wasteland Ends: Politics and Transcendence in Post-Industrial Society* (Garden City, N.Y., Anchor Books, 1973).

———. *The Making of a Counter Culture: Reflections on the Technocratic Society and Its Youthful Opposition* (New York, Doubleday, 1969).

Ruskin, John. *Unto This Last* (New York, Merrill, 1862).

———. *Essays on Political Economy* (Westport, Conn., Greenwood).

Schumacher, E. F. *Small Is Beautiful: Economics As If People Mattered* (New York, Harper & Row, 1973).

———. *The Age of Plenty: A Christian View* (Edinburgh, St. Andrew Press, 1974).

4

Comments on the Papers by Daly and Stiglitz

Nicholas Georgescu-Roegen

The two papers presented at this session are so opposed in outlook that a commentator could not possibly find himself in sympathy, even partially, with both of them. Given my own stand on the crucial role played by natural resources in the economic process, it may be superfluous to say with which of the two papers I am in substantial agreement. Yet I deem it necessary to state from the outset that I am entirely out of sympathy with the manner in which J. E. Stiglitz dealt with his topic.

True, his task could hardly be more thankless. But he has chosen to set up a line of multifarious but ineffective fires in defense of a position to which many standard economists still cling with the tenacity of original sin. This position is that the analytical models designed by standard economics are completely fit to deal with the issue of optimal allocation of natural resources among successive generations, an issue that affects the survival of the human species. It is my contention, expounded in several of my writings, that this position is dangerously false.[1] Neoclassical economics—or standard economics, as I prefer to call the discipline as practiced for the past fifty years—has paid practically no attention to natural resources. To be sure, legions of production functions in the neoclassical literature contain the factor land, by which is meant, however, only Ricardian land. But Ricardian land raises no issue for the intergenerational allocation of resources. This is *the* problem of natural resources.[2]

Stiglitz avoids the admission, embarrassing nowadays, that the main body of standard economists has paid no attention to this vital problem. For the defense that economists have long since recognized the seriousness of the limitations of resources, Stiglitz has little choice other than

---

The author held an Earhart Fellowship during the preparation of this paper.
[1] See especially Georgescu-Roegen [1].
[2] And since we cannot possibly control the flow of solar energy reaching the earth, the problem of natural resources is reduced to that of *mineral* resources.

mentioning, not a neoclassical economist, but Malthus. Curiously, even that defense witness has no glory, because Malthus's forebodings "have not been borne out—at least not yet." This bare assertion is to be expected. Standard economists, having paid no attention to the problems raised by the size of population, cannot recognize now any valid point in Malthus's position. In this connection, one may cite Blaug's glaring verdict: "The Malthusian theory of population is a perfect example of metaphysics masquerading as science" [2].

Before disposing of Malthus in such expedient fashions, one should take account of the fact that millions of humans are half-alive in abject misery, dying slowly of squalor and starvation. Above all, one should (if one can) imagine a United States populated as thickly as Bangladesh: it would contain not less than 5 billion people, more by one quarter than today's population of the whole earth. Actually, Malthus—we can say it now—was not Malthusian enough; he allowed for population to increase indefinitely provided it would not grow too fast.

By now it is fashionable among standard economists to say high and loud that one does not need to invoke thermodynamic laws in order to realize that exponential growth must eventually run into physical barriers.[3] Stiglitz does not want to be an exception. Like all the others, he also ignores the question that now cries for an answer: Why have we then labored for years to fabricate and sell a theory of economic development based on exponential growth?

The claim that standard economics is not concerned "with very long-run projections, but rather with the more immediate future," is another means of avoiding the main issue that would incriminate the standard position. The problem of resources is not confined to the "foreseeable future," as many other writers also insist, but concerns the entire future. Obviously, if one takes the foreseeable future to be just 24 hours, then, as Wilfred Beckerman assured us, we all could go to bed tonight without worrying in the least about what growth may do to those of us who will be alive the day after tomorrow. If the standard position concerns only what will happen to natural resources "in the immediate future" of this moment of the twentieth century, then all the din about how the market mechanism (especially that moulded on standard assumptions) can save us from ecological catastrophes is utterly idle. But if the claim is that exponential growth can prevail not only in our immediate future but also in any "immediate future" in the future, then the claim acquires a factual, nonparochial significance. The opposite position

---

[3] See, for example, Landsberg [3]. But, sadly, these writers ignore the fact that thermodynamics tells us some fundamental things about the economics of resources that are not as obvious.

is that exponential growth has been only one historical interlude caused by a unique mineralogical bonanza of the past hundred years.

I am the first to agree with Stiglitz that a specific policy geared for the future should ideally be based upon some solid projections. Since any *quantitative* projection whatsoever is ultimately based on some time-invariant matrix, Stiglitz is right in searching for some constant element. I further agree with him on the indescribable predicament of the econometrician trying to discover a *historical* law on the basis of past observations. Concerning parameterization, years ago I pointed out that the situation of the econometrician is analogous to that of a deft sculptor who can prove to you that there is a beautifully carved Madonna inside almost any log.[4] How can one then tell what is really inside a log?

Let me also make another of Stiglitz's points stronger. If we are able to predict that after a certain age people are likely to develop arteriosclerosis, it is only because we have been able to observe millions of humans growing old. Unfortunately, we have not observed and will never observe another people struggling to survive on a planet such as ours. This is why we cannot say for sure what is in the cards for us as a species. By observing a single human until he reaches the age of, say, thirty, we may very well conclude that he will never develop arteriosclerosis. It is legitimate to expect, therefore, that data pertaining to the period of minerological bonanza mentioned above—such as those so ably used by Harold Barnett and Chandler Morse in support of their famous thesis—should support any hypothesis of continuous growth.

It is therefore curious that after insisting on such difficulties, Stiglitz claims that the burden of proof is on "the resource pessimists," such as me, to convince the resource optimists that some elasticities are low. This sort of argument would be in order only if the optimists had already offered some acceptable proofs that those elasticities are high. Worse still, the issue does not even concern elasticities at all. It concerns the physical finitude and the irrevocable exhaustibility of natural resources.

Stiglitz, however, even raises the question of "how essential" natural resources are. Apparently, like Robert M. Solow (whom he cites in this respect), Stiglitz believes that physical production can be maintained at the same level if capital (or some other factor) is continually substituted for natural resources.

This conjuring trick devised by Solow is easily shown up. Exclusive preoccupation with paper-and-pencil (PAP) exercises habit has led to accepting these exercises without any concern for their relation to facts. On paper, one can write a production function any way one likes, without

4 See Georgescu-Roegen [1, chapters 10 and 12].

regard to dimensions or to other physical constraints.[5] A good example is the famous Cobb–Douglas function, but the Solow–Stiglitz variant adds the sin of mixing flow elements with fund elements, namely,

$$Q = K^{\alpha_1} R^{\alpha_2} L^{\alpha_3} \qquad (1)$$

where Q is output, K is the stock of capital, R is the flow of natural resources used in production, L is the labor supply, and $\alpha_1 + \alpha_2 + \alpha_3 = 1$ and, of course, $\alpha_i > 0$.[6]

From this formula it follows that with a constant labor power, L_0, one could obtain any given Q_0, if the flow of natural resources satisfies the condition

$$R^{\alpha_2} = \frac{Q_0}{K^{\alpha_1} L_0^{\alpha_3}} \qquad (2)$$

This shows that R may be as small as we wish, provided K is sufficiently large. *Ergo,* we can obtain a constant annual product indefinitely even from a very small stock of resources $R > 0$, if we decompose R into an infinite series $R = \Sigma\, R_i$, with $R_i \to 0$, use R_i in the year i, and increase the stock of capital each year as required by (2). But this *ergo* is not valid in actuality. In actuality, the increase of capital implies an additional depletion of resources. And if $K_i \to \infty$, the R will rapidly be exhausted by the production of capital. Solow and Stiglitz could not have come out with their conjuring trick had they borne in mind, first, that any material process consists in the transformation of some materials into others (the flow elements) by some agents (the fund elements),[7] and second, that natural resources are the very sap of the economic process. They are *not* just like any other production factor. A change in capital and labor can only diminish the amount of waste in the production of a commodity; no agent can create the material on which it works. Nor can capital create the stuff out of which it is made. In some cases, it may also be that the same service can be provided by a design that requires less matter or energy. But even in this direction there exists a limit, unless we believe that the ultimate fate of the economic process is an earthly Garden of Eden.

The question that confronts us today is whether we are going to discover *new* sources of energy that can be safely used. No elasticities of some Cobb–Douglas function can help us to answer it. As to the scarcity

[5] More on this point in Georgescu-Roegen [4, chapter 9] and [1, chapters 2, 4, 5].

[6] The slipshod manner in which the factors are defined is another consequence of the infatuation with PAP exercises.

[7] See Georgescu-Roegen [4, chapter 9] and [1, chapters 2, 4, 5].

of matter in a closed system, such as the earth, the issue may, in my opinion, prove in the end more critical than that of energy [1, chapters 1; 5].

No one could possibly argue with some of the statements of section II of Stiglitz's paper; if they are taken with a grain of salt they may give some useful indication of the direction in which a market may move because of government intervention or changes in the industrial structure. But this does not settle the great issue at stake, namely, whether the market mechanism can be an instrument for the intergenerational distribution of natural resources. In view of Stiglitz's insistence that the market is fit for this role, I can hardly overemphasize my reasons for its denial.

To be sure, those who share Stiglitz's position also argue that although markets admittedly have serious failures, if prices were right everything else—depletion and pollution—would also be right.[8] But no one has yet defined "right" prices. (I assume that by "right prices" they do not mean the "just prices" of the Scholastics.) The rub is that market prices depend on many factors: income distribution, taxation systems, industrial structures, taste spectrums, etc.[9] To wit, the price of gasoline would certainly be different if the geographical distribution of oil deposits were different from what it actually is. I cannot see how we could say which conditions would bring about the right prices. Were the prices right or wrong when large tracts of land were deforested? Were the prices of crude oil until the establishment of the OPEC right or wrong? What kind of perfect market would have prevented the squandering of crude oil over the past forty years?

From another approach, we may note that in order to arrive at the "true" cost of any material commodity, we must know the true values of natural resources *in situ*, which constitute the first cost item. Some economists trained in the neoclassical tradition have occasionally spoken of the "true scarcity value" of natural resources *in situ*.[10] Yet, to my knowledge, the determination of these values is a problem totally ignored by all tints of economic theory. For perhaps the only reasonable solution we may turn to a general, albeit rarely used, economic principle, which is that the value of an irreproducible good—whether Leonardo's Mona Lisa or some crude oil in its earthly pouch—is its auction price. However, the ordinary formulation of this principle omits to add the *sine qua non* condition that all those having a possible interest in the

[8] See references in [1, p. 13].

[9] I naturally exclude the thought that the economic process works over time, even in some acceptable approximation according to the simplified assumptions of the Leontief system.

[10] For example, Amouzegar [6].

commodity must be allowed to bid. Otherwise, if only my neighbor and I were to bid on the Mona Lisa, for example, I may obtain it for a few dollars, since my neighbor hates Renaissance paintings.

The moral is obvious. To arrive at the true scarcity value of any mineral resource, all users of the resource must bid, that is, all users in this generation as well as future ones.[11] Unfortunately, the future generations cannot be present to bid now. The current generation must therefore take into account their needs. Devising a way by which this can be done is admittedly a difficult but not impossible problem. Suffice it to say here that the solution lies in the domain of ethics rather than that of economics.

Stiglitz asserts that the foregoing argument about the independence of the present market from the demand of future generations is fallacious. His point is that since each owner sells to a future owner, who sells to another, and so on, the algorithm will take care of the interests of all future owners *now*. I submit that, on the contrary, it is his argument that is fallacious, the usual fascination with formalism being again responsible for the misinterpretation of the PAP algorithm. It is beyond doubt that each individual's actions are geared to the future. But his decisions are based only on whatever evidence the individual has at *that* moment and, moreover, they concern only the probable events within his time horizon. That is, his evidence does not encompass the whole future, nor is his time horizon unlimited (optimistically, it may be taken to cover about thirty years only). Hence, nothing beyond that time horizon bears upon the usual decisions of any individual. It would be preposterous to maintain that, even in a businesslike society such as the United States, the earlier owners of oil fields acted on the thought that one day this country might experience a dangerous shortage of fuels. Had they done so, the shortage would have probably not come so early.[12]

With one important exception (to be considered presently), Stiglitz never instructs us about the criterion of optimality served by the market mechanism and instead speaks only of "efficiency" and "efficient market" without explaining the meaning of these terms. This fact might be taken as an unintentional admission that, whatever the markets may do, they cannot be relied on for a reasonable intergenerational allocation of natural resources. But there is that exception, a mathematical model in which there is a criterion of optimality to be satisfied under the constraint of a given (finite) amount of resources.

[11] I must hasten to add that even this *Gedankenexperiment* is not completely satisfactory. The auction price still depends on the income distribution. But this seems to be the best we can do even in the abstract.

[12] The above argument can be easily supported by a graphical analysis, for which see Georgescu-Roegen [1, pp. 30–32].

The model goes back to the famous 1931 article of Harold Hotelling [7]. Beautiful mathematical piece though that article is, it set a fallacious pattern of approach to the economics of exhaustible resources. As Stiglitz and every other writer who has been stirred by the recent events argue,[13] resources must be distributed so that *the sum of discounted future utilities*

$$\int_0^\infty U(c_t)e^{-\rho t} dt \tag{3}$$

must be a maximum, where $U(c_t)$ is the *utility intensity* of c_t, and ρ is the constant discount rate of the future.[14]

As we all know, the idea that future pleasures and pains do not appear to an individual as vivid as present ones constituted a main point of Jeremy Bentham's hedonistic calculus. W. Stanley Jevons introduced it in economics with some very careful considerations [9]. He separated the discount factor into a probability coefficient that the event will actually occur and a coefficient to represent the underestimation of the future experience. But Jevons, while recognizing that the individual's decisions are influenced by both factors, argued that the underestimation of the future is an irrational trait. When tomorrow comes we will be as hungry and as thirsty as we are today. Hence, we should not fail to put aside equal amounts for future satisfactions.[15] However, the reduction resulting from the uncertainty of the future must be retained because of its statistical validity. For a most elementary illustration, let us consider a population of three individuals, one of whom will die each day. If they possess among them six daily rations, they should distribute them in time by discounting the future only according to the probability of survival. This yields the distribution 3, 2, 1, not 2, 2, 2. As we see, the saying "let's eat, drink, and be merry today because tomorrow we may die" makes sense, *but only because humans are mortals.*

For quasi-immortal entities—such as a nation and especially mankind—discounting the future is wrong from any viewpoint. There is no specific reason why such an entity will not experience the same needs at all times. Nor is it subject to a mortality table. The upshot is that equation (3) may apply to a single individual in managing his narrow affairs myopically, but when we come to ask how to distribute resources among generations, we must not in any way discount the future.

To be sure, if all future utilities are treated alike, the beautiful solution reached by Hotelling is of no use anymore. The focus of the problem

[13] For example, Koopmans [8].

[14] For my argument I need not preserve the factor corresponding to the population growth in St'glitz's formula.

[15] The point has been taken up in greater detail by Strotz [10].

is entirely shifted. The *analytical* solution is to spread resources evenly in time, which in the case of an infinite time horizon yields the paradoxical result that each year a null amount of resources should be consumed. The analytical impasse is eliminated by noting that what we may, for example, seek now is the maximum "amount of life," measured in man $\times$ years, which is tantamount to obtaining the longest life span for the human species [4, p. 304; 1, p. 23]. This solution presupposes that we know the standard level at which mankind must live as well as the future movement of population. Stiglitz's observation that resource planning requires a tremendous amount of information, most of which cannot possibly be available, is very welcome at this point. This is why whenever we may try to prescribe a quantitative policy for the economy of resources we can only play the tune by ear. Besides, instead of basing our recommendations on the ultrafamiliar principle of maximizing "utility," we should try *to minimize future regrets*. This seems to be the only reasonable (I do not think that we could call it rational) recipe for dealing with the most uncertain of all uncertainties—historical uncertainty. We should thus slow down the depletion of fossil fuels so as not to put ourselves in the impossible position of not having enough support for the search for other sources of energy, regardless of whether such a possibility is at present real or not. Had we tried to minimize regrets, we would not be so pressed today by the alarming dwindling away of crude oil resources.

Admittedly, all these considerations take us far away from the teachings of standard economics. But this is precisely the point that needed to be brought home at last.

Turning now to Herman Daly's paper, I do not think I am wrong in judging that by now he has associated his name with a steady-state economy, just as other economists have associated their names with the position "come what may, we will find a way, provided prices are right." For this reason I think that Daly's name should appear in the group "Humanist Economists" in his table of growth critics.[16]

This paper represents an improvement on Daly's earlier pleas. One new point deserves special attention. It is the map in which the hierarchy of ends and means is correlated with the categories of disciplines that keep the human mind continuously on the run. To have a single element by which everything is in the last analysis guided or judged has been a need felt by all truly philosophical schools. All great philosophers have imagined, if not a religious God, at least a philosophical one as the ulti-

---

[16] I have a few other ideas about that table but they are not important enough to mention here, save one: Agrarians in general, not only American Agrarians, deserve great credit for having opposed excessive economic growth.

mate criterion, not for what ought to be, but for what must be. There is an indisputable need for an ultimate end by which we can judge which of our actions are "good" and which are "bad." We always need a criterion of some sort or other. To take a simple but appropriate example: If the price ratio of coffee and meat is, say, 5 to 2, and I spend my budget at a point where my marginal rate of substitution between those commodities is 7 to 4, that is "bad." The criterion of maximum utility for my preference structure tells me so. But why should we not also ask the further question: Are my preferences good or bad? Daly's point is that for this question we must turn to the ultimate end. This paper thus strengthens the impression emerging from his previous writings that the essence of Daly's conception is not economic or demographic, but, rather, ethical—a great merit in a period in which economics has been reduced to a timeless kinematics. As a befitting commandment for the ultimate end of a religion that should help mankind to survive and lead a decent life, I would suggest "Love thy species as thyself" [5]. Such a religion would certainly bring about the amiable community for which Daly fights untiringly. But as intimated earlier, the most challenging enterprise is to establish any religious faith, any faith in an ultimate end.

This is perhaps why Daly does not limit his logistics at this point. He offers other reasons for his blueprint, and it is with respect to these reasons that I entertain some still unshakable doubts.

To begin with, I take exception to Daly's tenet (which actually is inherited from John Stuart Mill) that stationariness alone suffices to clear away all substantial conflicts between individuals or, especially, social classes. Quasi-stationary societies of the past proved that they were as vulnerable from this standpoint as the growing ones of recent times.

Second, there is nothing in Daly's setup to help us determine even in broad strokes the proper standard of living—"the good life"—and, worse still, the proper size of the population. In this last regard, I have suggested that at all times population must remain near the level at which it can be maintained biologically by organic agriculture (which does not necessarily imply a stationary population) [1, p. 34]. I do not know whether Daly subscribes to this necessary measure or not.

Third, a point in great need of clarification is his basic concept of a capital stock that remains constant in amount but may nevertheless undergo qualitative changes.[17] Currently, we measure the amount of capital over the years by values at some basic year. Is such a concessive practice sufficient for a blueprint that is meant to cover not only decades or even centuries, but millennia?

---

[17] The same difficulty does not arise in regard to constant population, not in any stringent sense. *This ignores progress in knowledge, or human capital power time*

While still hoping that mankind will ultimately and before it is too late progress toward an amiable congregation as envisioned by Daly and Mill, I have outlined elsewhere some basic reasons why I believe that a steady-state society is an unrealizable blueprint [5]. One of the proposals made in Daly's paper offers me an occasion for supporting my position from a different, more homely angle.

Figure 4-1 contains all the elements (with the same notations) of the diagram by which Daly explains how government may allocate natural resources optimally in a steady state. I take it that the curve *SS'* in his diagram represents only the average extraction cost for each successive unit of the resource in question. The natural resources *in situ* are free goods in the sense that they simply exist for us to mine at some cost whenever we wish. But let us consider now what will happen in the *next* period, after the amount *OQ* has been auctioned off and mined. The new extraction cost will be *BS''*, a curve obtained from *ES'* by horizontal translation to the left. For the same quantity *OQ,* the next generation will have to work much harder, and the government will receive a much smaller scarcity rent (represented by *CAB'E'*). The same mutation will take place for each successive period. How can we then think that such an economy may be in a steady state? To assume that technological progress will just bring the new cost curve *BS''* to the level of *SS'* would be utterly preposterous. It would mean joining the club of the believers in exponential progress.

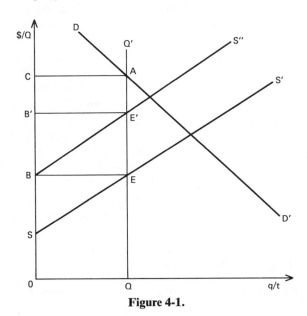

Figure 4-1.

The rub comes from the fact that we always mine "the highest grade and most accessible resources first," as Daly emphasizes. But from my foregoing observations it follows that to do so is not an economic imperative of a general validity. The practice is only one aspect of what I have called the dictatorship of the present over the future.

Conceivably, we could do away with it, too. The government should auction each year an identical representative sample of the entire mineralogical distribution of each kind of resource. But how can one know that distribution and how can the proposed sample be mined? There seems to be no way to do away with the dictatorship of the present over the future, although we may aim at making it as bearable as possible. Mankind's entropic problem will remain forever beyond the reach of any arithmomorphic manipulating model.

References

1. Nicholas Georgescu-Roegen, *Energy and Economic Myths* (New York, Pergamon, 1976).
2. Mark Blaug, "Malthus, Thomas Robert," *International Encyclopedia of the Social Sciences* (New York, Macmillan and Free Press, 1968) vol. 9, p. 551.
3. Hans H. Landsberg, "Growth and Resources," in National Academy of Sciences, *Mineral Resources and the Environment,* appendix to section I (Washington, D.C. NAS, 1975) p. A31.
4. Nicholas Georgescu-Roegen, *The Entropy Law and the Economic Process* (Cambridge, Mass., Harvard University Press, 1971).
5. Nicholas Georgescu-Roegen, "The Steady State and Ecological Salvation: A Thermodynamic Analysis," *Bioscience* vol. 27 (April 1977) pp. 266–270.
6. Jahangir Amouzegar, "The Oil Story: Facts, Fiction and Fair Play," *Petroleum Intelligence Weekly* Supplement, July 2, 1973, pp. 1–6. (Reprinted from *Foreign Affairs,* July 1973).
7. Harold Hotelling, "The Economics of Exhaustible Resources," *Journal of Political Economy* vol. 39 (April 1931) pp. 137–175.
8. Tjalling C. Koopmans, "Some Observations on 'Optimal' Economic Growth and Exhaustible Resources," in H. C. Bos, ed., *Economic Structure and Development: Essays in Honor of Jan Tinbergen* (Amsterdam, North-Holland, 1973) pp. 237–256.
9. W. Stanley Jevons, *The Theory of Political Economy* (London, Macmillan, 1871).
10. Robert H. Strotz, "Myopia and Inconsistency in Dynamic Utility Maximization," *Review of Economic Studies* vol. 23 (1956) pp. 165–180.

5

Fundamental Concepts for the Analysis
of Resource Availability

Donald A. Brobst

I
Introduction

Analysis of the future availability of mineral and energy resources
in the economy generally is made by examining the records of past production and probing the anticipated availability of these resources under
given sets of events and conditions. Through the years, analysts have
drawn an assortment of different conclusions from their efforts.

After studying the history of European mining, the geologist D. F.
Hewett [1] suggested that the production of metals in a nation endowed
with fuels will advance through successive cycles characterized by rises
followed by declines in exports of metallic ores; in amount of domestic
mining, smelting, and production of metal; and in imports of metallic
ores (figure 5-1). Hewett suggested nearly fifty years ago that the position of the United States in such a system was already advanced well
beyond the youth indicated by the early cycles.

Varying degrees of concern about the future availability of resources
have been expressed in the reports of the President's Materials Policy
Commission [2] and the National Commission on Materials Policy [3].
Extreme concern about the future availability of oil and gas was voiced
by Hubbert [4] after a study of petroleum discovery and production
records. Park [5, 6] questioned the world's ability to provide a universally
high level of affluence through continued exponential growth. Meadows
and others [7] sounded an alarm about possibilities for the collapse of
civilization as we know it from a computerized analysis of factors related
to population, industrialization, pollution, food production, and resource
depletion. Brooks and Andrews [8] concluded that long before resources
were depleted, pollution and social disorders would reduce current complexities to an overwhelming mass of unsolvable problems.

Many other authors, including Barnett and Morse [9] and Goeller and Weinberg [10], have reached more optimistic conclusions that relatively few resource problems loom ahead which cannot be overcome by economic adjustments and technological advancement.

The wide diversity of conclusions drawn from studies of resource availability has caused debate and confusion. The stage is set for controversy about resource use and policy between the extremes of the catastrophists, who foresee the death of our industrial society because of resource shortages, and the cornucopians, who foresee virtually no problems with resources that technology cannot overcome.

Events of the past few years are bringing the controversy over resources into the public arena. The importance of energy to the world economy now has become quite clear to many, although it is doubtful that the public has yet grasped the magnitude of the implications of possible restrictions on the future availability of energy materials. The world's economic life now consists of a system whose parts are interdependent, and tampering with any part may cause disruptions at many places. This latter point has been well demonstrated by such events as the sharp increase in petroleum prices, the nationalization of mineral- and energy-producing companies, and the attempts of mineral-producing nations to raise prices individually or through the formation of cartels. The results of social pressures here and abroad for more stringent environmental standards, especially with respect to mining and manufacturing activities, might reduce the ability of the world to meet its anticipated increase in demand for mineral and energy materials.

More and more the components of the economic system are being examined in detail to establish a better understanding of the relation of the parts to the whole system. This systems approach has been discussed by Churchman [11], who defined the method as simply a way of thinking about total systems and their components. The conclusions of a study

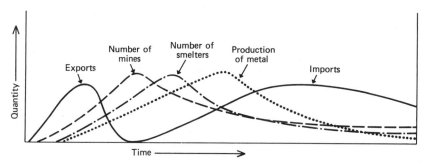

Figure 5-1. Cycles in metal production. (From D. F. Hewett, "Cycles in Metal Production," *Transactions of the American Institute of Mining and Metallurgical Engineers,* 1929, p. 89.)

done by a systems approach, however, will reflect the background of the analyst.

The study of mineral and energy resources brings together many disciplines, but especially economics, engineering, and geology, the latter itself a combination of physical sciences. Practitioners of each discipline will bring their own perspectives to the conclusions of a study. Economists generally have been most interested in the flow of resources from the mine portal and wellhead through the economic system. Engineers, depending on their specialty, have been most interested in how to mine, beneficiate, and use mineral and energy resources. Economists and engineers indicate a primary concern for the economic availability of resources. Geologists generally have been most interested in the scientific aspects of the occurrence of rocks, minerals, and energy materials and the application of geologic information to the search for deposits that will assure the availability of commercial supplies at the mine portals and wellheads. Geologists indicate a primary interest in the geologic availability of resources. There is overlap of interest, to be sure, but fundamental concepts as understood and applied by each analyst are bound to affect the conclusions drawn. I should like, therefore, to discuss from a geologist's perspective some concepts that are fundamental to making and evaluating analyses of resource availability.

The significance of the role of minerals and fuels in the U.S. economy can be overlooked easily in the gross national product (GNP). Table 5-1 shows the value of U.S. production and imports of fuels, nonmetals, and metals in wellhead and mine portal condition for 1972 and 1975. These years were chosen for comparison because 1972 was the last of the "normal" years prior to the oil embargo of 1973. The values for 1972 indicate the peak of economic growth at the last upward cycle. By 1975, the value of domestic production had nearly doubled to more than 62 billion dollars, whereas the value of imports had risen more than fivefold. In both 1972 and 1975, the largest values shown are for fuel materials, but notice the greatly increased value for both domestic and imported fuels in 1975. Another point that needs to be emphasized from these data is that the value of the nonmetals produced domestically in both 1972 and 1975 was nearly twice that of the metals. These relative values of materials are virtually unknown to the public, and perhaps unknown as well as to a large segment of those involved in certain aspects of business, economics, and government. The domestic production of these materials in 1975 had a value of 62.3 billion dollars in a 1.5 trillion dollar economy; only 4.1 percent of the GNP, but the basis of it all.

The statistical summary of the world's mining activity published annually in September by the *Mining Magazine* [12] offers some insights

Table 5-1. Mineral Materials in the United States Economy
(billions of dollars)

	1972	1975
U.S. production		
Fuels	22.1	47.9
Nonmetals	6.5	9.5
Metals (from U.S. ores)	3.6	4.9
Total	32.2	62.3
Gross national product (GNP)	1,152	1,516
U.S. production of fuels, nonmetals, and		
metals as percent of GNP	2.8	4.1
Imports		
Fuels	2.8	19.7
Nonmetals and metals	1.6	2.0
Total	4.4	21.7

Source: U.S. Bureau of Mines.

into the geographic distribution and current availability of twenty-three metals and minerals traded in world markets. The commodities are asbestos, bauxite (aluminum), boron, diamonds, fluorspar, phosphate, potash, iron, manganese, chromium, nickel, molybdenum, tungsten, titanium, copper, lead, zinc, tin, mercury, silver, gold, platinum, and uranium. The annual production of these twenty-three materials from only about 1,100 mines accounts for 90 percent of all mining output other than coal. Data from the Soviet Union, some nations in Eastern Europe, and the Peoples' Republic of China, however, are not included in the survey. The minimum annual production of mines on the list is 150,000 tons and the highest category of production includes those whose yield exceeds 3 million metric tons of ore annually. In this latter group are really the giant mines of the world, 191 of them with an average annual production of 7 million tons of ore. The United States has 185 (17 percent) of the 1,116 mines listed and 51 (27 percent) of 191 giant mines, but including some only for copper, iron, molybdenum, boron, potash, and phosphate.

The information in table 5-2 is a recapitulation of data about the 1,116 mines, their distribution by principal product, size of production, and location. The important considerations of coproducts and by-products in many metal mines, especially those of base and precious metals, had to be omitted from the table, but that does not greatly affect its usefulness. Some metals, such as iron, copper, lead, and zinc, are widespread and produced in many mines of all sizes. Other commodities, such as nickel, titanium, mercury, and fluorspar, are less widespread and come from the smaller size categories of mines. Some commodities are produced in highly restricted areas, such as molybdenum (North Amer-

Table 5-2. Summary of the Products, Distribution, and Annual Production of 1,116 the World's Major Mines

							Chief prod		
	Iron	Man-ga-nese	Chro-mium	Nickel	Mo-lyb-de-num	Tung-sten	Alum-inum	Tita-nium	C p
Mines—Size Aᵃ									
North America	15	—	—	1	3	—	—	—	
Central & South America	7	—	—	—	—	—	2	—	
Australasia	8	—	—	1	—	—	2	—	
Europe	10	—	—	—	—	—	—	—	
Africa	7	—	—	—	—	—	1	—	
Asia	2	—	—	1	—	—	—	—	
Total	49	—	—	3	3	—	5	—	
Mines—Size Bᵇ									
North America	26	—	—	16	—	—	—	—	
Central & South America	11	1	—	3	—	—	11	—	
Australasia	5	1	—	4	—	—	1	—	
Europe	33	—	—	2	—	—	2	—	
Africa	10	1	—	—	—	—	2	—	
Asia	10	—	—	—	—	—	1	—	
Total	95	3	—	25	—	—	17	—	
Mines—Size Cᶜ									
North America	21	—	—	11	2	3	2	5	
Central & South America	11	1	—	2	—	—	6	—	
Australasia	—	—	—	10	—	2	—	12	
Europe	39	—	1	3	—	3	7	1	
Africa	15	8	5	5	—	—	2	—	
Asia	14	7	3	1	—	1	6	1	
Total	100	16	9	32	2	9	23	19	
World total: Mines	245	19	9	60	5	9	45	19	2

Source: Mining Magazine
ᵃ Production greater than 3 million tons per year.
ᵇ Production 1 to 3 million tons per year.
ᶜ Production 150,000 to 1 million tons per year.

ica), chromium (chiefly Africa), manganese (Africa and Asia), boron (United States and Turkey), tin (predominantly Asia), platinum (almost exclusively southern Africa), and asbestos (Canada and southern Africa).

Compilations, such as those in table 5-2, which are based principally on records of mine production, only indicate where mining is in progress, what is produced, and provide an idea of current capacity of production by mine and commodity. These data also reflect something about the past success of the search for needed materials. The mine may or may not be located close to its markets, depending in part on economics and

Element or mineral commodity

Lead/Zinc	Tin	Mercury	Silver	Gold	Platinum group	Uranium	Boron	Potash	Fluorspar	Phosphate	Diamonds	Asbestos	Total mines
2	—	—	—	—	—	1	1	2	—	14	—	2	75
—	—	—	—	—	—	—	—	—	—	—	—	—	17
—	—	—	—	—	—	—	—	—	—	—	—	—	13
—	—	—	—	—	—	—	—	5	—	—	—	—	18
—	1	—	—	6	3	—	—	—	—	5	9	—	40
—	15	—	—	—	—	—	—	—	—	0	—	1	28
2	16	—	—	6	3	1	1	7	—	19	9	3	191
10	—	—	—	2	—	1	—	14	—	9	—	9	102
2	2	—	—	1	—	—	—	—	—	—	—	—	33
2	—	—	—	—	—	—	—	—	—	2	—	1	18
4	—	—	—	—	—	—	—	10	—	2	—	1	55
1	3	—	—	27	1	1	—	—	1	7	3	4	73
1	6	—	—	1	—	—	—	1	—	4	—	—	30
20	11	—	—	31	1	2	—	25	1	24	3	15	311
33	—	2	5	17	—	18	—	1	—	9	—	2	161
26	7	—	4	2	—	—	—	—	4	—	—	1	81
4	4	—	—	4	—	1	—	—	—	2	—	—	45
26	3	1	1	3	—	2	—	7	2	1	—	—	127
4	12	—	—	15	1	—	—	—	2	11	3	9	116
11	2	1	1	5	—	1	2	—	1	2	—	—	88
104	28	4	11	46	1	22	2	8	9	25	3	12	618
126	55	4	11	83	5	25	3	40	10	68	15	30	1120

in part on the geology of the commodity and its ore deposits and the ease of discovery of such deposits. The richest and easiest-to-find deposits of workable ores generally are mined first. The analysis of production data is informative and valuable, but it faces the past, and not the future. These data indicate little or nothing about the economic health of the mine under anticipated conditions or about the geologic features that do or do not assure the future productivity of the mine. The most useful analysis of the future availability of mineral materials, therefore, should include an examination of related economic and geologic factors. Some important and specific characteristics of mineral and energy resources must be more widely recognized, as well as better understood, before the controversy about resource issues can be reduced.

II
Characteristics of Resources

This discussion will be concerned only with the nonrenewable resources, the minerals and rocks of commercial value, including the fossil fuels—coal, oil, and gas. A mineral resource is a concentration of a naturally occurring solid, liquid, or gaseous material in or on the earth's crust in such form that economic extraction of a commodity is currently or potentially feasible. That word "potentially" is very important, but the definition and application is still highly subjective despite the generation of much new data about supply and demand and changes in economics that may favorably or adversely affect profitable extraction.

The definition of resources involves geologic and economic factors. To be available on the market, a mineral material must have both geologic and economic availability. Geologic availability concerns the very existence, mode of occurrence, and distribution of these materials in our planet. The earth is abundantly endowed with useful mineral and fuel materials, but the concept of geologic availability must not be taken for granted. Today's knowledge of the geologic occurrence and the distribution of minerals and fossil fuels suggests that most of these materials will not be available into the infinite future without improved technology and significant changes in the availability of energy and water. Economic availability involves the well-known, broad considerations of the availability of capital for exploration and development, the costs of production, and the expected market price of the material through time, as well as many other critical technological, environmental, social, legal, and political factors. All of these geologic and economic factors must be in favorable balance to allow the production of the minerals and fuels at a profit, and profit is a key word in the description of a free-enterprise, market economy. Industry cannot, however, supply materials that are geologically unavailable or technologically unrecoverable, irrespective of continued price rise.

Figure 5-2 shows a scheme for the classification of resources and the relation between the geologic and the economic factors of resources. The general features of this resource classification were proposed by V. E. McKelvey [13] and, with modifications, the classification was used in U.S. Geological Survey Professional Paper 820, "United States Mineral Resources" in 1973. After further modification in association with the

U.S. Bureau of Mines, this classification was jointly adopted by both bureaus as as a basis for discussing mineral resources (U.S. Geological Survey [14]).

Total resources consist of those materials that have already been identified and those that are as yet undiscovered, but which at some time might be discovered and used. Considering the identified materials, there are those that are currently of economic value and those of sub-economic value that cannot be brought to market now. The special name for the identified resources of economic value is reserves. They are that portion of the identified resource from which a usable mineral and energy commodity can be economically and legally extracted at the time of determination. The term ore is often used for reserves of some minerals. There are two categories of undiscovered resources. The hypothetical resources are those yet to be discovered in known mining districts or oil and gas fields. Speculative resources are those undiscovered deposits that still lie in undiscovered mining districts and oil and gas fields. Careful examination of figure 5-2 shows undiscovered resources of economic value as well as undiscovered resources of subeconomic value. The arrow along the bottom of the diagram indicates an increasing degree from right to left of geologic assurance of the existence of the deposit. The arrow on the right side of the diagram indicates an increasing degree from the

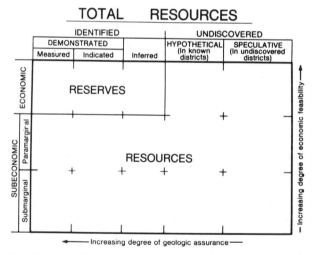

Figure 5-2. The classification of mineral resources as adopted by the U.S. Geological Survey, and the U.S. Bureau of Mines. (From "Principles of the Mineral Resource Classification System of the U.S. Bureau of Mines and the U.S. Geological Survey," Geological Survey Bulletin 1450-A, 1976.)

bottom to the top of the diagram of economic feasibility of recovering the material.

This scheme for the classification of mineral resources is not the only one available, but it can serve as a basis for further discussion. For those who wish to pursue further the philosophy and development of the terminology of resource classification, this and other suggested systems have been discussed critically by Schanz [15].

New reserves are sought from extensions of known deposits, through economic and technical changes that permit the conversion of identified subeconomic resources to reserves, or by the discovery of new deposits of economic value. These steps must be taken as old mines and old mining districts become geologically exhausted for lack of material or become economically exhausted by reaching their economic limits of production. In the short term, reserves of many commodities may likely be increased by concentrating effort on the search for undiscovered, now mostly hidden, deposits geologically similar to those now technically usable.

Geologic exhaustion is not imaginary. It happens. Many types of ore deposits have sharp physical boundaries. When mining reaches those boundaries in the three dimensions, the deposit is geologically, or physically, exhausted. In such cases, geologic and economic exhaustion are simultaneous.

Other geological types of deposits have gradational boundaries, commonly characterized by outward decreases in the content of the valuable material. In these types of deposits, therefore, geologic exhaustion commonly does not occur at the same time as economic exhaustion. The mine may cease to be profitable and operations cease, not necessarily for want of material, but because it has met an economic limit. Should economics change favorably, however, such a mine might have its identified subeconomic resources converted to reserves and mining operations might be resumed. Resumption of profitable operations requires that costs of rehabilitating the mine also be amortized. In some underground mines these costs can be especially high, perhaps too high to support the rehabilitation, in which case the mine remains in a state of economic exhaustion.

Deposits of petroleum are special cases in economic exhaustion. Primary recovery methods generally obtain only about 30 percent of the resource that occurs in the ground. Thus, an oil field generally is economically exhausted long before it is geologically exhausted. Secondary recovery methods may increase the recovery rate somewhat, but unless technology and other economic factors improve considerably, more of the identified resources may continue to remain beneath the surface than can be recovered.

Although geologic exhaustion is final, economic exhaustion may or may not be final, and only the changes of economic conditions through time provide the answers. In either case of exhaustion, wanted mineral and fuel materials cannot enter the supply system. It is necessary to understand the difference between the two kinds of exhaustion and how they relate to estimates of resource availability. Tilton [16] has recently discussed these concepts in detail.

The reserves of many mineral materials have been increased during past years despite increased production. It must be recognized, however, that should economic conditions change for what might be termed "the worse," materials also may easily drop out of the reserves and again become part of the identified subeconomic resources. Any change that reduces the value of material below the level of profitable production reduces the size of the reserve. For example, the sudden massive rise of energy costs and other increased production costs combined with depressed prices has reduced the reserves at many mines. How great is the reduction? This requires complete recalculations for each mine and commodity involved for every major change in conditions. The overall effect of changes may be slight or great, but constant checks are required. A reserve is calculated from a given set of conditions and it is necessary to know what conditions form the basis of the calculation. Without this information, it is virtually impossible to evaluate the meaning of a reserve figure. It is possible, however, to make a series of calculations for many varying sets of conditions and estimate what amounts of material might be available under many circumstances. All of these calculations for each deposit should take into consideration the basic geologic information about the tonnage, content (grade), spatial distribution, and mineralogical characteristics of the mineral materials in the ground.

Reserves are but a small part of the resources of any given commodity. Reserves and resources are part of a dynamic system and they cannot be inventoried like cans of tomatoes on a grocer's shelf. New scientific discoveries, new technology, and new commercial demands or restrictions are constantly affecting amounts of reserves and resources. Reserves and resources do not exist until commercial demand puts a value on a material in the market. Over the years, materials containing about 80 of the 92 naturally occurring elements have come into commercial use.

The diagram in figure 5-2 can be used to summarize the knowledge of the reserves and resources of any commodity. Resources are best treated on a commodity-by-commodity basis. The data may be summarized in a semiquantitative or a quantitative way, although filling in all the resource categories with accurate tonnages is currently impossible and is not likely ever to be possible. In the meantime, some information is needed to make value judgments. Quantitative reserve information can be assembled from the mining or petroleum companies for a given commodity. Companies in the United States are obliged neither to publish such data nor give it to government agencies, except in cases involving operations on public lands, but most companies cooperate with those agencies whose work involves a need to know about current and future availability of nonrenewable resources. It is understood, of course, that agencies receiving data considered confidential by a company will release such information to the public only in a composite way, so that records from individual companies are not specifically identifiable.

There are differences in virtually every resource and reserve estimate made because each is made for a specific purpose from the data available to the compiler. Each is biased somehow because of different approaches to analysis through the use of incomplete data that are not uniformly reported. There is little chance of escaping some subjectivity even when the compiler tries to be as objective as possible. If a geologist makes a resource estimate, it likely will be cast first in terms of material in place in the ground based on his best knowledge of the shape of the deposit and its grade and tonnage to a certain depth. Mining engineers are likely to think more in terms of how much of the commodity can be recovered through a period of time at today's or a future price. Estimates are likely to be in terms of ore of a certain grade or tons of the commodity or metal contained in the ore. The petroleum engineers will think in terms of oil or gas recoverable by primary and secondary methods. It is important to know what geologic and economic characteristics were used in making the estimate. All too often in the past a reader was left to decide for himself how the estimates were made by the author.

When the quantification of undiscovered resources is considered, one question looms over all others: How is the undiscovered resource quantified? Obviously the precision is low and much lower than estimates of the identified resources. Most of the estimates of undiscovered resources are based on geologic extrapolation. In the absence of better techniques, it seems reasonable that the earth scientists should be accorded the dubious honor of assisting in the assessment of these undiscovered resources through their best interpretation of the data available at the time. Better techniques to assess resources definitely are needed and they have a priority in the work of economic geologists, who are but a part of a relatively small profession. Although the need to assess the mineral resources of local areas, regions, and nations of the world has only recently been more widely recognized, scientists grappling with these problems through the years have produced some useful methods and thought-provoking papers.

More than twenty-five years ago, Lasky [17] discussed national mineral resource appraisal and Nolan [18] discussed the search for new ore deposits from a geological perspective. Lasky [19] also discussed cumulative resources of porphyry copper deposits as related to ore grade. The grade and tonnage relations among copper deposits were reexamined by Singer, Cox, and Drew [20]. Allais [21] brought a new approach to his study of resources in the Algerian Sahara. Harris [22] applied multivariate statistical analysis to mineral exploration and his ideas, developed in subsequent years, are reviewed in a later paper [23] that includes a pertinent bibliography of his own and other works. The state of the art of modeling mineral material systems has been surveyed and summarized in a report prepared for Resources for the Future by Vogely [24]. The evolution of techniques for assessing oil and gas resources was reviewed by Miller and coauthors [25], who also provided an extensive bibliography. A comprehensive posting of the literature on this subject is beyond the scope of this discussion, but the works cited can provide an entry into the complexities of estimating the availability of mineral resources.

Figure 5-3 can assist in clarifying several other points about the mineral resource diagram in figure 5-2, especially the nature of the right and bottom boundaries of the diagram. The right boundary of the diagram in figure 5-2 represents the limit of those undiscovered resources that occur in "conventional" ore deposits, those of types already known. Beyond the right boundary of this diagram lies an area of unconceived resources (in figure 5-3). This is the area in which lie those bodies of rocks and minerals that have not yet been recognized as types of deposits that may have potential commercial value. An example of such a deposit is the recent discovery of the mineral sphalerite, the sulfide of zinc, in fractures in coal in the Illinois Basin. These deposits were in years past not only undiscovered, but unconceived. When the deposits were discovered, however, they immediately became identified resources awaiting further evaluation to determine whether the sphalerite now constitutes a reserve, an economically recoverable resource, or a subeconomic resource.

In figure 5-3, the line labeled potential economic threshold coincides with the lower boundary of the resource diagram in figure 5-2. This threshold marks the lowest concentration of potential economic value of a desired material in a deposit. Below this concentration there is, at the time of determination, little or no expectation that the material will become commercially valuable. Thus, calculations of resources do have a lower limit based on economic considerations.

Geologic and technologic considerations have important effects on this economic boundary for each element or commodity sought. In some cases, the selection of this boundary varies for different types of deposits which contain the same, as well as different, materials from which the desired constituent is to be recovered. Many people in science and industry currently consider the value of this economic threshold for copper to be 0.1 percent. At this concentration, most of the copper still occurs in separate mineral particles that technologically can be separated from the rest of the associated minerals. The copper-bearing minerals referred to here are principally the various sulfides, sulfates, carbonates, and oxides, as well as native copper, which unlike many elements, does occur in its elemental form in nature. Any of these minerals may be abundant enough to be a major component of the copper ore in a deposit. The economic threshold of cobalt resources, however, was placed at 0.01 percent by Vhay and coauthors [26, p. 150], a value considerably below that of copper. Because of its geology and economics, cobalt rarely is the primary product of a mine, but has been, or might be, a by-product from some types of metallic ore deposits at home and abroad. Cobalt commonly occurs in many deposits, both in small amounts of minerals con-

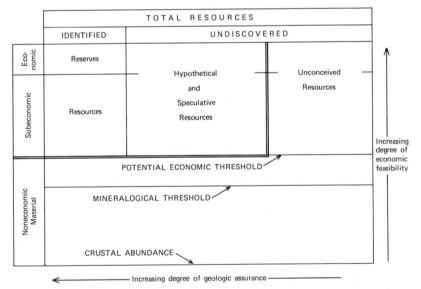

Figure 5-3. Diagram showing the relation of resources to noneconomic materials.

taining abundant cobalt and in more abundant minerals that contain little cobalt. Barite, the sulfate of barium, occurs in three major geologic types of deposits, each with its own economic threshold for purposes of calculating resources [27, pp. 81–82].

Figure 5-3 also shows two other boundaries, the mineralogical threshold, which lies in the field of noneconomic materials, and crustal abundance, which forms the base of the field of noneconomic materials. The mineralogical threshold in this context refers to the minimum natural conditions that will permit the formation of separate particles of specific minerals of the type that, if abundant enough, could be mined and processed by current methods as ores, commercial sources of a wanted material. This statement also implies that the mineralogical threshold might or might not coincide with the economic threshold, depending on the material under discussion and length of time being considered for potential development. Under the constraints of current technology, the economic threshold for most elements is not likely soon to fall below the mineralogical threshold. As the concentration of chemical elements decreases to levels below that which allows the formation of separate particles of ore minerals, the elements are dispersed in the crystal structures of the other kinds of minerals that comprise the noneconomic, ordinary rocks constituting the bulk of the earth's crust. At these low levels of concentration elements are said to occur at their crustal abundance.

The materials in the field bounded by the mineralogic threshold and crustal abundance have geologic characteristics so different from those in all of the fields above the mineralogical threshold that some examination of the composition of the earth's crust and the distribution of its chemical elements is necessary in order to recognize current limitations on resources. This information is especially pertinent to the frequently touted idea that the ultimate answer to man's resource problems lies in the mining of vast tonnages of rock to recover the many elements available only in the low concentration ranges of crustal abundance. Geologic reasons suggest that such a vision is not likely to be fulfilled in the foreseeable future without at least the availability of cheap energy in virtually unlimited quantities.

III
Crustal Abundance and Resources

Four of the many estimates of the composition of the earth's crust found in the literature are shown in table 5-3. Two recent estimates of the average composition of the earth's crust are given, along with two esti-

Table 5-3. Average Composition of the Earth's Crust and the Continental
Crust in Weight Percent

	Earth's crust		Continental crust	
	Mason[a]	Vinogradov[b]	Skinner[c]	Taylor[d]
Oxygen	46.60	47.00	45.20	46.40
Silicon	27.72	29.50	27.20	28.15
Aluminum	8.13	8.05	8.00	8.23
Iron	5.00	4.65	5.80	5.63
Calcium	3.63	2.96	5.06	4.15
Sodium	2.83	2.50	2.32	2.36
Potassium	2.59	2.50	1.68	2.09
Magnesium	2.09	1.87	2.77	2.33
Titanium	0.44	0.45	0.86	0.57
Hydrogen	0.14	NG	0.14	NG
Total	99.17	99.48	99.03	99.91
All other elements	0.83	0.52	0.97	0.09

NG, Not given.
[a] From Brian Mason, *Principles of Geochemistry* (New York, Wiley, 1958).
[b] From A. P. Vinogradov, "Average Contents of Chemical Elements in the Principal
Types of Igneous Rocks of the Earth's Crust," translated from the Russian in *Geochemistry*, no. 7 (1962), pp. 641–664.
[c] From B. J. Skinner, "A Second Iron Age Ahead," *American Scientist*, vol. 64
(1976), pp. 258–269.
[d] From S. R. Taylor, "The Abundance of the Chemical Elements in the Continental
Crust—A New Table," *Geochemica et Cosmochemica Acta*, vol. 28 (1964), pp. 1273–1285.

mates of the composition of the crust underlying the continents, which
now provides our useful mineral materials. The values for each of the ten
most abundant elements are of the same order of magnitude. The data
also make it quite clear that the ten most abundant elements comprise
the bulk of the crust, more than 99 percent. Only a glance at table 5-2 is
necessary to see that many of the elements most useful in industry do
not appear in table 5-3. In fact, the remaining 82 naturally occurring
elements comprise less than 1 percent of the crust. Consider, then, that
these scarce elements, if evenly distributed throughout the crust, rarely
would occur in amounts in excess of a few grams per metric ton. Conventional ore deposits currently of commercial value for given elements
contain concentrations that are about 5 to more than 2,000 times greater
than the estimated crustal abundance of the element. The occurrence of
any of the scarce elements in concentrations sufficient for mining is
exceptionally rare and of great importance to us, so much so that large
amounts of time and money are devoted to their study in order to discover
and use them.

Recently Parker [28] and Vokes [29] have discussed, summarized,
and cited much pertinent information about the chemical composition of

the crust. These chemical data about the abundant and scarce elements are the basis for calculations of the apparently astronomically large amounts of metallic and nonmetallic resources in the earth. There are virtually as many sets of data as there are estimators because each selects data and a method of approach to prepare for interpretation. Many chemical analyses are available from surface samples, but few are available from samples recovered from the depths of the earth. The accuracy and precision of the methods used to determine the concentration of each element, not only the scarce, but also the plentiful ones, in rock samples have been discussed in considerable detail in many reports. One of the most recent of these reports [30] contains a great deal of discussion and many bibliographic citations. Few samples are analyzed for every element. Analytical methods to determine some elements are complex and difficult. Defining accurately and precisely the chemical composition of the earth's crust becomes difficult at best, considering the problems of inadequate sampling and the variety of analytical and computational methods available. The interpretation of data used to estimate the composition of the earth's crust was discussed by Miesch [31], who suggested several ways to minimize inadequacies inherent in such an undertaking. In a discussion of the theory of error in geochemical data, Miesch [32, p. A16] warned that the effects of overall bias in geochemical errors are usually not severe, unless the purpose of the investigation is to estimate absolute mean concentrations of constituents to several significant figures.

Notice in table 5-3 that the estimates by Skinner and Taylor of the scarce elements in the continental crust vary by a factor of about ten. It is truly perilous to try to characterize the average composition of large volumes of rock because even small differences in the estimated abundance of the scarce elements will greatly affect the amount of the element anticipated to be available. The chemical composition of many minerals has some limited variation. Different minerals form rocks that have a wider range in composition, and the abundance of rock types varies in different parts of the crust. The problems compound quickly.

Despite these problems, some useful general and specific information is available. Ore minerals of many abundant elements are about as small a group as that of some scarce elements. Although iron, aluminum, and magnesium are among the more abundant elements in the earth's crust, their presence in many common minerals does not mean that any combination of minerals constitutes ore. The most desirable ores of iron and aluminum are oxides, but most of these two elements are bound with other elements in common and abundant silicate minerals of relatively little or no economic value as sources of the two metals. Much magnesium also is fixed in refractory silicate minerals, so much so that sea water and natural brines are its major ores.

The scarce elements are found concentrated many times more than their crustal abundance in various commercially valuable ore minerals that commonly, but not exclusively, are oxides, sulfides, sulfates, carbonates, and, in some cases, native elements. The mineralogical threshold, like the economic threshold, generally occurs at concentrations of 0.01 to 0.1 percent. Concentrations greater than 0.1 percent of a scarce element in a chemical analysis generally indicate that the sample might contain ore-type minerals of the element. Gold and uranium are two exceptions to this generalization, in that they may form separate minerals at concentrations well below 0.1 percent. In concentrations below the value of the mineralogical threshold, however, most scarce elements are dispersed in the crystal structure of other minerals according to physical laws that allow substitution of some elements for others under certain conditions. In many cases of such substitution, these small amounts of an element are not economically recoverable because of the manner in which the elements are bound tightly together in the crystal structure. This is especially true of small amounts of metals dispersed in silicate minerals, minerals that make up most of the earth's crust.

Mineralogy and chemistry are highly important in determining the occurrence of chemical elements in ore-type minerals or as substitutes for other elements in the structure of other minerals, especially silicate minerals. For example, as much as several tenths of 1 percent barium could occur in a rock where it could all be replacing some of the potassium in feldspar, a complex aluminum silicate mineral. In order to recover such barium, the feldspar would have to be recovered and then the barium from the feldspar. The same could be true for small amounts of lead. The removal of metals from silicate structures will require much more energy than the recovery of a similar amount of material from the minerals of a conventional ore deposit, not only because of the larger amount of material that must be processed, but also the greater difficulty of separating the metal from the atomic structure of the silicate.

Table 5-4 is a compilation of some industrially useful nonferrous and ferrous metals and their concentration in grams per metric ton of the average continental crust according to the estimate of Lee and Yao [33]. In this list only iron, aluminum, and titanium are among the most abundant elements; the others are among those scarce elements that are less than 1 percent of the earth's crust. The table also presents a calculation of the number of metric tons of average crust that would have to be processed at the unlikely recovery rate of 100 percent to obtain 1 ton of the desired element. The calculations indicate that if crust of this

Table 5-4. Crustal Abundance and Minimum Grades of Ore of Selected Metallic Elements

	Grams per metric ton in continental crust[a]	Metric tons of average crustal rock required to produce 1 metric ton of element[b]	Metric tons of minimum grade ore required in 1977 per metric ton of element[c]
Aluminum	83,000	12	7
Titanium	5,300	188	180
Zinc	81	12,000	40
Copper	50	20,000	200
Lead	13	77,000	50
Tin	1.6	625,000	10,000
Silver	0.065	15,000,000	1,300
Platinum group	0.028	36,000,000	100,000
Gold	0.0035	285,000,000	100,000
Iron	48,000	20	4
Manganese	1,000	1,000	5
Vanadium	120	8,300	100
Chromium	77	13,000	14
Nickel	61	16,000	100
Niobium	20	50,000	1,200
Cobalt	18	55,000	200
Tungsten	1.2	830,000	200
Molybdenum	1.1	910,000	400

[a] Data from Tan Lee and Chi-lung Yao, "Abundance of Chemical Elements in the Earth's Crust and Its Major Tectonic Units," *International Geology Review*, vol. 12, no. 7 (1970) pp. 778–786.
[b] Assuming 100 percent recovery, which is not likely.
[c] Based on data in D. A. Brobst and W. P. Pratt, eds., *United States Mineral Resources*, U.S. Geological Survey Professional Paper 820, 1973.

composition were available, the number of tons to be processed per ton of some metals recovered would be staggering. The right column of table 5-4 presents for comparison the number of tons of ores of minimum grade mined in 1977 from some typical kinds of commercial deposits to yield 1 ton of the element. Notice that titanium, one of the abundant elements, is the only one listed whose current grade of ore closely approaches its estimated abundance in the crust.

IV
Distribution of Abundant and Scarce Elements

All of these geochemical considerations lead to several additional aspects of the resource system. Skinner [34] recently discussed two significant concepts on the distribution of the elements. The distribution of the most geochemically abundant metals such as iron, aluminum, and titanium can be illustrated by the unimodal curve shown in figure 5-4.

For these materials, mining has been carried on in the types of materials of the highest grade that would lie on the right side of the figure. For these elements, Skinner [34, p. 262] suggested that the same kinds of ore-type minerals occur in the rocks of the crust, regardless of the degree of concentration of that element. The concentrating techniques used in current beneficiation and refining processes to extract metal from high grade ores also can be used in the future with less rich material and even

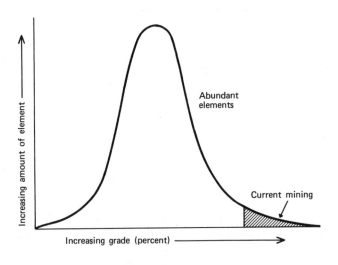

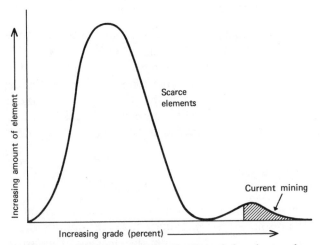

Figure 5-4. Possible geochemical distribution of abundant and scarce elements. (From B. J. Skinner, "A Second Iron Age Ahead?" *American Scientist* vol. 64, 1976, p. 263.)

common rock, but at increasing cost, especially in energy. As the grade or percent of metal in an ore declines arithmetically, the curve suggests that the amount of metal available at a given grade will increase geometrically down to a grade corresponding to the peak of the curve and then decline in both grade and tonnage.

Skinner's suggested distribution for the geochemically scarce elements in the earth's crust also is shown in figure 5-4. This is a bimodal distribution, with the large peak showing the distribution of these elements in common rocks, where they are trapped as atomic substitutes for more abundant metals in the crystal structure of minerals. The small peak represents that part of the scarce elements in the earth's crust that has been freed from such atomic substitution and is recombined as separate minerals. Material under the small hump may be considered the part of the scarce element that is concentrated by the geologic processes which form ore deposits.

If the bimodal distribution of the scarce elements is correct, then the richest grades of ore, represented by the area under the small hump, have been tapped first. There will be an early period during which mining of declining grades will yield larger and larger tonnages of ore. This is the condition that miners seem to have had for most of this century. Eventually, however, the distribution curve turns down again and further reductions in grade also bring declining tonnages of ore at a given grade. There are indications that this might already be happening in the mining of several metals, such as mercury, gold, and silver. The second feature of the bimodal distribution is the indication that a point will eventually be reached where reduction in grade reaches the mineralogical threshold, that point beyond which a scarce element occurs only in positions of substitution and is, therefore, no longer easily amenable to concentration. In figure 5-4, the mineralogical threshold for scarce elements lies somewhere between the humps of the bimodal curve.

Some indirect lines of reasoning suggest that the order of magnitude of the amount of metal concentrated in commercially valuable ore deposits might at least be estimated. Many geologists believe that some of the mass properties of ore deposits, such as size of the largest known deposits, the number of deposits that contain a million or more tons of a given metal, are features that seem to be related to the crustal abundance of the element. V. E. McKelvey [35] was the first to suggest that the discovered reserves of the scarce metals are proportional to their crustal abundance. Skinner [34, p. 266] went on to say that if the conclusion about the size of the hump (figure 5-4) representing the ore deposits of the scarce elements is acceptable, then the size of the humps for other scarce elements can be estimated. The report by the Committee on Mineral Resources and the Environment (COMRATE) of the National Academy of Sciences [36, pp. 128–130] has shown how this might be done. It is estimated that the mineralogical threshold for copper is reached at a grade of 0.1 percent. It also is estimated that no more than 0.01 percent of the total copper in the continental crust will be found concentrated in ore bodies with grades of 0.1 percent copper or more. The reasoning was based on the volume percent of mineralized rock in the most intensely mineralized regions so far discovered and on the distribution frequency of copper deposits in the crust. This value of 0.01 percent must be taken as the maximum possible yield, but it is not likely to be too large by more than a factor of 10. Thus, the size of the ore deposit hump may possibly fall between 0.001 and 0.01 percent of the amount of any scarce metal in the crust.

An important feature of the hypothesis of bimodal distribution for the scarce elements is the mineralogical threshold, or barrier as Skinner [34] called it. But even a recognized mineralogical threshold does not necessarily mean that chemical data from samples that cross such a threshold will produce a bimodal distribution. Analyses that detect amounts of an element contributed by the minutest amount of an ore-type mineral, and that resulting from an abundant substitution are indistinguishable. Even careful microscopic study might fail to detect a few minute grains of an ore mineral. The number and size of the samples selected for chemical study from different environments could well make a difference in the trends indicated by the analytical results. My colleague D. A. Singer [37] has suggested that the greater the variety of geological environments in which an element occurs, the more likely that the distribution of its concentration will be unimodal. This may be a reason for the unimodal distribution of the abundant elements proposed by Skinner [34, p. 263] as shown in figure 5-4.

Bimodal distribution is not evident in the histograms of analytical values for the content of various elements given in many geochemical studies reported in the literature. Few studies are extensive enough to be cited as definite proof because they examine only a suite of a few elements, generally in a restricted or specific environment. Among the larger studies, the histograms for 30 elements analyzed in an examination of 863 samples of surficial materials in the conterminous United States [38] offered no evidence of bimodal distribution of those elements. Histograms of the logarithms of the values suggest that the scarce elements are either log normally distributed or form a log normal distribution censored by analytical limits of their detection. Singer [37] also has pointed out that individual studies in specific geological environments do not prove the lack of a bimodal distribution, but they do suggest that if the distribution is bimodal, the high grade peak might be so small that many tens of thousands of carefully selected samples would be needed to identify it.

Proof for both the bimodal and log normal distributions is lacking, mostly because analytical sampling of the earth's crust is still in its most rudimentary stages, a point strongly made by Skinner [34, p. 265]. Only considerably more sampling will ultimately indicate what the distribution of the scarce elements is. Obtaining this information is important because it bears directly on how successful mineral exploration can, but not necessarily will, be in the next century in finding deposits of needed metals, nonmetals, and fuels that can be used commercially. This knowledge can be used to assign priorities to the types of deposits sought, to estimate the location, size, and grade of deposits remaining to be found and the chances of finding them at reasonable cost of time and money, and to estimate the amount of labor needed to develop new methods to search for hidden ore deposits of conventional and new types. Failure to maintain a satisfactory rate of success in the discovery of mineral and fuel deposits of sufficient size to permit production to meet anticipated future demands would be a devastating constraint upon the continuous economic growth desired and expected by many people.

V
Energy, Technology, and Minerals

These discussions about the geologic occurrence and availability of elements suggest that a steady rise in the amount of energy will be needed to mine larger volumes of lower and lower grade ores and to process their larger volumes by crushing and concentration. Page and Creasey [39] discussed the energy consumption for the utilization of lower and lower grade ores. They concluded that the energy required to produce a unit of metal can be used to determine a lower limit on the grade of ores used to calculate potentially economic resources. This lower limit of grade can be evaluated and that figure can be used as a limiting factor in the search for low-grade minerals that might be mined in the foreseeable future.

The energy requirements for the recovery of the scarcer elements might be very different from those for the abundant metals, as shown qualitatively in figure 5-5. The two curves are parallel until the conventional ores of scarce elements have been worked out. Once a mineralogical threshold is reached, however, a tremendous jump in energy consumption will take place to recover the scarce elements because traditional mineral concentration processes can no longer be used. The scarce metals will have to be sought in silicate minerals that will have to be broken down in order to release these tightly bound metals. The magnitude of energy increase will naturally vary with the kind of host minerals; but for most silicates, the energy demand will jump by a factor of 100 to 1,000. Few data are available pertaining to these energy needs, but they will no doubt be much higher than the needs for processing a conventional ore deposit. It seems unlikely that the mineralogical threshold will be exceeded simply because costs might become unbearable if only the current and traditional sources of energy are available.

To emphasize further the relationship of energy and concentration of elements in ore deposits, look at a set of examples for copper. If the concentration of copper in the continental crust is correctly estimated to be 50 grams per metric ton, 20,000 tons of rock would have to be processed to recover 1 metric ton of copper from silicate minerals. Consider the possibility that 0.1 percent copper will be the lower limit of grade of the ore (the mineralogical threshold), then 1,000 tons of rock will have to be processed to obtain 1 ton of copper from disseminated sulfide minerals. At a grade of 0.5 percent copper, as in a typical porphyry-type deposit mined today, only 200 tons of rock will have to be processed to obtain 1 metric ton of copper from sulfide minerals. Thus, the copper in the sulfide ore of porphyry deposits is concentrated 100 times more than that in crustal abundance.

Granting the point that a mineralogical threshold does not exist for ore-type minerals of abundant elements, it seems quite probable that the recovery of these minerals well may be constrained under certain condi-

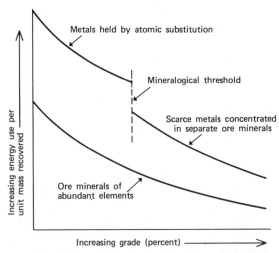

† ·**Figure 5-5.** Diagrammatic presentation of energy requirements for recovering abundant and scarce elements. (Modified from B. J. Skinner, "A Second Iron Age Ahead?" *American Scientist* vol. 64, 1976, p. 267.)

tions by an economic threshold, especially when those minerals are simply too disseminated to be recovered economically. We must not forget that vast amounts of even the most abundant elements in the earth's crust also are fixed as constituents of the common silicate minerals and that they will be just as difficult and relatively expensive to separate and recover from the tight bonds of the silicate crystal structures as the lesser amounts of the scarce elements. Without the readily available large amounts of inexpensive energy heralded by Goeller and Weinberg [10], the mineral materials geologically and economically available to the consumers of the world are much more distinctly limited than many people realize.

It seems likely that lower grade materials from conventional ore deposits probably will continue to be used before unconventional or new types of deposits will be opened, even in times of rising prices, because the technology and plants are available. It is hard to resist using tried and true methods, even with rising energy costs.

The increasing use of even the most abundant metals will lead to increased use of energy, although a better performance in recycling some metals could help to reduce energy demands. Aluminum refining has a deserved reputation as a high energy consumer, twice as much as copper and six times as much as steel with the same tonnage of product. This certainly has to be considered when aluminum is suggested as a substitute for copper. It will, moreover, require more energy to extract and produce aluminum from possible alternative aluminum-bearing minerals, such as alunite, a hydrated sulfate of aluminum and potassium, or dawsonite, a hydrated sodium-aluminum carbonate, each with an aluminum content of about 15 percent, than it does to extract the 25 percent of metallic aluminum from bauxite, the currently used oxide ore. But collected aluminum scrap can be reprocessed at perhaps as little as 5 percent of the energy cost needed to produce primary aluminum. Titanium, whose abundance makes it a prospective substitute for scarce metals, currently requires twice as much energy per ton to manufacture as primary aluminum from current sources. After collection, the recycling of copper takes about 5 percent as much energy as the production of primary copper.

The trash piles of our consumption-oriented society contain resources which would be valued highly if discovered in their native state. There is almost as much heat value in a ton of municipal trash as there is in a ton of lignite. The trash lies generally within a few miles of the point of potential use. Currently junked automobiles weigh about 4,000 pounds (1,800 kg) and contain about 80 percent iron and steel. Certainly the discovery of a deposit of iron ore in our nation yielding half that value in metallic iron would be welcomed. Instead, taconite containing 30 percent or less iron is mined and beneficiated. These ores, moreover, require five times as much energy to make a ton of molten steel than to make a ton of steel from collected scrap. The reuse of such materials helps to solve not one problem but three. Our needs for scarce materials are satisfied, energy is saved, and some much needed clean-up work is done at the same time.

More intensive recycling of mineral materials is possible. A system for recycling many materials has not been developed because of past conditions, when recycling was considered uneconomic, that is, unnecessary. Changes in economic conditions could bring about a rapid reappraisal of the value of recycling mineral materials.

The success of the long- and short-term search for ore deposits and energy resources will have to depend in good measure on the development of new technology. Starr and Rudman [40] of the Electric Power Research Institute recently pointed out in *Science* magazine that the application of technology is generally ten years behind the drawing boards in research departments. This backlog is a reservoir of information which will have to be utilized more fully and at faster rates in the future than in the past. There is no time for lag in the development of resource-related technology.

New and better techniques to search for and find hidden deposits of minerals and oil and gas will be required if increased supplies of resources are expected to reach the market in the future. Explorationists currently are using some sophisticated-looking geochemical and geophysical techniques, but they are mostly tools that produce information that must be interpreted "correctly" to obtain the desired results. These tools are still quite limited in their application. Looking to copper, for example, in the search for porphyry deposits, geologists can quite easily find those that crop out. It is generally possible to identify those with an exposed geochemical halo (figure 5-6), a sort of crown of other elements that commonly occurs at the outer margins of many types of metal deposits. Good geologic reasons indicate that other porphyry deposits, with or without these halos, are hidden beneath younger sedimentary or volcanic rocks. New techniques are needed to locate good sites for further detailed exploration and drilling. Oil and gas fields and hidden ore deposits are located by drilling, and increased success is, of course, desirable. As has been said many times about mineral and fossil fuel deposits, they are first found in the minds of men.

Undoubtedly the greatest requirement to assure a supply of raw materials where and when they are wanted is to develop an abundant supply of cheap energy. Without this energy, the task of supplying a growing population with abundant material becomes difficult, if not impossible. The development of these abundant sources of energy will take work and capital investment over time. Some of the material requirements for these energy systems are tremendous. Before abundant, cheap energy arrives, more of our conventional energy sources will have to be tapped in greater quantity. This will require not only more technology, but more mineral materials to develop the coal mines, drill new oil and gas wells, build the power plants and the distribution systems. These little-heralded requirements will put extra demands on the mineral suppliers.

The magnitude of the demands and supply of nonfuel mineral materials for the U.S. energy industry through the years 1975 to 1990 has been estimated by Albers and coauthors [41] and Goudarzi and coauthors [42], respectively, for the option to pursue business-as-usual as presented in Project Independence [43]. The reports contain basic information compiled from industry and government sources in order to estimate the physical quantities of minerals needed for the production of energy from various types of fuels. The anticipated needs are compared with the identified resources (reserves plus subeconomic resources, see figure 5-2).

The Federal Energy Administration (FEA) report in 1974 urged doubling domestic coal production by 1990 to 1.3 billion short tons per

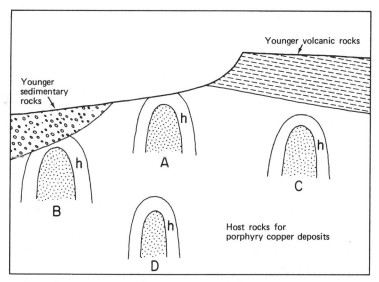

Figure 5-6. Hidden porphyry copper deposits. Deposits of type A can be found with current technology. The discovery of deposit types B-C, and D will require assistance from more advanced technology. The symbol "h" refers to the geochemical halos. The copper deposits are shown in the stippled areas.

Table 5-5. World and U.S. Barite Production, and U.S. Imports, 1850–1975
(millions of tons)

	Production		U.S. Imports
	World	U.S.	
1850–1914	6.5	1.2	0.2
1915–1918	1.2	.7	.0
1919–1944	16.7	7.1	.9
1945–1975	86.2	27.6	15.2
Total	110.6	36.6	16.3
Percent of total since 1945	78	75	94

year. The increase was expected to require the development of seventy-four open-pit facilities, each capable of producing 4.5 million short tons of coal per year and eighty-two additional underground mines producing 2.7 million short tons of coal per year. The needs for nineteen metals in this task are summarized by Albers and coauthors [41, table 7, p. A6].

It is estimated that 2.6 billion feet of oil and gas wells will be drilled between 1977 and 1988 [41, table 11, p. A8]. The equipment involved will require 81 million metric tons of iron, about equal to the iron content of two years' domestic production of iron ore at current rates, 39 million metric tons of concrete, 33 million metric tons of solid ingredients for drilling mud, and lesser amounts of many more metals; and so the recital goes for refineries, power plants, pipelines, and nuclear facilities. The total mineral needs climb quickly and all are presumably in addition to normal needs, which also are expected to grow.

These increasing mineral needs can be put into a comprehensible frame of reference by surveying barite production (table 5-5). Barite is used as a weighting agent in drilling mud for oil and gas wells. About 85 percent of the world's supply goes to this use. The American Petroleum Institute estimates that barite needs in the United States during the next eleven years (1977–88) will be 23 million metric tons (25.3 million short tons). This is not just an indifferent, shoulder-shrugging number. Table 5-5 shows my estimate of the world barite production since 1850 based on a survey of the literature and data from the U.S. Bureau of Mines. Seventy-five percent of the total domestic barite production amounted to 27.6 million short tons in the past thirty years, and that just barely exceeds the expected domestic demand for the next eleven years. World demand is also rising because of increased well drilling. Continued import of at least 30 percent of our current needs may be more costly and less practical in the future due to world competition for supplies. There is good geological reason, however, to believe that world supplies can meet the demands, but not without work. A look at the statistics for most other commodities and oil and gas would reveal the same trends of growth, but the chances for meeting demands for all commodities are not equally good.

VI
Exponential Growth

Many trends of increased demand are indicators of exponential growth. Exponential growth is dangerous, especially when it takes people off their guard. If we were to start with what appeared to be a 1-billion-year supply of any commodity, based on current rates of consumption, and used it in increasingly large amounts, say at the rate of 3 percent growth annually, which has been the rate of economic growth in the United States in the not too recent past, that billion-year supply would be consumed in just under 600 years. A 2-billion-year supply would last only another 23½ years, because that is the time interval required for the last doubling, at which point the supply has vanished. That, of course, is not the way mineral resources are exhausted, but the example shows the importance of giving careful consideration not only to the size of the supply, but to the rate at which it is consumed. The rate at which things are consumed of course depends on the ability to produce through time.

A study currently under way by Dennis Cox and Nancy Wright of the U.S. Geological Survey and George Coakley of the U.S. Bureau of Mines (written communication) indicates that the demand for copper in the U.S. might exceed mine capacity by about 1981 and exceed total capacity from known and drilled deposits by 1987. After that time, a widening gap could occur between the demand and the minimum annual production curves. Although the magnitude of this gap cannot be precisely determined because of incomplete information, discovery and development of the new deposits possibly might provide sufficient production to fill the widening gap. By the year 2000, the gap between domestic production capacity and the anticipated primary demand might equal about 2 million short tons of annual production, which is about equal to current U.S. production capacity. Such needs could be met by the discovery and development of eight giant copper deposits or thirty to forty average-size deposits. To put it another way, current production is provided by thirty-eight deposits containing 68 million tons of copper. Another thirty-eight deposits or the same amount of ore must be found and developed within twenty-four years. Because of the ten- to fifteen-year lead time between discovery and first production of many mineral deposits, most of these new deposits must be identified by 1985.

The factor of lead time, that time between discovery and production, is invisible to many people. The lead time is lengthening because of many geological and economic factors, some of which have already been discussed. Exploration is time consuming and costly, as is development. Ultimate success is elusive. Investments of time, money, and labor through several to many years may be lost at any stage of the exploration and development process because any one or a combination of factors could force a halt to an individual project. The successful company scores enough success to cover the costs of its failures. Paul Bailly [44] of Occidental Minerals Corporation has presented a detailed summary with examples of some of these problems.

Success ratios for industries are not generally available, but under the federal government's Strategic Mineral Development Program from 1939 to 1949, about 10,000 prospects were examined [45, p. 8]; of these, 1,342 deposits were investigated in detail, but only 1,053 contained enough tonnage to be of commercial interest. The Defense Minerals Exploration Act authorized a similar program of support for exploration between 1951 and 1958. Requests were received for financial assistance from 3,888 applicants who wanted to explore for strategic and critical minerals. Assistance was granted for 1,159 projects, of which 399 resulted in certification of discovery of valuable minerals. In 1959 only forty-five of these were still in production. Historically, only about 1 percent of the "new field wildcat wells" drilled discovered a field estimated to have ultimate reserves of more than 1 million barrels of oil or 6 billion cubic feet of gas. In 1975, this discovery rate increased to about 1.8 percent. However, all the fields discovered in 1975 are small, and only one field is reported to have ultimate reserves of 25 to 50 million barrels of oil. In the face of rising need, a favorable discovery rate is not enough; the discoveries should preferably be economically significant. Not all discoveries are of economic value to the discoverer. Unless subsequent development is possible, a discovery adds nothing to the supply.

Some statistics on Canadian successes are available. In 1951, one in 100 prospects led to a mine development and by 1969 the ratio had been reduced to one in 1,000 [46, p. 134].

VII
Other Factors Bearing on the Resource System

A few other factors bearing on the resource system should be noticed. Political factors are becoming more evident, and these, too, have their geologic aspects. The world's energy and mineral resources are not evenly scattered around the world. Virtually every nation has some resource problems and varying degrees of resource potential. The United States has done well and has been blessed with good potential in many commodities, but not in all. Domestic reserves of many ferroalloy and several other elements are small or nonexistent. In 1974, there were no domestic reserves of chromium, manganese, niobium, and only small reserves of tin, cobalt, nickel, and bauxite for aluminum [47]. It is beyond the scope of this paper to delve into the details of the availability of all these elements, but the sources of these elements should be carefully considered in policy options if our domestic industry is to stay supplied satisfactorily. Stability in national governments is an integral part in the arrival of minerals in world markets. When deposits of a material are localized, and the commodity is important, supply problems may be critical. For example, nearly 97 percent of the world's identified resources of chromium lie in Rhodesia and the Republic of South Africa. The United States and the rest of the world look to those deposits for their supplies.

Problems with land use and environmental standards are adding as much as an estimated five years to many mineral projects and forcing the abandonment of others. Everyone is in favor of clean air and water, but some tradeoffs probably will have to be made. Rules that curb efforts to find, develop, and use fuels and minerals will have repercussions in the market. If oil and gas become unavailable soon, coal or nuclear sources will have to supply more energy, or we will have to do without it. Well-intended laws preventing open-pit coal mining remove some geologically available coal from use, because very shallow coal beds can be mined only by open-pit methods. Tight standards for sulfur content in coal may require costly long hauls of cleaner burning coal to areas whose coal may fail standards by a small degree. Removal of public land from mineral entry will reduce the potential for development of domestic mineral and energy resources, not only of those already known, but those yet to be discovered [48, pp. 81–93]. The nation might be forced into importing some materials at increasingly higher cost as competition grows for supplies in the world market. These are but the tip of an iceberg of rising social issues that now influence world industrial activity and that will do so increasingly in the future. It is no longer possible to consider geologically available supplies of resources as automatically available, even if the economics are favorable. This is a difficult part of the system to assess. How are the political and social problems to be ameliorated or overcome?

The availability of water is vital to the production and use of mineral and energy materials. This subject is much too complex to discuss in detail here, but the importance of water should be neither ignored nor minimized. Water is not available in sufficient amounts in many parts of the world to support either a mining or a manufacturing industry. Large-scale desalinization of salt water also likely must await the arrival of abundant, cheap energy.

VIII
Keeping the Resource System Functional

Geoscientists will be expected to press the search successfully for new supplies of mineral and fuel materials so that they will be available in time at reasonable prices to fill the needs and desires of a growing population. The task of keeping the resource system functional in the coming decades will be more difficult than ever, especially with rising energy costs and the need to recover more products from conventional deposits of minerals which are progressively becoming harder to find, develop, and use. The burden may be lightened when energy becomes abundant and cheap, but that day cannot be expected to arrive soon.

In the meantime, creative thought from many disciplines will have to be translated into action to meet the economic challenges ahead. Geoscientists can offer much assistance in the solution of resource problems. The earth is bountiful, but all of its treasures are not available to us. There is time to think and take action. Recognition of the following issues and research on them could well assist in successfully meeting the coming challenges.

IX
Issues for Study and Research

1. Geologic reasons discussed in this paper suggest that exponential growth at the anticipated rates in the world use of mineral and fossil fuel materials cannot continue indefinitely, although the national governments of the world appear committed to domestic and international policies that look forward to growth on a business-as-usual basis in the years ahead. Much of the reasoning for these policies of an expanding economy is founded on the premise that the past is the key to the future. The fact that we have done extremely well in attaining the goals of an affluent society by these policies in the past is, however, no guarantee that they will be just as completely successful in the future. Perhaps we should not overlook the possibility that the principles of economics do not tell us all that we need to know about mineral resources. Alternatives to the ever-expanding economy might well be examined before geologic and/or economic exhaustion of some materials forces the issue, at which time it might no longer be possible to avoid unwanted economic, social, and political upheavals. The words of Churchman [11, p. 8] seem appropriate

to this issue, "When you postpone thinking about something too long, then it may not be possible to think about it adequately at all."

2. New sources of abundant, inexpensive energy must be developed to enable the recovery of needed minerals from lower grade ores in conventional types of deposits and from new types of deposits yet to be discovered and found usable, and then to process these materials into useful goods. Without such sources of energy and major advances in technology, there is now little hope of successfully exceeding the limitations of the current economic thresholds in ore deposits by a large factor. There is even less hope of exceeding the mineralogical threshold, and no hope of using ordinary "average" crust of the earth as an ore. It is a snare and a delusion to maintain a blind faith in the near-term, abundant, economic availability of metals at the grade of crustal abundance in the silicate minerals of ordinary rocks.

3. Effort should be expended to use what is available in the best possible ways.

a. The recycling of many materials is well below the levels possible. Recycling has been called uneconomic for many reasons, mostly those left over from days when such activity was not done or little fostered because it was not deemed necessary. Only small volumes were involved in the past. As time has moved on, the volumes available for recycling have grown, but the necessary infrastructure has not yet really been instituted to make recycling economically attractive for most metals.

b. Substitutions are possible in which more abundant materials may be used for those that are scarce. Basic information about the geologic occurrence of the elements and minerals of the earth's crust and their physical and chemical properties must be examined carefully, case by case, and related to technical requirements and costs when considering various substitutions. Consideration of such aspects as geologic occurrence, ease of handling, and differences in energy requirements for recovery and fabrication might make some substitutions vastly more or less desirable than first thoughts would indicate.

c. Conservation is an important method of extending the available supplies of energy and minerals, but it is not a substitute for new supplies. An important aspect of conservation involves influencing the attitudes, tastes, and desires of the public.

d. It is necessary to foster a more ready availability and acceptance of coproducts as a regular source of supply for many minerals, such as fluorspar, barite, cobalt-bearing materials, and many minor metals (see Brooks [49]).

e. In the past, technology has been developed which required that explorationists set up crash programs to seek special minerals and make them more readily available, even if they are quite restricted in their geologic availability. An emphasis in technical development should include use of the most geologically available and least energy-intensive materials whenever possible.

4. Problems in mineral assessment and exploration must be solved more rapidly and efficiently in the coming years than in the past. New and better methods of expressing mineral assessments are needed. Values given for reserves and those given for undiscovered resources do not embody the same limits of confidence. To assume the potential economic availability of astronomical amounts of elements based on levels of crustal abundance can only lead to a complacency that is fraught with peril. How is the unknown quantified? We must learn to live with incomplete data while better use is made of available information from a reservoir that is growing constantly. Although much of the earth's crust remains to be explored at depth, most of the easy-to-find deposits of fossil fuels and minerals already have been identified. Geologic extrapolation suggests that more reserves and resources of useful mineral substances remain to be found. Without new tools to find the hidden deposits, the work of finding them will be costlier and take longer than in the past. The results of the search for some commodities may not lead to increasing the supplies necessary to accommodate exponential increases in use.

5. The need for prudent and reasonable tradeoffs of ecological and land-use factors for a domestic, or even a world, ability to produce what circumstances of the times may require must be better understood. Everyone wants clean air and water, but at what sacrifice? Nobody wants to live next to the stone quarry or the copper mine. Nobody will want to live next to those potential enormous open pits. But everyone wants the benefits of the products of resource operations at lower cost. Some adjustment of public values and sentiments may occur as the cost is recognized. The consumer pays, and we are the consumers!

6. Public understanding is absolutely essential to assure the best rate of success in meeting the challenges of discovering and using wisely mineral and energy resources in the years ahead. An informed public will be able to understand the options available to an industrial society. The public and its policy makers must understand that although the earth is not going to run out of mineral resources on a given day, the physical constraints of geologic and economic availability do place limits upon which of them can be useful to our needs in the foreseeable future. The effort to develop new energy sources and new technology for more efficient use of energy and minerals likely will be long and expensive. That effort should begin now. The next few decades are critical. Unless the problems of the short to middle term are bridged, an industrial society

may not survive to reach that longed-for utopian period of cheap, abundant energy.

The public must have some understanding of the options, and their consequences, related to such issues as:

a. Living with growth rates in consumption that will strain the limits of the world's mineral and energy resources;
b. Permanently withdrawing land from exploration for and development of minerals and energy materials;
c. Excessive dependence on foreign sources of mineral and fuel materials and, perhaps, even capital;
d. Trying to maintain an independence of choice in policy when there is no longer sufficient economic independence to support such an option;
e. Making foreign policies that might not recognize the necessity for access to sources of materials that will be needed in the future.

The facts of mineral and energy resources as they relate to maintaining the style of life in the United States, and improving it in many other parts of the world, must be brought out as soon as possible. The public and its elected representatives formulate public policy. Success in the future will require tremendous cooperation between the public, industry, academia, and all levels of government. Each will have to make its unique contribution in order for us not only to succeed in solving our problems, but to survive. Make no mistake about it, an industrial society lives on energy and mineral resources. We shall have to make intelligent choices, because there are no simple solutions for these problems.

References

1. D. F. Hewett, "Cycles in Metal Production," *Transactions of the American Institute of Mining and Metallurgical Engineers* (1929) pp. 65–98.
2. President's Materials Policy Commission, W. S. Paley, chairman, *Resources for Freedom* (Washington, GPO, 1952, 5 vols.).
3. National Commission on Materials Policy, *Material Needs and the Environment Today and Tomorrow* (Washington, GPO, 1973).
4. M. K. Hubbert, "Degree of Advancement of Petroleum Exploration in the United States," *American Association of Petroleum Geologists Bulletin* vol. 51, no. 11 (1967) pp. 2207–2227.
5. C. F. Park, Jr., *Affluence in Jeopardy* (San Francisco, Freeman Cooper, 1968).
6. C. F. Park, Jr., *Earthbound Minerals, Energy and Man's Future* (San Francisco, Freeman Cooper, 1975).
7. D. H. Meadows, D. L. Meadows, Jørgen Randers, and W. W. Behrens, III, *The Limits to Growth* (New York, Universe Books, 1972).

8. D. B. Brooks and P. W. Andrews, "Mineral Resources, Economic Growth, and World Population," *Science* vol. 185, no. 4145 (1974) pp. 13–19.
9. H. J. Barnett and C. Morse, *Scarcity and Growth: The Economics of Natural Resource Availability* (Baltimore, Johns Hopkins University Press for Resources for the Future, 1963).
10. H. E. Goeller and A. M. Weinberg, "The Age of Substitutability," *Science* vol. 191, no. 4428 (1976) pp. 683–689.
11. C. W. Churchman, *The Systems Approach* (New York, Delta Books, Dell Publishing, 1968).
12. *Mining Magazine*, "International Mining Survey," September issue (London) 1976, pp. 233–245.
13. V. E. McKelvey, "Mineral Resource Estimates and Public Policy," *American Scientist* vol. 60, no. 1 (1972) pp. 32–40.
14. U.S. Geological Survey, *Principles of the Mineral Resource Classification System of the U.S. Bureau of Mines and the U.S. Geological Survey,* Geological Survey Bulletin 1450-A, 1976.
15. J. L. Schanz, *Resource Terminology: An Examination of Concepts and Terms and Recommendations for Improvement,* EPRI Report 336 (Palo Alto, Calif., Electric Power Research Institute, 1975).
16. J. E. Tilton, "The Continuing Debate over the Exhaustion of Nonfuel Mineral Resources," *Natural Resources Forum* vol. 1, no. 3 (1977) pp. 167–173.
17. S. G. Lasky, "National Mineral Resource Appraisal," *Mining Congress Journal* vol. 35, no. 1 (1949) pp. 35–37.
18. T. B. Nolan, "The Search for New Mining Districts," *Economic Geology* vol. 45 (1950) pp. 601–608.
19. S. G. Lasky, "How Tonnage and Grade Relations Help Predict Ore Reserves," *Engineering and Mining Journal* vol. 151, no. 4 (1950) pp. 81–85.
20. D. A. Singer, D. P. Cox, and L. J. Drew, *Grade and Tonnage Relationships Among Copper Deposits,* U.S. Geological Survey Professional Paper 907-A, 1975.
21. M. Allais, "Method of Appraising Economic Prospects of Mining Exploration over Large Territories: Algerian Sahara Case Study," *Management Science* vol. 3, no. 4 (1957) pp. 285–347.
22. D. P. Harris, "An Application of Multivariate Statistical Analysis to Mineral Exploration," (Ph.D. dissertation, The Pennsylvania State University, 1965).
23. D. P. Harris, "Geostatistics in the Appraisal of Metal Resources," in W. A. Vogely, ed., *Mineral Materials Modeling,* Resources for the Future Working Paper EN-5 (Baltimore, Johns Hopkins University Press for Resources for the Future, 1975).
24. W. A. Vogely, ed., *Mineral Materials Modeling,* Working Paper EN-5 (Baltimore, Johns Hopkins University Press for Resources for the Future, 1975).

25. B. M. Miller, H. L. Thomsen, G. L. Dolton, A. B. Coury, T. A. Hendricks, F. E. Lennartz, R. B. Powers, E. G. Sable, and K. L. Varnes, *Geological Estimates of Undiscovered Recoverable Oil and Gas Resources in the United States,* U.S. Geological Survey Circular 725, 1975.
26. J. S. Vhay, D. A. Brobst, and A. V. Heyl, "Cobalt," in D. A. Brobst and W. P. Pratt, eds., *United States Mineral Resources,* U.S. Geological Survey Professional Paper 820, 1973, pp. 143–156.
27. D. A. Brobst, "Barite," in D. A. Brobst and W. P. Pratt, eds., *United States Mineral Resources,* U.S. Geological Survey Professional Paper 820, 1973, pp. 75–84.
28. R. F. Parker, *Composition of the Earth's Crust,* U.S. Geological Survey Professional Paper 440-D, 1967.
29. F. M. Vokes, "The Abundance and Availability of Mineral Resources," in G. J. S. Govett and M. H. Govett, eds., *World Mineral Supplies: Assessment and Perspective* (New York, Elsevier, 1976) pp. 65–98.
30. F. J. Flanagan, ed., *Descriptions and Analyses of Eight New USGS Rock Standards,* U.S. Geological Survey Professional Paper 840, 1976.
31. A. T. Miesch, *Methods of Computation for Estimating Geochemical Abundance,* U.S. Geological Survey Professional Paper 574-B, 1967.
32. A. T. Miesch, *Theory of Error in Geochemical Data,* U.S. Geological Survey Professional Paper 574-A, 1967.
33. Tan Lee and Chi-lung Yao, "Abundance of Chemical Elements in the Earth's Crust and Its Major Tectonic Units," *International Geology Review* vol. 12, no. 7 (1970) pp. 778–786.
34. B. J. Skinner, "A Second Iron Age Ahead?", *American Scientist* vol. 64 (1976) pp. 258–269.
35. V. E. McKelvey, "Relation of Reserves of the Elements to Their Crustal Abundances," *American Journal of Science* vol. 258-A (1960) pp. 234–241.
36. National Academy of Sciences, *Mineral Resources and the Environment,* Report by the Committee on Mineral Resources and the Environment (COMRATE), Commission on Natural Resources, National Research Council, National Academy of Sciences, 1975
37. D. A. Singer, "Long-Term Adequacy of Metal Resources," *Resources Policy* vol. 3, no. 2 (June 1977).
38. H. T. Schacklette, J. C. Hamilton, J. G. Boerngen, and J. M. Bowles, *Elemental Composition of Surficial Materials in the Conterminous United States,* U.S. Geological Survey Professional Paper 574-D, 1971.
39. N. J. Page and S. C. Creasey, "Ore Grade, Metal Production and Energy," *U.S. Geological Survey Journal of Research* vol. 3, no. 1 (1975) pp. 9–13.
40. Chauncey Starr and Richard Rudman, "Parameters of Technologic Growth," *Science* vol. 182, no. 4110 (1974) pp. 358–364.
41. J. P. Albers, W. J. Bawiec, and L. F. Rooney, *Demand for Nonfuel Minerals and Materials by the United States Energy Industry, 1975–90,* U.S. Geological Survey Professional Paper 1006-A, 1976.

42. G. H. Goudarzi, L. F. Rooney, and G. L. Schaffer, *Supply of Nonfuel Energy Minerals and Materials for the United States Energy Industry, 1975–90,* U.S. Geological Survey Professional Paper 1006-B, 1976.
43. U.S. Federal Energy Administration, Project Independence Report— Project Independence Blueprint, Final Task Force Report (Washington, GPO, 1974).
44. P. A. Bailly, "The Problems of Converting Resources to Reserves," *Mining Engineering* vol. 21, no. 1 (1976) pp. 27–37.
45. U.S. Geological Survey, *Mineral Resource Perspectives, 1975,* U.S. Geological Survey Professional Paper 940, 1975.
46. W. E. Roscoe, "Probability of an Exploration Discovery in Canada," *Canadian Mining and Metallurgical Bulletin* vol. 64, no. 707 (1971) pp. 134–137.
47. W. P. Pratt and D. A. Brobst, *Mineral Resources: Potentials and Problems,* U.S. Geological Survey Circular 698, 1974.
48. U.S. Department of Interior, *Mining and Minerals Policy,* Annual Report of the Secretary of the Interior under the Mining and Mineral Policy Act of 1970 (Washington, GPO, 1976).
49. D. B. Brooks, *Supply and Competition in Minor Metals* (Baltimore, Johns Hopkins University Press for Resources for the Future, 1965).

6

The Age of Substitutability: A Scientific Appraisal of Natural Resource Adequacy

H. E. Goeller

As the twentieth century has progressed, life, society, and technology have become ever more complex compared with the relative simplicity of earlier times. Institutional, economic, societal, environmental, and technological problems have increased to the point where one wonders whether the twenty-first century, let alone the more distant future, can be safely attained in any sort of civilized form.

In a recent paper entitled the "Age of Substitutability," A. M. Weinberg and I inquired into some of these problems [1]. Because of our backgrounds we addressed mainly the technological and to a lesser extent some of the economic problems of the future, and alluded only peripherally to societal problems, which we regard as the most difficult of all. Our general conclusion has been that, at least technologically, even the far distant future can be bright, and that the material aspects of life do not have to be drastically different from today's. However, if social disruption is to be avoided, this state, we are sure, can only be achieved through unprecedented foresight and planning. We regard "business as usual" and "muddling through," particularly in the short term, to be increasingly inadequate and even dangerous options. Our outlook places us, technologically at least, among the more avid Cornucopians, provided extremely good planning is done.

The great debate on the future of society came to a head with the publications of the Club of Rome—first, *Limits to Growth* [2] in 1972 and later a more toned down, disaggregated, and detailed analysis, *Mankind at the Turning Point* [3] in 1974—both of which provided very pessimistic outlooks for mankind's future. The strongest reply to the Club of Rome thesis is *The Next 200 Years* by Herman Kahn [4]. Although we do not feel capable of judging all of his results, we do agree wholeheartedly with his arguments on the future of physical resources, energy, and materials.

Many futurists now concede that many economies must break away from their historic exponential growth patterns and that some areas, such as world population and even economic growth itself, will ultimately arrive at zero growth positions. Modern western society tends to forget that growth is the unusual rather than the usual state of most civilizations and that nongrowth does not necessarily imply sterile and static utopias with no change and no progress.

Weinberg and I envisioned our ultimate Age of Substitutability as that time in the future when the material requirements of society would be provided almost exclusively from unlimited nonrenewable resources, renewable resources, and through recycled rarer materials used nondissipatively. We also assumed that by that time the world's population would have leveled off at about 10 billion persons.

There appear to be three stages on the road to the ultimate Age of Substitutability. The first is a short-term period—perhaps thirty to fifty years—of initial transition. This is a period during which the existing investments of industry run through their amortization, but it is also a period of rapid technological change for new plants and facilities based on the best long-term schemes for conserving limited material and energy resources. As is shown later, this is the period during which all petroleum and natural gas is depleted and decisions are made on the development and deployment of transient (coal, oil shale, and nuclear burners) and ultimate energy systems. The second stage—encompassing perhaps a century—would be the final transition period during which coal and economic oil shale would be completely used up, when large in-use pools of elements used nondissipatively (generally metals) would be built up to reduce dependence on high-cost, low-grade virgin materials, and when the search for substitutes, particularly for elements in limited supply and used dissipatively, would reach its zenith—in short, the final transition period into stage 3, the true, nearly closed system for limited materials, the Age of Substitutability.

It is very unlikely that any futurists, including ourselves, can see so far ahead with any degree of precision. Thus much of what is said here is highly speculative at the least. However, in certain ways such long-term speculation, done above the turmoil of short-term commodity markets and the purchasing agents' anguish, may have more validity than at first seems plausible.

Certain basic resource facts are undeniable. For example, at least twenty chemical elements in the air, seas, and/or lithosphere, including several metals (iron, aluminum, magnesium, and possibly titanium), already exist in essentially infinite supply. This list may increase in the future with new technology, that is, nickel may be obtained from peridotites, manganese, and perhaps other metals from sea-floor nodules. Some futurists even envision obtaining everything we need from dirt or country rock, particularly if many products are recovered simultaneously [5]. Such a possibility seems unlikely for the near term, but given centuries for technological development, even this option may ultimately become economically feasible.

Table 6-1 compares the percentages of 1974 demands for such non-renewable materials in terms of quantity and value used in the United States and the world at large. Percentages are used because they change more slowly with time than quantities or prices. It is perhaps surprising that fossil fuels; sand, stone, and related products; iron, aluminum, and magnesium; and eight of the other most widely used elements (seven of which have near infinite resources) constitute more than 99.5 percent of all nonrenewable materials currently used by society. The remaining sixty or so elements (mostly with limited resources) account for only 0.35 percent of the nonrenewable materials used in the United States and 0.38 percent used throughout the world. As shown in table 6-1, however, the monetary value of the sixty rarer elements is considerably higher: 10.7 and 9.1 percent respectively.

Table 6-1 also lists the ultimate resource bases for all of the most used materials which are not based on all types of rock, but only on the more suitable "ores," such as salt or limestone, and seawater or air. Certainly those with resource to demand (R/D) ratios of a million or more may be considered infinite for all intents and purposes.

The outstanding fact to be drawn from table 6-1 is that by far the greatest resource scarcity is the impending scarcity of fossil fuels or CH_x,[1] particularly since the seemingly secure R/D ratio of 2,500 dwindles to a mere 100 years or so when future world growth in fossil fuel demand is taken into consideration. Admittedly there exists an additional 200 times as much reduced carbon in shales as in conventional fossil fuels,[2] but only a tiny part of this exists as economic oil shale; it is not enough to appreciably change the R/D ratio noted. On the other hand, the amount of oxidized carbon, principally in limestone, is enormous (R/D is 4×10^6).

Since about 90 percent of fossil fuels currently consumed is used to provide energy and since about 90 percent of the world's total energy is presently obtained by burning fossil fuels, the scarcity of extractable CH_x is synonymous with the limited long-term availability of the major present

---

[1] Oil that can be obtained from shale now or in the future at costs competitive with petroleum or synthetic oil from coal.

[2] Fossil fuels are a chemical combination of carbon and hydrogen, thus the symbol CH_x where $x = \sim 1$ for coal, ~ 2 for petroleum and 4 for natural gas.

Table 6-1. A Comparison of U.S. and World Demand for Nonrenewable Materials With Their Respective World Resource Bases, 1974

Material	Demand — United States		Demand — World total		World "usable" resources		
	% of total quantity	% of total value	% of total quantity	% of total value	Resource base	Quantity (tonnes)	Resource to demand ratio (years)
Fossil fuels (CH_x)							
Coal and peat	13.05	8.12	17.02	11.37	Coal	10^{13}	2500
Petroleum	21.33	42.06	14.56	40.41	Oil		
Natural gas	11.14	5.99	4.87	2.75	Gas		
Subtotal	45.52	56.17	36.45	54.53	Limestone	2×10^{15}	4×10^6
Sand and gravel (SiO_2)	23.03	1.34	32.28	1.98	Sand, sandstone	1.2×10^{16}	5×10^6
Crushed stone ($CaCO_3$)	24.52	1.93	23.58	1.95	Limestone	5×10^{15}	4×10^6
Clay, gypsum, pumice	1.93	0.44	2.94	0.75			
Subtotal	49.48	3.71	58.80	4.68			
Iron	2.14	18.97	2.63	24.44	Basalt, laterite	1.8×10^{15}	4.5×10^6
Aluminum and magnesium	0.14	3.82	0.08	2.31	Clay/seawater	3.7×10^{15}	$\sim 3 \times 10^8$
Subtotal	2.28	22.79	2.71	26.75			
Other major							
Chlorine	0.26	1.17	0.14	0.66	Rock salt, seawater	2.9×10^{16}	4×10^8
Sodium	0.53	0.68	0.36	0.49	Rock salt, seawater	1.6×10^{16}	3×10^8
Nitrogen	0.51	2.08	0.37	1.91	Air	4.5×10^{15}	1×10^8
Sulfur	0.29	0.29	0.26	0.27	Gypsum, seawater	1.1×10^{15}	3×10^7
Oxygen	0.38	0.23	0.26	0.16	Air	1.1×10^{15}	3.5×10^7
Hydrogen	0.17	1.59	0.10	0.98	Water	1.7×10^{17}	$\sim 10^{10}$
Potassium	0.12	0.26	0.10	0.23	Sylvite, seawater	5.7×10^{14}	4×10^7
(Phosphorus)	0.11	0.36	0.07	0.24	Phosphate rock	1.6×10^{10}	1300
Subtotal	2.37	6.66	1.66	4.94			
All other	0.35	10.67	0.38	9.10	Limited resources		

Source: Calculated from data in U.S. Bureau of Mines, *Commodity Data Summaries, 1976* and *Mineral Trends and Forecasts; October 1976.*

sources of energy. For the interim, coal can be used either in direct combustion or as a source of synthetic oil and gas. Thus we have about a century to develop and totally deploy the ultimate energy-providing substitutes for fossil fuels. Natural steam geothermal and tidal energy systems can provide only miniscule amounts of energy; hydroelectric projects, particularly in developing countries, and nuclear burner reactors generally, are considerably more important, but only solar, fusion, nuclear breeders, and possibly dry hot rock geothermal systems can be capable of providing the world with limitless energy.

The remaining 10 percent of fossil fuels now consumed in the world is used as the basic raw material for producing a wide range of modern petrochemical products from oil and gas and as metallurgical coke derived from coal and used principally in producing iron and steel. In the Age of Substitutability, when practically all economic supplies of fossil fuels have been consumed, it will be necessary to produce essential petrochemicals from CO_2 obtained from calcined limestone, followed by conversion to methane (CH_4), and from there to more complex organic compounds. At that time hydrogen obtained by electrolysis of water will become the main reductant for metal ores. Both of these ultimate "substitutes" will require large amounts of cheap energy from nonfossil fuel sources.

The only other element listed in table 6-1 that has a limited R/D ratio is phosphorus. Phosphorus is extremely important because it is the only one of the three major plant foods or fertilizers (nitrogen, potassium, and phosphorus) that is not in near-infinite supply. However, it is generally conceded that speculative resources of phosphate rock are very large and that a shortage of economic phosphatic fertilizer may occur only in the very, very far term. At this point we may, as H. G. Wells noted, have to return all bones to the soil [6].

In all probability, shortages in the supply of some trace elements (Cu, Zn, Co, etc.) necessary for agriculture will occur before a shortage of phosphorus. This possibility certainly deserves a great deal of study, particularly since agricultural use dissipates a number of metals that could be currently recycled. Of all the activities of society, none looms larger in importance than an agriculture that provides sufficient food for the world's people.

As already stated, one of the chief attributes of the Age of Substitutability will be the absence or near absence of economically extractable fossil fuels. Table 6-2 is a revision of the demand data in table 6-1, with fossil fuels omitted. Thus, if all nonfossil fuel resources are used in the same proportion as now, the same sixty elements with limited resources would account for 0.65 percent of all nonrenewable materials used in the

Table 6-2. U.S. and World Demands for Nonfossil Fuel Nonrenewable
Resources, 1974

| | United States | | World total | |
Material	% of total quantity	% of total value	% of total quantity	% of total value
Sand and gravel (SiO_2)	42.28	3.08	50.86	4.37
Crushed stone ($CaCO_3$)	45.00	4.43	37.15	4.31
Clay, gypsum, pumice	3.54	1.01	4.64	1.65
Subtotal	90.82	8.52	92.65	10.33
Iron	3.93	43.48	4.15	53.97
Aluminum and magnesium	0.26	8.87	0.13	5.09
Subtotal	4.19	52.35	4.28	59.06
Other major				
Chlorine	0.48	2.68	0.22	1.47
Sodium	0.96	1.56	0.57	1.09
Nitrogen	0.93	5.09	0.59	4.22
Sulfur	0.53	0.67	0.40	0.60
Oxygen	0.70	0.52	0.40	0.35
Hydrogen	0.31	3.65	0.16	2.16
Potassium	0.22	0.60	0.16	0.51
(Phosphorus)	0.21	0.82	0.11	0.52
Subtotal	4.34	15.59	2.61	10.92
All other	0.65	23.54	0.46	19.69

Source: Calculated from data in U.S. Bureau of Mines, *Commodity Data Summaries,
1976* and *Mineral Trends and Forecasts, October 1976.*

United States and 0.46 percent in the world. We consider these percentages an upper bound for use of limited materials in the Age of Substitutability since appropriate substitutions, and to a lesser extent recycling, will tend to decrease these percentages.

At first glance, substitution is generally thought of as the use of an alternate material, normally but not always a more more plentiful one, for a more expensive and generally scarcer one. Often, however, it involves the substitution of a better performing material (for example, oil and gas for coal), even if it is scarcer or more expensive, or both. One must always take into account the difference between best performance and adequate performance since the latter is all that is normally necessary. Substitution in a broader sense often involves the functions provided by materials, since in many instances an alternative *way* of doing things may greatly reduce and occasionally eliminate the use of a material altogether. Thus, large-scale use of mass transport in lieu of private automobiles would provide a large savings in materials and the energy needed to make and use them. Similarly, use of radio and microwaves for communications saves large quantities of copper, and to a lesser extent, aluminum. One aspect of substitution that is chiefly societal and highly

Table 6-3. Distribution of U.S. and World Demand for Materials with Limited Resources that Constitute <1 percent of all Nonrenewable Materials Used by Society, 1974

	United States		World total	
	% of total quantity	% of total value	% of total quantity	% of total value
Other ferrous metals	17.59	14.39	24.49	12.86
Other nonferrous metals	33.47	70.25	30.74	73.09
Total other metals	51.06	84.64	55.23	85.95
Other refractory elements	12.25	9.69	12.86	6.98
Other elements	4.20	2.48	2.13	1.25
Other silicates	32.49	3.19	29.78	5.82
Total	100.00	100.00	100.00	100.00
Percent of all nonrenewable materials				
Including fossil fuels[a]	0.35	10.67	0.38	9.10
Excluding fossil fuels[b]	0.65	23.54	0.46	19.69

Source: Calculated from data in U.S. Bureau of Mines, *Commodity Data Summaries, 1976* and *Mineral Trends and Forecasts, October 1976.*
[a] From Table 6-1.
[b] From Table 6-2.

subjective lies in the area of aesthetics. For example, about 90 percent of titanium goes for titania pigment, but as far as metals protection goes, red iron oxide is every bit as good as brilliant titania white.

Since the discovery of phosphorus in 1669 about sixty "new" chemical elements have been discovered, most of them with relatively limited resources [7]. Following the discovery of each new element—an act of basic science—applied scientists and businessmen have rapidly sought ways to produce the element cheaply and evolve practical uses for it. In some cases the new uses were, at least temporarily, uniquely essential to an evolving materialistic society; in other cases, however, they were not, although the new materials may have been marginally better and cheaper than older substances. In a few cases, such as arsenic and thallium, new uses have been hard to find. As long as resources are large compared with demand, any use, no matter how frivolous, can be tolerated; but as demand presses supplies ever harder, the contest between frivolity and need must yield to uses that conserve supply. In most cases, but not all, price in the marketplace is a trustworthy arbiter.

Of the sixty or so elements derived from nonrenewable resources in limited supply (the "all other" category of tables 6-1 and 6-2), the structural metals, so important to modern technology, are dominant in both quantity and monetary value. As shown in table 6-3, these metals account for about half the total quantity of limited materials used by society and

Table 6-4. U.S. and World Demand for Virgin Metals, 1974

	United States		World total	
	% of total quantity	% of total value	% of total quantity	% of total value
Ferrous metals				
Iron	87.06	60.39	91.79	71.14
Manganese	1.43	0.44	1.66	0.57
Chromium	0.54	0.25	0.44	0.23
(Silicon)	0.66	1.43	0.32	0.78
Nickel	0.21	2.29	0.13	1.54
Other	0.07	1.37	0.04	0.84
Subtotal	89.97	66.17	94.38	75.10
Nonferrous metals				
Aluminum	5.62	11.89	2.76	6.50
Magnesium	0.12	0.42	0.05	0.20
Titanium	0.02	0.28	0.01	0.15
Copper	1.87	8.93	1.17	7.53
Zinc	1.40	3.11	1.04	4.01
Lead	0.89	1.24	0.55	1.02
Tin	0.05	1.20	0.04	1.07
Other	0.05	6.76	0.03	4.42
Subtotal	10.03	33.83	5.62	24.90
Fe, Si, Al, Mg & Ti	93.48	74.20	94.93	78.77

Source: Calculated from data in U.S. Bureau of Mines, *Commodity Data Summaries, 1976* and *Mineral Trends and Forecasts, October 1976.*

about 85 percent of their monetary value. Further, the amount of energy needed to obtain and reduce metal ores is much greater than that needed to process most of the remaining materials with limited resources. Iron, aluminum, and magnesium are omitted from the above analysis because they all occur in near-infinite supply.

Table 6-4 gives further data on the structural metals for both the United States and the world. Silicon, a nonmetal, is also included because of its extensive use in steelmaking. Iron accounts for about 90 percent of the quantity and about two-thirds of the value of all metals and is one of the main metals used by society. It is reassuring that the metals derived from near-infinite resources—iron, silicon, aluminum, magnesium, and probably titanium—account for nearly 95 percent of the quantity and three-quarters of the value of all metals consumed.

As will be shown later, even when society is forced to use low-grade resources of these plentiful metals, energy and other costs will not increase by a factor of more than about two because near-infinite resources are not too different in either quality or concentration from presently used ores.

As Frasché [8] and others have pointed out, society never physically runs out of any nonrenewable resource; however, all of the elements are so mixed in rocks and seawater that as we go to ever leaner ores, the costs per unit of product in dollars, energy, and environmental degradation continually increase, with occasional respites when new technology, better suited for the leaner ores, is developed and adopted. Further, considerable attention is now being given to determining whether there are grade cutoffs from very low grade ore to near natural abundance [9]. In any event, the limited materials become more and more expensive and are gradually replaced by cheaper substitutes wherever possible. In a few cases, however, as with phosphatic fertilizers and trace metals for agriculture, there is no possible substitute and even extreme measures toward finding substitutes must certainly fail. Thus, we never run out; instead, certain materials become too expensive, compared with substitutes, for any except the most exotic uses, and for those few cases where there are no substitutes for an absolutely essential use, society just has to pay the price.

In a relatively recent study involving thirty-two-year predictions of future demands for all nonrenewable resources—admittedly made before the general alarm was sounded for conservation of energy and scarcer materials—only two materials were given negative growth rates over the prediction period [10]. This prediction, as most, was certainly "business as usual" for another third of a century—stage 1 of the Age of Substitutability. It is unfortunate that such predictions may become self-fulfilling prophecies when a diminishing use of scarce substances, particularly those with nonsubstitutable uses, appears a more appropriate forecast for long-range planning.

In assessing future demands for materials derived from limited resources, one must be careful not to simplify issues. First, one must set down the various uses of an element or material in decreasing order of quantity. Then he must determine for each use its ultimate importance to society: is it a frivolous or purely aesthetic use or is it an important basic one? Then it is necessary to determine whether it is a dissipative use or one which permits recycling so that the same material can be used again. Finally, he must determine whether adequate substitutes exist or appear likely to be developed.

Thus, basically adequate stainless steel flatware can be substituted for more aesthetic sterling silver, thereby making silver available for its more essential use in photography. On the other hand, although silver used in works of art is recyclable, it tends to be hoarded as heirlooms, thereby denying its more dissipative use in photography.

Similarly, mercury, a relatively scarce metal, has many uses. Over the long term, probably 95 percent of present uses can be satisfactorily replaced by alternative substances or functions. For example, a third of U.S. mercury consumption is in caustic-chlorine production cells; this use could be totally eliminated by returning to the adequate but somewhat less satisfactory diaphragm cells. A quarter of the mercury is used in special batteries; there are many other types. And so on. Such arguments do not imply that industry could immediately get along with only 5 percent of the present mercury supply; but, conversely, delaying presently feasible substitutions, even if they are slightly more costly, is inappropriate in the long-term interest of society.

To be thorough, one must then examine all the uses or at least the major uses of the other sixty or so scarce elements to determine for each the present possibilities and future likelihoods of more plentiful substitutes or unique new functional alternatives. A NATO research group has recently made such a study for eleven scarce metals [11].

In the thirty-two-year U.S. and world demand projections mentioned earlier, the average price increase for the sixty limited elements was about 50 percent by the year 2000. Thus, in table 6-2, the 23.5 percent monetary value contribution of these elements in the United States would increase by the year 2000 to about 31 percent, assuming that the percentages of limited materials and the price of plentiful materials remain fixed. If the limited elements continue to be used as extensively as now into the long term, their eventual contribution to the total value of all nonrenewable materials could easily become dominant.

The game for the future, then, is to discourage unnecessary uses of scarce elements by appropriate and early substitution in order to minimize increases in absolute monetary value. In many cases this will be done by normal pricing mechanisms.

Naturally this game can never be played perfectly; however, thorough and continuing study of these problems should be carried on to minimize unpleasant surprises. It is unpleasant to find too late that the price of some irreplaceable material affecting a key industry has skyrocketed to the point that an entire economy is seriously affected. The net effect of a well-planned regimen of substitution is that even though the cost of widely used plentiful materials will rise slightly because we must go to somewhat lower grade ores to obtain them, the continually decreasing requirements for high-priced limited materials will result in an overall cost increase for the aggregate nonrenewable resource base of a factor of only two or three.

But what about energy requirements in the Age of Substitutability for mining and converting ores into materials useful to society? Again, we resort to a comparison based on metals, rather than on all materials, because the production of metals is more energy intensive than most

Table 6-5. Energy Requirements for the Production of Abundant Metals and Copper

Metal	Source	Gross energy[a] (kWh/ton of metal)	E_L/E_H[b]
Magnesium ingot	Seawater	100,000	1
Aluminum ingot	Bauxite	56,000	1
	Clay	72,600	1.28
Raw steel	Magnetic taconites	10,100	1
	Iron laterites	11,900	1.17 (with carbon)
			~2 (with electrolytic hydrogen)
Titanium ingot	Rutile	138,900	1
	Ilmenite	164,700	1.18
	Titanium rich soils	227,000	1.63
Refined copper	Porphyry ore, 1 percent Cu	14,000	1
	Porphyry ore, 0.3 percent Cu	27,300	1.95

Source: J. C. Brevard, H. B. Flora II, and C. Portal, *Energy Expenditures Associated with the Production and Recycle of Metals* (Oak Ridge, Tenn., Oak Ridge National Laboratory, 1972) ORNL-NSF-CP-24.
[a] At 40 percent thermal efficiency for generation of electricity.
[b] Energy required for low grade ore/energy required for high grade ore.

other materials. Now and in the future iron is destined to be the preeminently used metal. Use of aluminum has grown rapidly all through this century and the metal is now in second place. Use of magnesium found in near-infinite supply in brines and seawater and titanium use since midcentury have been disappointing to producers, but both appear to have high potential for growth as the limited metals become scarcer and more expensive.

We believe the problem is well portrayed in table 6-5 taken from a study by Brevard, Flora, and Portal [12]. This table indicates how much of an energy increase can be expected in the future as society is forced to turn to lower grade ores. No change is envisioned for magnesium since its ore—seawater—is essentially infinite and homogeneous. For the near-infinite terrestrial ores of iron and aluminum, a 28 percent increase is projected for aluminum from clay rather than bauxite and a 17 percent increase for iron from laterites rather than magnetic taconites. But for copper, a relatively limited element, a 95 percent increase in energy use is anticipated, probably by the year 2000 for U.S. ores.

A second important point is that the energy increase given for iron is for a continuing use of coal coke as the ore reductant. When all economic fossil fuels are exhausted in the Age of Substitutability, hydrogen rather than coke must be used as the metal ore reductant (incidentally, a technology already exists), a process that will probably double the present energy demand [13]. In any event, because of the dominance of iron and aluminum metals, it is hard to see how the energy requirements for producing all metals can increase by much more than a factor of two, particularly since in the long run it is expected that scarcer metals (Cu, Zn, Pb, Sn, etc.) will be replaced to a large extent by more plentiful substances.

One dichotomy exists between aluminum and copper at the present time which is a good illustration of short-term advantages made at the expense of long-term good. Production of aluminum is considerably more energy intensive than production of copper; yet aluminum resources are vastly greater than those of copper. Because of the high rise in energy costs over the past few years, however, the tendency is now to produce copper more extensively than aluminum.

In the recent NATO report on the problems of future supply for the eleven scarce metals noted earlier, a major conclusion was to seek methods to reduce the dissipative uses of these metals so that more would be available for recycling, thereby extending the resource base further into the future.

The recycling of materials derived from near-infinite resources, such as iron and aluminum, is not required in order to conserve resources, as it is for copper, zinc, and lead, but to conserve energy and minimize disposal problems.

Although environmental problems are beyond the scope of this paper, a few comments on mine spoils and land disruption seem in order. Probably the major problems of land defacement still lie ahead of us, but not in the ultimate Age of Substitutability. It is highly likely that the most serious period of land defacement will occur in the late stage 1 and early stage 2 periods when the surface mining of coal reaches its greatest extent, particularly when the ratio of overburden to coal that can be economically mined may be on the order of 50 to 1, and when much more coal is needed to replace diminishing or exhausted supplies of oil and natural gas. The quantities of material so disrupted seem certain to be as great or greater than the mining of all other materials later on, even with greatly increased demand for nonfuel substances, and particularly as we place greater dependence on the use of near-infinite resources as substitutes for limited elements.

Disposal of mine spoils is only one of many environmental problems that must be faced and solved in the future. Appropriate and adequate solutions to these problems will certainly require great ingenuity from physical and biological scientists and engineers for a long time to come.

In the Age of Substitutability, with a population of possibly 10 billion persons (2.5 times the present world population) and with very good planning, it is quite likely that the world's people can be provided with the requisite quantities of nonrenewable resources for a comfortable life, and that an increase in average world social equity to about half that presently being experienced in the United States seems achievable. The amounts of energy and materials needed to reach such a goal will be much greater than those now consumed, but given several centuries to make the transition, this goal does not appear impossible. It will require an additional 2 kilowatts of installed energy-generating capacity per person in the United States and about 3 kilowatts per person elsewhere to provide everyone in the world with about half the nonrenewable materials per capita now being consumed in the United States alone plus the desalination of sea water for the increased agricultural requirements. An additional amount of energy for both the United States and the rest of the world would also be needed for other purposes. Thus, energy demand in the United States would increase from the present 11 kilowatts to 15 kilowatts of capacity per person, and in the world from 1.5 to 7.5 kilowatts per person. For 10 billion persons, this would require an installed energy capacity of 75×10^9 kilowatts, about 12 times the present capacity. This large increase would require an enormous endeavor but would not, in our opinion, be impossible, given a century or more in which to accomplish it.[3] In addition, it appears to be environmentally feasible since this much energy is still only 0.1 percent of the total solar energy absorbed and reradiated by the earth. The physical crux of the problem will certainly be based on our ability to develop and deploy one or more economic and essentially infinite nonfossil fuel energy systems before all economic supplies of fossil fuels are consumed. Since there are at least four contenders—solar, fusion, nuclear breeders, and possibly dry hot rock geothermal—the probability that at least one of these can be developed successfully seems extremely good; however, it is important that all possibilities be pursued for a considerable time in order to determine which can produce future energy needs most safely and cheaply.

One of the chief concerns in analyzing the future supply of nonrenewable resources is a politico-economic one; whether or not the free market system as it now operates, with its high discount rates, is always an adequate institution for formulating and implementing the most rational long-term resource policies. With high discount rates, decisions are almost always made in the interest of short-term advantages; the copper/aluminum argument previously given is such an example. Thus, unless lower rates soon prevail or tax and other incentives are established, the road to the Age of Substitutability may be filled with short-term road-

---

[3] A twelvefold increase in 150 years represents an average annual growth rate of only 1.7 percent.

blocks, making the journey far more arduous. Whether industry will be able to discipline itself in taking a longer term view of resource management in the interest of future generations is a moot question. If it cannot, then it seems necessary for governments to intervene; however, governments also suffer from a short-term outlook and are generally slow to take action. Only the most superb leadership, foresight, and planning seem capable of adequately and rapidly facing and solving such issues head on.

In this paper "rational" long-range materials policy implies, insofar as it is currently possible, development of plans for management of resources and their uses in a manner in which future generations are not penalized by today's economic and political actions. Until recently, it was a tenet held by most economists that future generations would always be better off and that therefore they could adequately take care of their economic needs despite present policies; this tenet now seems less certain with dwindling energy and limited materials resources.

Another example illustrates some of the problems involved. Helium is a rare commodity obtained exclusively from certain natural gas deposits; failure to recover it before the gas is burned releases it to the atmosphere where it is diluted from 10 to 1000-fold, depending on its content in a given natural gas. It has been an important material in the U.S. space program and may have large and important uses in certain future nuclear reactors and in the cryogenic (very low temperature) transmission of electricity under superconducting conditions, with great savings of transmission materials.

Until recently the U.S. government operated a helium stockpile program and amassed about a twenty-year supply at mid-1960 demand levels (around 5,000 tons/year). This program has now ceased and industry now separates only enough helium to meet current demands at prices which are well below the government price of $30/1000 ft^3. U.S. natural gas from conventional sources will be exhausted in twenty to thirty years and world supplies probably a decade later, at which time all the contained helium will have been vented to the atmosphere. If large needs then develop, it will be necessary to recover it from air at a few parts per million. At such low concentrations enormous facilities and expenditures of 50 to 100 times the current amount would be necessary to recover helium from air. The general argument against recovery now is that with high discount rates, the cost of today's smaller facilities is *more* than the cost of much larger facilities later discounted to today's value of money. Although such an argument may be sound under the rules of classical economics and a free market system, it does not sufficiently address the fact that recovery of helium from air would require expenditures of vastly larger amounts of energy and construction materials later on than would present recovery from natural gas. Further, the amounts of co-separated oxygen, nitrogen, and argon made available would be far in excess of demand so that the cost would have to be borne almost exclusively by the helium product. Although this example is an extreme one, it points out some of the problems which may ultimately be faced in maintaining a supply of those limited elements that are unrecyclable and have no known substitutes for essential uses.

As mentioned earlier, it may be important in some cases to depend on government intervention in normal free market operations to safeguard future supplies of certain key materials. It was also stated that government action is often slow to be instituted and is generally oriented toward short-term results. However, whereas industry is driven by short-term profit motives, whether or not it is in the best long-term interests of society, government has at least some responsibility for the well-being of posterity. Thus, although free market mechanisms are adequate, except in environmental matters, to control production of materials derived from near-infinite resources, they are increasingly less so in the control of rarer materials with present or future essential uses such as trace elements for agriculture and perhaps ultimately for the essential plant food phosphorus. The U.S. government has shown considerable wisdom in this decade in addressing environmental woes, but has not yet developed a fully coherent or adequate energy policy. It is important to continue to study materials policies and to reach conclusions before acute shortages in necessary materials can develop. Individually, such crises are certain to be less severe than the energy crisis, but collectively they could be even more severe. Only governments have the right to enact controls, regulations and tax incentives, and penalties to achieve public good.

As has been stated several times, it seems unlikely that the final Age of Substitutability will be achieved without extremely good planning which must include both technological research and development and studies in economics, environmental problems, and social and political issues. Technical efforts should include development of processes for the longer term which have high yields and are environmentally satisfactory, and development of products which have longer lives, are energy efficient, and are readily recyclable. These efforts go beyond the near-term research of industry and should not, therefore, compete unduly with their short-term goals. Economic studies should investigate in greater depth the adequacy of the free market and high discount rates in achieving long-term good as, for example, in the helium example given above. Economic/energy studies should be combined to see whether saving money or saving energy in the future is more important, particularly over the next twenty-five to thirty years until energy systems based on near-infinite resources are operable. Many social studies should also be made; for example, determination of the best methods to educate the public on energy and resource issues and investigations on how advertising might be modified to achive this end seem very pertinent now.

In summary, our conclusions on the future availability and management of nonrenewable resources are as follows:

1. By far, the greatest resource problem is the increasing shortage and ultimate depletion of fossil fuels or CH_x which is used both as the current primary basis for production of energy, and as the sole raw material for petrochemicals and metal reductants. Thus, an enormous effort is required to rapidly develop and deploy one or more "infinite" nonfossil fuel energy systems. Ultimately CO_2 must become the source for petrochemicals and hydrogen from water electrolysis the chief reductant for metals ores. Both are highly energy intensive. A corollary is that unless nuclear breeders are developed, the nuclear burner age will be shorter than the petroleum and natural gas age.

2. Use of twenty or so elements with near-infinite resources as substitutes for those with limited resources must be vigorously promoted. The greatest need here is the early substitution of iron, aluminum, magnesium, concrete, glass, and possibly titanium for nonferrous metals and some steel alloying agents. If this is appropriately accomplished, the unit monetary and energy "bill" for all nonrenewable resources (except fossil fuels) should not increase by more than a factor of two or three over the next several centuries.

3. Probably the single most important long-term problem is perpetual assurance that supplies of the elements necessary for modern agriculture are always available. We would envision shortages of certain trace elements as a first "crisis" in this area and possibly a shortage of phosphorus in the very long term, but could recycle bones in the latter case.

4. The production of metals is highly energy-intensive compared with other nonrenewable resources. However, because iron and aluminum now constitute 94 percent of the metals used world-wide, greater substitution of these metals plus magnesium and titanium should assure that our unit "energy bill" for all metals will be less than twice the present need.

5. Recycling, applicable only to elements used nondissipatively, is an admirable goal, but should not be overemphasized as a materials conservation measure because unless it is very efficient (say greater than 90 percent recovery) it is relatively ineffective over many recycles. However, for metals it is a large energy-saving expedient.

6. With regard to land spoilage, especially by strip mining, the most environmentally damaging era will probably be the next fifty years, the period when near-surface coal is depleted.

All of the above solutions are principally technological. Little progress seems likely to be made in any of them, however, if we continue to pursue standard production practices, including many of our present economic concepts which stress so strongly short-term advantages. Physical scientists and engineers can provide the requisite new technologies, environmentalists and sociologists will provide more than enough conscience, but the final decision in our modern civilization must be made by the economists and politicians. Let us hope that in order to achieve a smooth road to a not-physically impossible Age of Substitutability they can rise to new heights of success in planning and action.

References

1. H. E. Goeller and A. M. Weinberg, "The Age of Substitutability," *Science,* vol. 191 (February 20, 1976) pp. 683–689.
2. D. H. Meadows, D. L. Meadows, Jørgen Randers, and W. W. Behrens III, *The Limits to Growth* (Universe Books, New York, 1972).
3. M. Mesarovic and E. Pestel, *Mankind at the Turning Point* (New York, Dutton, 1974).
4. Herman Kahn, W. Brown, and L. Martel, *The Next 200 Years* (New York, William Morrow, 1976).
5. Harrison Brown, *The Next Ninety Years* (Pasadena, California Institute of Technology, 1967) p. 17.
6. H. G. Wells, J. S. Huxley, and G. P. Wells, *The Science of Life* vol. 3 (Garden City, N.Y., Doubleday, 1931) pp. 1031, 1032.
7. N. A. Lange, *Handbook of Chemistry* (3rd ed., Sandusky, Ohio, Handbook Publishers, 1939) p. 34.
8. D . F. Frasché, (Washington, D.C., National Academy of Sciences-National Research Council, 1963) Pub. 1000-C, p. 18.
9. B. J. Skinner, "A Second Iron Age Ahead," *American Scientist,* vol. 64 (May/June 1976) pp. 258–269.
10. U. S. Bureau of Mines, *Mineral Facts and Problems, 1970,* Bulletin 650 (Washington, GPO, 1970).
11. NATO Scientific Affairs Division, *Rational Use of Potentially Scarce Metals,* (Brussels, Belgium, May 1976).
12. J. C. Brevard, H. B. Flora II, and C. Portal, *Energy Expenditures Associated with the Production and Recycle of Metals* (Oak Ridge, Tenn., Oak Ridge National Laboratory, 1972) ORNL-NSF-EP-24.
13. R. A. Labine, "New: Making Iron in a Fluidized Bed," *Chemical Engineering* vol. 67 (February 8, 1960) pp. 96–99.

7

Comments on the Papers by Brobst and Goeller

Bruce M. Hannon

Each author is so expert in his field and these fields are so foreign to me that I can only comment on what I perceive to be their omissions.

Basically, Brobst writes of resource availability. He believes that the cost of accelerating the discovery rates of larger and larger supplies of critical resources, particularly those for new electric energy supplies, is very high.[1] He is consequently rather pessimistic about our abilities to meet the resource demands of growth. Goeller is more optimistic. He argues that substitutability of resources can allow continued aggregate economic growth.

Both authors work entirely in physical units and avoid reference to changing dollar resource prices as resources become scarce. Neither author emphasizes the difference between energy and nonenergy resources. While short-run substitution of one of these for the other is possible, in the long run there is no substitute for energy resources. This fact, I believe, provides a reason for the unique position of energy resources in economic production functions, as distinct from other resources.

The inclusion of the rapidly rising direct (Brobst's paper) and indirect resource inputs into resource price trends (see Barnett's paper) should surprise resource economists who believe these trends change gently. Neither speaker discussed the effects that continued or accelerated resource use would have on land use.

Both authors only touched on recycling as a means of extending a resource life. They were pessimistic about the ability of recycling to significantly extend resource availability, however. The importance of recycling increases only as economic growth rates slow.

In deciding on the amount of effort which should be devoted to

---

[1] Note that the average heat rate for average U.S. electric power plants has declined over the past several years. This is a signal that the energy inputs to electrical power plants are becoming less effective in meeting demand patterns for electricity. This is a physical measure of declining resource utility.

160

recycling, or to resource substitution, it seems to me that the objective should be to minimize the physical resource costs among the alternative ways of obtaining a desired good or service. Of particular interest to the resource engineer would be the relative direct and indirect energy costs of competing alternatives. An economist would wish to minimize the dollar cost. The effectiveness of recycling depends on a complex array of factors little understood by today's policy makers. Basically, we should act to minimize the entropy or disorder created in performing economic services. This prescription implies using materials for as long as possible and then dismantling, sorting, and returning them to their original point of manufacture. Inevitably, foreign materials degrade recycled materials or they suffer structural breakdown and are diverted into downgraded secondary markets. These markets tend to become saturated as a result of the independence of the demands for the original and the secondary products. This concept of saturation points defines the physical limit of the utility of recycling. Market defects which are detrimental to recycling, such as inaccurate freight rates for virgin and recycled materials, inadvertent tax subsidies favoring virgin material use, and the vertical integration of virgin sources with final production, also ought to be remedied.

A major need of special importance to geologists is the present and predicted costs (direct and indirect, in physical units) of use of a particular resource, including the effects of recycling. Input–output models are probably an effective tool for this determination. The next step would be to establish the ranked and quantified importance of physical resources by analyzing economic final demand scenarios.

Alternatively, one could rank the types of resources on the basis of the demands of a subsistence economy, yielding the absolute minimum nature of the demand. With such a ranking, one can compare the demands with the known remaining amount of these resources. Goeller has done this for a single period, but, of course, without knowledge of the relative demand for these resources in a dynamic economy and without detailed knowledge of the ability to substitute among these resources. To gain this latter knowledge, we would need large and expensive modeling efforts, at the very least.

One of the principal economic concerns is the effect of resource shortages on labor productivity. Increases in capital and labor inputs have historically explained only 10 to 20 percent of the change in rising labor productivity [1]. Changes in resource inputs, particularly energy, may have accounted for the bulk of the change, with "technological change" playing a much smaller role than usually believed. If resources, particularly energy, are now becoming scarce, at least in the United States, then other factors of production, capital and labor, will be substituted for the resources. In the past, technological change may well have been the strategy by which the resources were substituted for capital and labor, making the latter more productive. But we must remember that a unit of technology itself can have significant, perhaps even increasing demands for resources, labor, and capital. If technology is not able to counteract declining capital and labor productivity (and capital and labor depreciation) in the face of declining resources, the returns to capital or/and labor would decline. This is the basic flaw in the paper by Stiglitz. Further, it is not at all clear that technology can reverse its major direction, the substitution of resources for labor and capital, and overcome its own costs plus the increasing inputs of capital, in order to guarantee future income levels. The present direction of technology produces a return on investment in the technology itself. Can the same be true in a resource-short economy?

If technology does not achieve the above goal, then income of capital holders and labor will decline, although employment may increase. Besides the distinct possibility for inequitable income distribution, this decline would produce a reduction in long-run aggregate demand. This decrease in final demand would mean a decline in the aggregate resource demand. It also means, perhaps more importantly, that the composition of the reduced demand would change. Consequently, the composition of the resource demand would also change, possibly even exacerbating the supply shortage of certain critical resources. Taxes on those resources, especially on energy, could be used to reduce the demand for critically short resources on an individual basis. In addition, direct demand controls, some of which are already being seriously considered (e.g., container deposits, peak load pricing of electricity) could specifically redirect demand away from critical resources.

In general, too much of this conference was dedicated to conditions of resource supply, addressing the question: Can we have economic growth? A full examination of the issues surrounding economic growth requires that consideration be given to the possible mechanisms, natural and policy induced, for influencing society's pattern of final demands. Once such an investigation is recognized as an integral component of any evaluation of economic growth, then growth strategies can be appraised, based on the answers they imply for the questions: What are the real economic and social benefits and costs of growth in material use rates? Is such growth necessary or indeed desirable?

References

1. Kuznets, Simon, *Modern Economic Growth Rate, Structure and Spread,* (New Haven, Conn., Yale University Press, 1966).

8

Scarcity and Growth Revisited

Harold J. Barnett

I
Background for the Scarcity and Growth Analysis

A. Introduction. *Scarcity and Growth: The Economics of Natural Availability* (hereafter *S and G*) was one of several publications by members of Resources for the Future (RFF) that were prepared during RFF's first five-year term (approximately 1955–60) in response to the implicit mandates of the President's Commission on Materials Policy. While several articles by Barnett and Morse preceded its publication in 1963, this volume summarizes their overall evaluation of natural resource adequacy.

In this paper, "Scarcity and Growth Revisited," I seek to review and supplement that analysis with the benefit of fifteen to twenty years' hindsight. While this paper is a modest effort, and incomplete, I do hope to offer some perspective on the earlier analysis and to present some evidence on the intervening period.

This section reviews the findings of *Scarcity and Growth*. In section II we discuss the evidence on the adequacy of natural resources for the United States that has become available since 1957. Section III considers the movements in various measures of real unit costs and relative prices of resources for a selected sample of countries throughout the world.

I am grateful to several organizations: Washington University, for sabbatical leave; the International Institute for Applied Systems Analysis, Laxenburg, Austria, where a substantial portion of the paper was prepared in very congenial conditions; and Resources for the Future, for arranging this conference and requesting the paper.

In addition, I have personal obligations for help and friendly cooperation to Professor Chandler Morse, coauthor of *Scarcity and Growth;* Professor V. Kerry Smith, who arranged the Conference and very generously edited and improved my paper; Dr. Morris Norman, who most kindly computer programmed my untidy data on European and world productivity, which appears in section III; and Messrs. Loeser, Popper, and their IIASA library colleagues, for helping me to find these basic European and world data.

After summarizing the nature of these results, I reconsider the environmental effects of meeting the need for natural resources.

B. Brief Summary. I begin with a summary concerning one central element from the original *S and G* volume—the doctrine of increasing economic scarcity of natural resources. There are many and diverse views on the social aspects of natural resources. Among these, a major interest resides in the concept of a natural resource scarcity and its economic effects. The belief seems to be that natural resources are economically scarce; that economic scarcity increases with passage of time; and that this impairs levels of living and economic growth. These views have been widely held for a long time in western societies. Professor Morse and I found them present in the conservation movement and among the classical economists and others. Moreover, the concerns arising from these beliefs are also present among many economists, policy makers, and a segment of the general populace today.

The analysis in *Scarcity and Growth* suggested that the classical theory of increasing economic scarcity of natural resources was invalid except in highly constrained, unrealistic models. For real economies, theory cannot answer whether or not there is increasing economic scarcity of natural resources. The question must be answered factually, on the evidence.

For the United States in the period from the Civil War to 1957, the evidence denies the doctrine of increasing economic scarcity in agriculture, minerals, and the aggregate of extractive industries. The principal reasons for this were: (1) substitutions of economically more plentiful resources for less plentiful ones; (2) increased discoveries and availability of domestic mineral resources; (3) increased imports of selected metallic minerals; and (4) a marked increase in the acquisition of knowledge and sociotechnical improvements relevant to the economics of resource discovery, development, conversion, transportation, and production. These factors have made it possible for the economy to produce larger and larger volumes of extractive goods at declining real marginal costs.

While these observations were among the major findings of *Scarcity and Growth,* we also discussed problems associated with use of natural resources and the attendant implications for intergenerational equity. We found that, in U.S. history, each generation has passed to the next improved conditions of natural resource availability and economic productivity. Moreover, the phenomena of accumulated knowledge, scientific advances, and self-generating technological change have more than overcome tendencies of increasing costs for utilization and exhaustion of specific resources. It is not by chance that advances in knowledge, market processes, and government policies provide solutions to actual and prospective natural resource cost problems. The motivations, mechanisms, and choice of solutions appear to be endogenous in modern efficiency-seeking economies.

Finally, *Scarcity and Growth* discussed the implications of these patterns of technical change and growth for a broad class of social and environmental factors which we grouped under the heading "quality of life" effects. We noted that while society had been very successful in avoiding increased economic scarcity of natural resources in terms of cost of extractive goods, other problems relating to natural resources were appearing.

We identify several such cases of impact which have emerged during the past generation: urban agglomeration; waste disposal and pollution; changes in income distribution, particularly in relation to distressed areas; water supply; land use; international relations with underdeveloped nations. [1, pp. 253–254]

Moreover, sometime earlier I concluded:

I am greatly impressed by a "new" form of resource scarcity—the problem of space, privacy, and nature preservation. . . . This category of doctrine already includes a quality scarcity concern over fouling streams, disfiguring land, and air pollution. And I guess it should also include concern over atmospheric and land contamination by radioactivity. [2]

In *S and G* we chose to identify and describe these problems but did not integrate them into our analysis.

C. Statistical Measures and Tests. *Scarcity and Growth* defined increasing resource scarcity as increasing real cost of extractive products. The hypothesis of increasing resource scarcity (hereafter simply resource scarcity) can be tested by examining time series of the real cost of these products. The resource scarcity hypothesis was defined in a strong and in a weak form.

The Strong Hypothesis of Increasing Economic Scarcity. The strong hypothesis states that the real cost of extractive products per unit will increase through time due to limitations in the available quantities and qualities of natural resources. For the strong hypothesis, we measure real cost in terms of labor (man-days, man-hours, or man-years) or labor plus capital (depreciated investments adjusted for price level) per unit of extractive output. This formulation offered the traditional form of the hypothesis. In it, increasing scarcity is visible in an increasing

Table 8-1. Summary of Movements in Real Unit Costs
(1929 = 100)

Years	Total extractive	Agriculture	Minerals	Forestry
1870–1900	134	132	210	59
1919	122	114	164	106
1957	60	61	47	90

trend of L_E/O_E or $L_E + C_E/O_E$.[1] In the classical economies described by Smith, Malthus, and Ricardo, it was not necessary to attach the "E" subscripts. The extractive sectors—agriculture, forestry, fishing, mining—and the total economy were nearly equivalent in quantitative terms, with the extractive sector bulking very large in the full economy.

The strong or traditional form of the hypothesis has been rediscovered by a number of contemporary movements. These include ecological, environmental, no-growth, ZEG, ZPG, Crisis of Mankind, and steady-state movements led variously by the Club of Rome, Forrester–Meadows, Hardin, Ehrlich, Daly, and others. These popular no-growth movements of the day must subscribe to the strong hypothesis—to increasing real cost defined as above—because only such increasing cost trends, in association with growing population, could significantly restrain and ultimately stop economic growth in modern economies.

The U.S. output in extractive sectors increased markedly from the Civil War to 1957. The increase in agriculture, following Engel's law, was slower than the increase in real gross national product (GNP). Minerals output, on the other hand, increased roughly as fast as real GNP. The stage was clearly set in extractive products for operation of the classical economic doctrine of increasing cost or diminishing returns. The extensive frontier of the nation is believed to have disappeared by the end of the nineteenth century. Given a substantial expansion in population and economic activity, the strong hypothesis proposes increasing labor and labor plus capital costs per unit of output of extractive goods.

The statistical record fails to support, and in fact is contradictory to, the classical hypothesis. Real costs per unit of extractive goods, measured in units of labor plus capital, did not rise. They fell, except in forestry (which is less than 10 percent of extraction). Table 8-1 briefly summarizes the evidence. Interestingly, the pace of decline in real costs accelerates following World War I, compared with the preceding period. The classical scarcity hypotheses would suggest that the tendency to increase

[1] Editor's note: The unit costs defined as $(L_E + C_E)/O_E$ have been adjusted to resolve the units of measurement problem. Thus this formulation corresponds to Brown and Field's definition on page 220 of this paper. The exact procedure in the original Barnett–Morse study is described in their appendix B.

in real costs becomes greater as size of the economy increases. These results are opposite to this view, with the appearance of a more favorable
record in the later period.

The foregoing observations are important historical evidence or
events, not statistical artifacts. We tested whether different weighting
systems could affect the aggregate unit cost indexes which we presented.
Figure 8-1 shows the index of labor plus capital cost per unit of output
in extraction, based on three different sets of weights for output. In each
case, every individual commodity's output in the extractive cost index is
weighted by the price of that commodity relative to other prices in the
extractive sector, the prices being those of the widely separated years,
1902, 1929, and 1954.

The comparisons in figure 8-1 show that the weighting system for the
output indexes has not been primarily responsible for the declining trend
in cost of extractive products. The extractive cost index declines at simi-

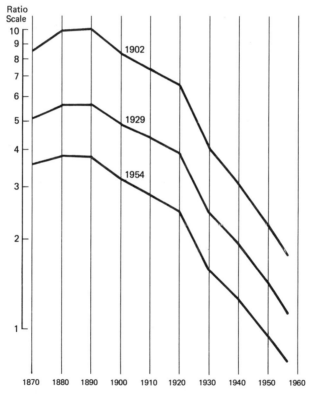

Figure 8-1. Labor and capital cost per unit of U.S. extractive output,
1902, 1929, and 1954 weights.

lar rates irrespective of the weighting system. In the 1902 price weighted index (of gross output), the unit cost of the extractive goods index has an average decline of 1.32 percent per annum since 1890; this compares with 1.25 percent for the 1954 index, and an intermediate figure for the 1929 index. We obtained similar results in both agriculture and minerals by varying the weight of output of individual commodities according to their prices in 1902, 1929, or 1954. The 1954 weighting system which we have used does not primarily account for the fact of declining unit cost in total agriculture. The situation is similar in minerals as an aggregate. All three weighting systems show substantial and similar declining unit costs.

Figures 8-2 through 8-7 show that the contradiction of the strong scarcity hypothesis holds for the great majority of extractive commodi-

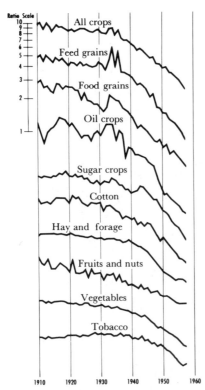

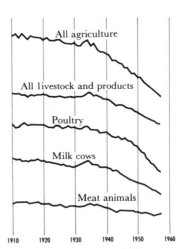

Figure 8-2. U.S. agriculture: labor cost per unit of output in all crops and nine major commodities, 1910–57.

Figure 8-3. U.S. agriculture: labor cost per unit of total output and of output of livestock and products, 1910–57.

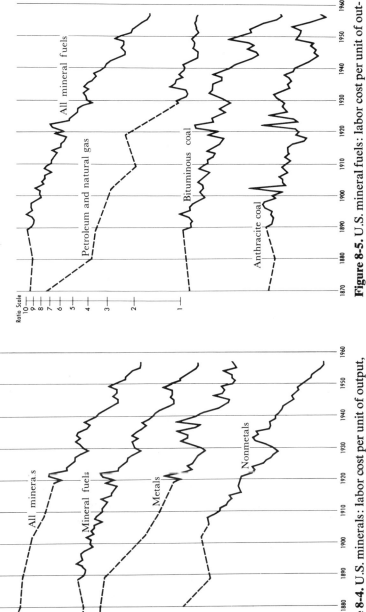

Figure 8-5. U.S. mineral fuels: labor cost per unit of output, 1870–1957. Solid lines connect points in annual series; dashed lines connect points over a year apart.

Figure 8-4. U.S. minerals: labor cost per unit of output, 1870–1957. Note: Solid lines connect points in annual series; dashed lines connect points over a year apart.

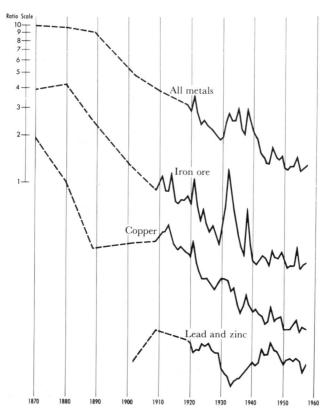

Figure 8-6. U.S. metals: labor cost per unit of output, 1870–1957. Solid lines connect points in annual series; dashed lines connect points over a year apart.

ties, excluding forestry. In these charts, only labor costs and gross outputs can be used, since neither capital input data nor net output figures are available for individual commodities. (For reference, we show the comparable labor cost per unit of gross output in the corresponding aggregate categories.)

The Weak Hypothesis of Increasing Economic Scarcity. The weak hypothesis suggests that while increasing resource scarcity does tend to increase real cost (L_E/O_E or $L_E + C_E/O_E$), this increase is more than offset by sociotechnical progress or other favorable, economy-wide changes. While the tendency for real costs of extractive outputs to rise as a result of increasing scarcity is more than offset by the dynamic forces in the economy, nonetheless, the resulting rate of decline in real costs of

Figure 8-7. U.S. nonmetals: labor cost per unit of output, 1880–1957. Solid lines connect points in annual series; dashed lines connect points over a year apart.

extractive goods may be less than in the rest of the economy. We can test this hypothesis by assuming that these favorable dynamic forces (the progress of civilization, to use Mill's term) are operating equally in both extractive and nonextractive sectors. In this case we can test for increasing scarcity by examining the trend of $(L_E/O_E) \div (L_N/O_N)$, or the equivalent with labor plus capital. (The subscript N represents the nonextractive sector of the economy.) If the weak scarcity hypothesis is valid, then

Table 8-2.   Real Unit Costs in Relative Terms
(1929 = 100)

Years	All extractive goods	Agriculture	Minerals	Forestry
1870–1900	99	97	154	37
1919	103	97	139	84
1957	87	89	68	130

the unit cost of extractive goods *relative* to nonextractive will rise, even though the absolute unit cost is declining. With certain other assumptions, the weak scarcity hypothesis can also be tested by examining the trend of P_E/P_N or P_E/P, that is, the trend of relative price of extractive products. If the weak scarcity hypothesis is true, the price of extractive goods will rise relative to the price index of all goods (P).

The weak hypothesis can be interpreted as a more sophisticated measure of real cost than the traditional one. Modern economists would say it is a better measure than that of classical economics. In the weak hypothesis, real cost is measured as "opportunity cost," that is by reflecting the goods and services which are forgone in order to produce a unit of extractive product, where L is valued at its productivity in the overall economy at each respective date. Similarly, in defining real costs as P_E/P, we consider the extractive product relative to the value of goods and services forgone to obtain it. These two real cost measures for the weak scarcity hypothesis—relative cost and relative price—are equivalent to each other as indicators, under certain assumptions.[2]

These "opportunity cost" measures of real cost are quite different from the cost measures which are relevant to the strong hypothesis of classical economics or the present-day alarmists—Meadows [4], Erlich [5], Hardin [6]—mentioned earlier. Only the strong form of natural resource scarcity, in which the costs of extractive goods rise absolutely and eventually dominate the expenditures comprising GNP, can halt and reverse economic progress. The weak form, in which the costs of extractive goods decline in absolute terms although they rise relative to the costs of other goods, offers, at worst, a slow rate of economic progress, but could never halt it, let alone bring about the decline which the alarmists say has been occurring or will occur soon.

Table 8-2 shows the historical trends of unit costs in the United States for the weak scarcity hypothesis. The figures are indexes (1929 = 100) of labor plus capital cost in extractive sectors *relative to the non-extractive sector of the economy:*

[2] The assumptions and alternative measures are discussed in *S and G*, pp. 202–16, and in Barnett [3].

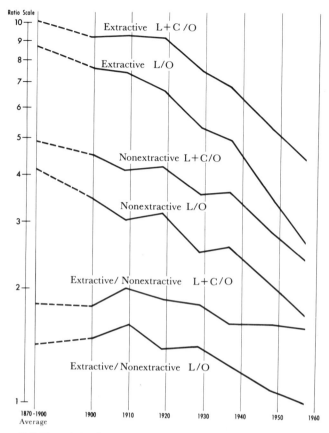

Figure 8-8. Trends in the cost per unit of extractive output relative to nonextractive output in the United States, 1870–1957.

The weak scarcity hypothesis fails in all extraction, agricultural, and mineral sectors. Costs per unit of output in these sectors decline no less rapidly than in the economy at large. Only in forestry is the weak scarcity hypothesis supported.

Figure 8-8 presents the absolute and relative unit cost data (both labor plus capital and labor alone) for the aggregate extractive and non-extractive sectors. The weak scarcity hypothesis fails for all extraction. The relative price data are shown in figure 8-9. These show that over the whole period relative prices did not rise in the full extractive sector, agriculture, or minerals, but did in forestry. These data tend to confirm the relative cost data. The weak scarcity hypothesis fails for extraction, agriculture, and minerals, but is supported in forestry.

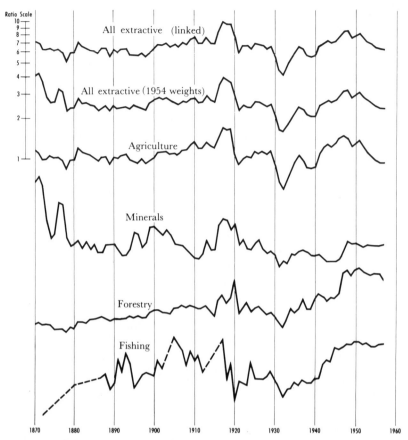

Figure 8-9. Trends in unit prices of forest products relative to nonextractive products in the United States, 1890–1957. Solid lines connect points in annual series; dashed lines connect points over a year apart.

II
Extension of U.S. Statistical Tests to 1970

Based on the evidence in section I, the hypothesis of increasing resource scarcity in the United States, 1870–1957 is not supported by the data. The findings fail to support increasing resource scarcity for the United States over the period involved. However, it now becomes relevant, fifteen years later, to reconsider the statistical analysis. In this section, we examine U.S. real cost data since 1957. In the next section, we compile and analyze data for other countries of the world since World War II, to offer further support for these findings.

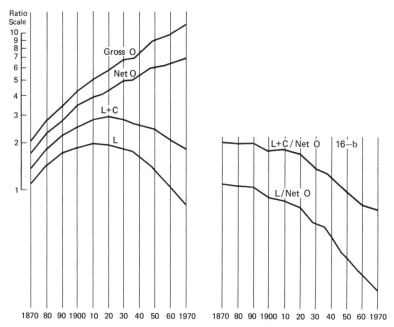

Figures 8-10 and 8-11. U.S. extractive industries: output, labor, and capital inputs, and cost per unit of output, 1870–1970.

Manley Johnson and Frederick W. Bell, of Florida State University, have updated certain of the original labor, capital, and output data in *Scarcity and Growth* to 1970. Their extensions have been graphed in a manner consistent with the earlier analysis (in *S and G*) and are given in figures 8-10 and 8-11.[3]

These results indicate that, in general, the record of declining real cost, measured as L_B/O_B or $(T_E + C_E) O_E$, observed in the 1870–1957 period, continues. The rapid rates of decline in labor costs per unit of extractive, agricultural, and mineral output appear to persist unabated, but the rates of decline for $L + C$ per unit of net output seem to have slowed in the 1960–70 decade. There is no sign of upturn to support the strong scarcity hypothesis.

With respect to the weak scarcity hypothesis, Robert R. Manthy of Michigan State University has extended the relative price data in *S and G* to 1973. V. Kerry Smith's analysis [7] of their trends suggests that the erratic relative price trends in Barnett and Morse continue (see figure

[3] Reproduced from R. R. Wilson and D. A. Samuelson, "America's Natural Resources: Boom or Doom," paper presented to Southern Economic Association Meetings, 1976. The citation is to Johnson's unpublished Ph.D. dissertation, 1976.

8-9). There is *no* increase, and the weak scarcity hypothesis fails to be supported.

Smith has analyzed the 1900–73 data intensively, using statistical techniques beyond simple observation, plotting of the observed values, and fitting of moving averages and trends. His view appears to be that the relative price data are so volatile as to cause him to question our ability to draw any conclusions from the data. He explains this at length in his paper. However, it seems the interpretation of these findings is not at variance with the *S and G* conclusions. That is, we can observe 100 years of extractive and nonextractive prices, and long-term segments within the period; relate them to national events; and interpret the economic trends in extractive and other prices. These movements can, in turn, be related to long-term trends in real costs, and we can further interpret all of these relative to economic scarcity hypotheses. It may be that Smith's agnosticism results from emphasis on short-term and second-order fluctuations (and possibly statistical niceties) not related to the economic history and scarcity concepts.

III
Labor Cost of Minerals and Agricultural Products in World Regions and Various Countries

The findings reported in this section should be regarded as a preliminary appraisal of the evidence on resource scarcity in various nations of the world.[4] It is an exploratory effort, but nonetheless suggestive of the movements in real resource costs elsewhere.

A. Strong Hypothesis of Increasing Economic Scarcity. *Labor Cost of Mineral Production in Major World Regions.* One of the more interesting of the data sets which are used in testing the increasing scarcity hypotheses is published by the United Nations. These statistics report, for major regions of the world, labor productivity (reciprocal of labor cost) in each of four mineral categories: coal mining (CO), petroleum and gas extraction (PG), mining of metallic minerals (MM), and all minerals extraction (MI). The data begin with a "world" region (W), then are broken into types of economies: market (M), centrally planned (CP), developed market (DM), and developing market (GM), and then into continental groupings. The 1974 Year Book presents data for a sixteen-year period, 1958 through 1973, but omits 1959, 1961, 1962, 1964–67, and 1970.

---

[4] I am most grateful to my colleagues in the IIASA (Laxenburg, Austria) library—to Messrs. Loesser, Popper, and their associates for help.

These data have been evaluated for the world region and for each of the four "market types." With four mineral classes and five regions, there are twenty individual time series. The trends and parameters estimates are shown in appendix B. The series are numbered 11 through 35.[5]

All of the time series fail to support the strong hypothesis of increasing scarcity for minerals. Indeed, all are consistent with an opposite hypothesis, that of increasing resource availability. Productivity in minerals production not only does not decline, but increases rather strongly and somewhat persistently in all five of the regions for all four of the mineral classes. This is equivalent to decline in real labor cost, measured in conventional man-hour or man-day units.

The trends of labor productivity increase are not uniform among the series. A simple trend model of the form: $y = ae^{bt}$ was estimated with ordinary least squares. The following observations summarize the statistical evidence:

(1) The rates of increase in labor productivities per year can be tabulated as:

Rate	Number of cases
2.00–2.99%	3
3.00–4.99%	14
> 5%	3

(2) All but one of the R^2 (coefficient of determination) for these relations exceed 0.9; all of the coefficients are statistically significant.

(3) Finally, there may be a deceleration in the rates for the *linear* trend lines in the following nine cases:

Identification number	Series	R^2
14	Metals mining, W	0.967
21	Minerals, M	0.987
22	Coal, M	0.941
24	Metals mining, M	0.942
27	Coal, DM	0.909
29	Metals mining, DM	0.963
32	Coal, GM	0.951
33	Petroleum and gas, GM	0.977
34	Metals mining, GM	0.844

Labor Cost of Coal Production in Selected Countries. The U.S. Bituminous Coal Association, a trade association of coal mining compa-

---

[5] A labor cost in manufacturing series appears also in each region, with the symbol MA. This is used later in examining labor productivity in minerals relative to manufacturing.

Table 8-3. Productivity Movements for Coal

Data source	Productivity change in last four years, to 1973
U.S., underground	Down
U.S., strip	Level
U.S., auger	Erratic level
U.S., overall	Down
Belgium	Level

nies, has published comparative productivity figures in coal mines in the United States and six European countries over the period 1944–73. The figures for U.S. mines are in four series— underground, strip, auger, and total. These time series are identified as numbers 1 through 10 in the statistical appendix (B). In addition, there are two other productivity series in appendix B—one for the European Coal Community (no. 36, 1960 to 1966) and one for Great Britain (no. 212, 1964–73).

Least squares trend lines using the same model as that given above were fitted to all of these series. In all cases there were strong upward trends in labor productivity. The t statistics ranged from 5 to 31, and the R^2 statistics ranged from 0.70 to 0.97. The annual rates of increase in productivity ranged from 2 to more than 8 percent, with the majority falling in the 3 to 5 percent range. These data all deny the strong scarcity hypothesis.

In addition, these series have been plotted against *linear* trend lines. In the U.S. and Belgium series, labor productivity turns down or levels off in the late 1960s or 1970 and this continues to 1973. If one were to fit these past several years instead of the whole period, the story is somewhat altered as shown in table 8-3. The earlier findings for Great Britain, France, the Netherlands, Germany, Poland, and the European Coal Community remain unchanged. In order to evaluate the significance of the U.S. and Belgium productivity data, more information is needed. We have to ask, "What may have changed each of these series?" One possibility is resource scarcity. Other possibilities are environmental constraints, changes in safety regulations, stage of the business cycle, and so on.

Labor Cost of Agricultural and Mineral Products in West Germany. The analysis for West Germany is based on labor productivity series for agriculture and minerals. The agriculture series is in two parts, one component (designated 242) from 1956–62 and a second (number 243) from 1962–71. The minerals series (number 245) is from 1957–71. Agricultural productivity rises at 8½ percent a year in the first part of the period ($t = 10.4$; $R^2 = 0.78$) and 6 percent in the second ($t = 10.4$; $R^2 = 0.92$). The improvement in productivity is persistent and rather regular. Moreover, output was rising during the period.

The results for labor productivity in the minerals sector are quite similar. It increases at 4.3 percent; $t = 20.7$ and $R^2 = 0.97$. Output was rising in the early years and became erratic without apparent trend in the later ones. Thus there is no support for the strong scarcity hypothesis in the productivity movements for agriculture and minerals sectors in West Germany.

B. Relative Cost Measures to Test the Weak Scarcity Hypothesis. *Relative Labor Costs of Minerals Output in Major World Regions.* In this section results for *relative* labor productivity measures across regions will be related to the *weak hypothesis* concerning increasing natural resource scarcity. We test the weak scarcity hypothesis by examining *relative* labor cost of minerals or its reciprocal, *relative* labor productivity in minerals.

Each of the mineral productivity series previously discussed has been divided by the manufacturing (MA) productivity series in the same year and region. These data were compiled from the same sources. The results of regressing these series on time are also shown in appendix B. Table 8-4 summarizes these results. From this evidence, we are unable to accept the weak scarcity hypothesis. The only exception to this conclusion comes with the cases of coal and possibly minerals in centrally planned economies, and coal in developing market economies.

Examination of the graphs of linear trends and the actual observations of these relative productivity data reveal some evidence which would be favorable to the weak scarcity hypothesis beginning to emerge for some of the minerals. That is, although the series for 1958–72/73 generally provide evidence against the weak hypothesis, the last two years or so of some of the series are more favorable to the weak hypothesis. Table 8-5 summarizes the relative productivity series showing declines to 1972 or 1973 for two or more years.

These results may be a signal of impending weak scarcity. However, two years of divergence are too brief a period to be taken seriously in this type of analysis. The change in relative productivity can be due to many things other than scarcity, as mentioned earlier.

Relative Agricultural Prices in Selected Countries of the World. Two basic series measuring relative agricultural prices have been used for the weak scarcity hypothesis. The first is the ratio of agricultural prices to

Table 8-4. Relative Labor Cost in Major Regions of the World[a]

Outcome	
Statistically significant support for increasing scarcity hypothesis[b]	
Support ($R^2 > 0.5$, $b > 0.01$)	Coal in centrally planned economies (219).[c]
Support ($R^2 < 0.5$, $b < 0.01$ or both)	Minerals in centrally planned economies (218) and coal in developing market economies (229).
Statistically significant evidence adverse to increasing scarcity hypothesis	
Adverse ($R^2 > 0.5$, $b > 0.01$)	Petroleum and gas in each of world (215), market (225), developed market, (230), developing market (235), and centrally planned economies (220).
	Minerals in market (223) and developing market economies (233).
	Coal in developing market economies (234).
	Metallic minerals in centrally planned economies (221).
Adverse ($R^2 < 0.5$ or $b < 0.01$)	Minerals in world (213).
Statistically insignificant results;[b] no support $t < 2.0$.	Coal in world (214) and market (224) economies.
	Metallic minerals in world (216), market (226), developed market (231), and developing market economies (236).
	Minerals in developed market economies (228).

[a] The above regression parameters were taken from ordinary least squares estimates of the model $y = ae^{bt}$.
[b] In all cases "statistically insignificant" means $t < 2.0$.
[c] Numbers in parentheses indicate series.

Table 8-5. Summary of Declines in Relative Productivity

Extractive output	Region[a]	Length of period
213 Minerals	W	2 years
214 Coal	W	2 years
216 Metallics	W	2 years
218 Minerals	CP	(see table 8-4)
219 Coal	CP	(see table 8-4)
223 Minerals	M	2 years
224 Coal	M	2 years
226 Metallics	M	2 years
228 Minerals	DM	2 years
229 Coal	DM	(see table 8-4)
230 Petro + Gas	DM	2 years
231 Metallics	DM	4 years
236 Metallics	GM	2 years

[a] W—world; CP—centrally planned; M—market; DM—developing market.

prices of other goods. If increasing resource scarcity is present in the agricultural sector, we would expect agricultural prices to rise compared with the prices of all other goods, where price movements of resources will play a much smaller role.

Each of the two relative agricultural price series is in two parts, for selected countries:

(1) Ratio of prices received by farmers to prices paid (RP)
   • Series 143–164 from approximately 1950 to 1963, 15 countries
   • Series 165–191 from approximately 1963 to 1972, 25 countries
(2) Ratio of agricultural prices to the general wholesale price index of the country (AGW)
   • Series 264–285 from approximately 1950 to 1962, 22 countries
   • Series 286–316 from approximately 1961 to 1972, 31 countries.

It seems reasonable that the "prices received/prices paid" (series 143–191) should be ignored. While these data would be strongly adverse to the weak scarcity hypothesis, they are not directly relevant to it. There are two reasons underlying this judgment. First, the "prices paid" figure can include "wages," which makes this relative price series inappropriate for a test of the weak scarcity hypothesis. Second, the "prices paid" data may emphasize goods which use natural resources intensively, such as fuels, fertilizers, and seed. This property tends to make the deflator in the "prices received/prices paid" less representative of *non* resource-intensive goods.

The second series consists of prices of agricultural products relative to the general wholesale price index for the country. Table 8-6 is a summary list for the 53 identified cases. Thirty of these cases offer no support for the weak hypothesis, but 23 do. Table 8-7 indicates that support for the scarcity hypothesis is more concentrated in the later period, 1961–72, and its rejection is somewhat more in the former. This time sequence is itself a piece of supporting evidence for the weak, increasing scarcity hypothesis.

In table 8-8 the countries and periods for the "support" cases discussed above are identified specifically. In addition, the table reports the regression parameters for each of the eight countries which experienced relatively rising agricultural prices in the first period. Several overall observations can be made:

1. All eight countries are advanced in development. However, *most* of the developed countries are *not* in this list of countries providing evidence for the weak scarcity case.
2. Five of the countries are European. Four of them do not repeat their scarcity evidence in the second period, and the fifth (Spain) exhibits

Table 8-6. Test of Scarcity Hypothesis: Trends of Ratios of Agricultural
Prices to General Wholesale Prices, Series 264–316

Statistically adverse to scarcity hypothesis		Statistically support scarcity hypothesis
Statistically insignificant	Sign is opposite to hypothesis	
264	267	266
265	269	268
270	274	271
275	277	272
280	279	273
282	281	276
283		278
284	287	285
	296	
286	304	288
290	316	289
291		293
292		295
294		297
299		298
303		300
307		301
309		302
310		305
312		306
314		308
		311
		313
		315
(20 cases)	(10 cases)	(23 cases)

Table 8-7. Summary of the Evidence for Relative Prices of Agricultural
Products by Time Period

	Number of cases		
Type of evidence	1950–62	1961–72	1950–72
Adverse evidence	14	16	30
Support evidence	8	15	23
Total	22	31	53

rather weak evidence with low b, t, and R^2. How should we interpret
evidence which appears in 1950–62 and disappears in 1961–72 relative to a long-term scarcity hypothesis? One possibility is that evidence
of resource scarcity is a transient phenomenon in market economies
because its appearance induces economic forces, that is, technical
change, substitution, and so on, which tend to mitigate the long-term
effects.

Table 8-8. Identification of Support Cases

Country	(Series No.) First period	(Series No.) Second period	Parameters[a] b	Parameters[a] t	Parameters[a] R^2
Germany (D)	266	—	0.008	3.3	0.55
Italy (I)	268	—	0.006	2.0	0.25
Spain (E)	271		0.007	2.3	0.64
		313	0.004	2.1	0.23
Sweden (S)	272	—	0.012	0.45	0.64
Yugoslavia (YU)	273	—	0.037	2.7	0.57
Mexico (MX)	276		0.007	3.4	0.46
		289	0.007	5.4	0.72
Argentina (AR)	278	—	0.014	2.9	0.55
Japan (JP)	285		0.018	3.4	0.51
		300	0.032	8.4	0.86
Costa Rica (CR)	—	288			
Chile (CE)	—	293			
Ecuador (EC)	—	295			
India (IN)	—	297			
Iran (IR)	—	298			
Korea (KR)	—	301			
Philippines (PP)	—	302			
Belgium (B)	—	305			
France (F)	—	306			
Greece (GR)	—	308			
Netherlands (NL)	—	311			
United Kingdom (GB)	—	315			

[a] The model used is of the form $y = ae^{bt}$

3. One of the countries, Japan, is generally viewed as a classic agricultural scarcity case. Thus it is not surprising to find it repeats evidence in the second period. By contrast, Mexico is usually viewed as agriculturally strong, and so scarcity evidence here seems surprising.

Finally, with respect to the other twelve cases which provide evidence of scarcity in the second, but not in the first period, five are European and developed. It is difficult to evaluate these results without further in-depth analysis. There may well be particular circumstances relative to some of these countries in this period which explain the apparent support for the scarcity hypothesis and which are not directly related to the question of the adequacy of the natural resource base.

Relative Labor Cost of Agriculture and Minerals Output in Germany. Two alternative series for agricultural productivity relative to industrial productivity, 1956–62 (numbers 247 and 248), another series for 1962–71 (number 249), and one for productivity in the minerals sector in Germany have been analyzed to test the weak scarcity hypothesis. Table 8-9 presents the results. In the agricultural series none of the series

Table 8-9.   Relative Labor Productivity in Germany

Definition of time series	Slope coefficient[a]	t	R^2
Agriculture			
No. 247	0.04	1.80	0.27
No. 248	0.04	2.00	0.35
No. 249	0.008	1.20	0.04
Minerals			
No. 250	−0.0067	−3.20	0.40

[a] The model used to estimate the trend in labor productivity in the extractive sector relative to nonextractive is $y = ae^{bt}$.

supports the scarcity hypothesis. The correlations and t values are not only too low to be useful, but the signs on the b coefficient estimates fail to support the hypothesis. The data on relative minerals productivity (1957–71) offer weak support for the weak scarcity hypothesis.

$$\text{No. 250 } R^2 = 0.40, b, = -0.0067, t = -3.2$$

Plots of the component series comprising the relative productivity measure in minerals have been examined. Both minerals productivity (245) and industrial productivity (200) observations are regular and persistent, including the later years. The *relative* productivity series (250) is erratic. It falls sharply from high above its trend line to far below, 1957–60; rises sharply above the line in 1961–63; falls sharply below the line in 1964–68; and rises sharply above it in 1970–71. Thus it is difficult to offer an explanation for these results.

Relative Prices of Raw Materials and Minerals in Germany. Raw materials (RM) are not all identical with agricultural, forestry, and mineral products, but they may be closely related. In an effort to provide supplemental information for the weak scarcity hypothesis, I have examined some of the relative price data for raw materials (RM), as well as minerals (MI). These are each deflated by prices of manufactured goods (MA), wholesale prices (W), or retail trade prices (RT) in the even numbered series 252–262. Two of the series are 1960–71, the other four are 1949 or 1950 to 1971. The findings are given in table 8-10.

It seems that raw material products and prices account for a substantial fraction of the total costs of manufactured and wholesale goods and therefore influence their price movements. Deflation using the manufacturing price series apparently leaves only noise. Thus it seems reasonable to ignore series 252–256.

Series 258–262 offer mild support for the proposition that minerals

Table 8-10. Relative Price Movements for Extractive Outputs in Germany

Time series[a]	b	t	R²
252 RM/MA	0.0007	0.61	0.03
254 RM/W	−0.0022	−1.35	0.07
256 RM/RT	−0.0051	−2.62	0.22
258 MI/MA	0.0189	6.57	0.66
260 MI/W	0.0110	3.80	0.55
262 MI/RT	0.0149	3.83	0.38

[a] RM—raw materials; MA—manufactured goods; W—wholesale prices; RT—retail trade prices; MI—minerals.

prices have moved up relative to nonextractive prices. This may reflect scarcity, according to the weak hypothesis.

C. Summary. I have examined world-wide agricultural and minerals data in the post-World War II period relative to the hypothesis of increasing scarcity. The findings may be summarized as follows:

	Support of strong hypothesis
Labor cost of several classes of mineral production in all world regions.	No in 20 cases.
Labor cost of coal production in major producing countries.	No in 10 cases.
Labor cost of agricultural and mineral products in West Germany.	No in 2 cases.
	Support of weak hypothesis
Relative labor cost of several classes of minerals output in all world regions.	No in 17 cases. Yes in 3 cases.
Prices of agricultural goods relative to general wholesale price index.	No in 30 cases. Yes in 23 cases.
Relative labor cost of agricultural and minerals output in West Germany.	No in 3 cases. Yes in 1 case.
Relative prices of raw materials and minerals in Germany.	No in 3 cases. Yes in 3 cases.

I commented on the foregoing findings when I presented them and I refer the reader to the trend estimates in the statistical appendix. It is also desirable to repeat the earlier warning. These results should be regarded as preliminary since the series involved are available for short periods and in several of the cases are of uncertain quality. Nonetheless, pending an in-depth analysis of the recent evidence, it seems we can tentatively accept three general insights which emerge: (a) the strong scarcity hypothesis is contradicted; (b) the weak hypothesis is not supported in most cases; and (c) in several selected cases the most recent data appear to offer limited support for the weak hypothesis.

IV
Environmental Pollution

As I noted at the outset of this paper, the Barnett–Morse *Scarcity and Growth* volume identified environmental pollution and abatement as a significant social problem. Using the term "quality of life" to describe these factors, we argued that these concerns were more genuine and pressing than alleged Malthusian–Ricardian dilemmas of increasing resource scarcity and the cost of extractive products. It seems useful at this point to update these views in two respects. First, I present some estimates of present and future costs of pollution abatement. Second, I discuss the nature of the social function for pollution abatement over time.

On the first question we have a number of estimates, including data from the Council on Environmental Quality and the Environmental Protection Agency, studies done at Resources for the Future by Ridker [8], and others. In 1970, annualized costs of pollution abatement, both public and private, were about $10 billion. At this level of outlay the public believed it had unsatisfactory levels of water, air, and land quality. Moreover, if the policies and technology of the 1960s continued to the year 2000, air and stream pollution would become very much worse as the economy grew. The increased pollution would be quite unacceptable to most of us.

Prompted by this outlook, remedial measures have been taken. These were officially put forward in the standards of the early 1970s and in the 1973 water and 1975 air emission standards of the Environmental Protection Agency. They are all technologically feasible. They relate to presently known techniques, without any dramatic technical breakthroughs. But, of course, they entail substantial costs.

In annual terms such policies would raise abatement costs from the $10 billion in 1970 and $26 billion in 1974 to about $55 billion (1974 prices) in 1983. Annual costs would then rise perhaps to $100–120 billion (1974 prices) in the year 2000, depending on the rate of population growth. Put another way, annual pollution abatement costs would rise from 1 percent of the nation's output in 1970 to 2 percent in 1974, to 3 percent by the end of the century. Large though these figures are, they are quite small relative to our income and economic growth. We would have to give up less than a tenth of one percentage point in annual growth of national output to pay for this active abatement policy.

What would we get—what are we getting—for this large absolute but small relative payment? The data in the annual reports of the Council on Environmental Quality show that already environmental quality is significantly improving, and further gains are a prospect. For example, from 1970 to 1974, the national ambient levels of the major air pollutants —particulates, sulfur dioxide, and carbon monoxide—declined significantly (Sixth Annual Report, figure 4, page 311). From 1961 to 1974, river quality—including the protection of aquatic life and suitable drinking water—in the nation increased significantly (Sixth Annual Report, figure 19, p. 352). The data on air, stream, and land pollution are generally favorable, but not uniformly so over every pollutant and region. As some problems are solved, others become more apparent and need to be addressed. We have now become aware of problems of fine particulates, synergistic reactions, and trace chemical and metal contaminants. In some quarters there is concern that the pace of improvement is not rapid enough, and that public support for the costs of environmental clean-up may be waning. For our purposes here, however, we observe that increases in environmental pollution levels can be avoided and, in fact, reduced in our growing economy. The expenditure levels are well within our means and need not appreciably affect rates of growth in income and output per capita. Indeed, the probable situation may be more favorable than I have described. Some technical breakthroughs in pollution control will in fact occur, some cost reductions will occur, and improved policies can be adopted as necessary.

In summary, large improvements in environmental quality of air, streams, and land are fully compatible with economic growth in the United States. This may be seen in table 8-11 in which we show real national GNP and environmental maintenance and improvement costs in the years 1974 and 2000. It seems reasonable to conclude that growth in per capita income and improvement in technology provide the economic and technical means to seek improvement in the environment.

It is also necessary to consider the nature of social cost functions for pollution abatement. The "doomsday sayers" are pessimistic about pollution abatement. They have stated that environmental clean-up cannot run a winning race against pollution from economic growth. The argument goes as follows. The atmosphere or waters have a limited capacity to be self-cleaning, dictated by their natural characteristics. Abatement efforts must remove all pollution emissions above this rate of discharge. Pollution emissions, however, are proportionate to economic activity and increase in proportion to real GNP. Therefore, abatement efforts must

Table 8-11. An Analysis of Annual Costs of Environmental
Inprovement Relative to Real GNP
(in billions)

	1974	2000	Comments
Real GNP before deducting environ- mental costs	$1,407	$3,900	$(1.04)^{26} = 277\%$
Less environmental improvement costs	28	120	Based on CEQ data
Real GNP remaining after paying en- vironmental improvement costs	$1,379	$3,780	Increase to 274%

remove larger and larger percentages of the pollutants in gross emissions, in order to keep the net emissions below the percentage which the atmosphere and waters can cleanse by nature's processes. The cost function, these people allege, is exponential with respect to percentage of pollutants to be cleaned from emissions:

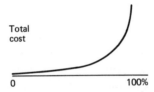

Cost rises asymptotically to infinity at 100 percent cleansing.

The argument is essentially the same as Malthusian-type limits on natural resources for agriculture, forestry, or minerals production.[6] In conventional Malthusian-type models, the natural resource and sociotechnical parameters are viewed as fixed, there is only one other factor (labor or "doses" of labor plus capital), and the production function exhibits constant returns to scale with constant quality factors. Thus, after a point, output does not rise proportionate to the increase in the variable input. In this pollution model, gross emissions are of constant quality in parts per million pollutants relative to pure air or water. But they have to be "cultivated" or "mined" more and more intensively to remove more of the impurities, in order that the total pollutant discharges to air and water should not exceed the fixed limit of nature's capacity to clean itself. Inevitably, given the Malthusian assumptions, costs eventually rise.

If it is viewed as a Malthusian model, the argument of increasing pollution costs is subject to all the deficiencies of the Malthusian model when applied to agriculture, forestry, and minerals. These have been discussed at great length in parts 2 and 3 of *Scarcity and Growth*. Actually, Malthusian pollution models may be even more defective than other

[6] *Scarcity and Growth* discussed these same issues.

Malthusian models. One aspect of their limitations concerns their accounting of space. Some of the manmade enterprises which emit pollution can be concentrated, or their emissions concentrated, so that pollutants become concentrated in sewers or area sectors. Thus, particular water courses can be made sewers, with the sludge eventually extracted for chemical processing. Other enterprises, such as power plants, can be concentrated in regions where the ambient air is still capable of self-cleaning very large discharges. Or tall smokestacks can disperse dilute pollutant discharge over large areas, not exceeding the satisfactory self-cleaning level. The oceans, except at some coastal points, have enormously greater self-cleansing capacity than is being used. Concentrations of population and production in urban places aggravate pollution problems initially. But then, when substantial abatement efforts are undertaken, they may provide important economies of scale or conjuncture for remedy.

Another error in the allegations of Malthusian pollution cost functions is the omission of technological changes and innovations. Here the opportunities are much wider than in, say, Malthusian agriculture models. Our chief air pollution offenders are four-cycle private automobile engines and coal power plants. The increasing cost argument assumes that we must make stack and car pipe discharges cleaner and cleaner by afterburners, catalysts, and filters. But, of course, we need not have gasoline engines in cars, nor even private cars, and the fuel that goes into power plants need not be high sulfur coal. The chief offenders for water pollution are electric power thermal discharge and chemical plant and municipal sewer discharges. Cooling towers, settling tanks, and secondary sewage treatment are not subject to increasing costs under constant technology, and actually would be subject to declining costs per unit of economic activity as a result of technological change.

The complete substitution of new products and processes denies that it is necessary to traverse an increasing cost curve. Nonetheless, even if for some commodities and processes the cost curve does increase, there is no reason to assume a priori that the product is a large proportion of the social bill of goods. Unless it is large, cannot be substituted for, and cannot be made more efficient, it need not be troublesome. The air and water pollutants from conventional power plants, autos, and sewers are merely social costs to be taken care of from the growing GNP, in the many ways which we know.

In summary, an advancing economy can select among the services or functions it wants from its GNP; among the products to provide the services; among numerous processes and branches to provide products; among basic resources; among locations for each of many stages of economic activity; and among innumerable pathways through time. Assuming constant ratios of pollutants to GNP and increasing cost functions for pollution abatement is an excessively simple-minded form of economic analysis.

Nuclear dangers are sometimes lumped with other environmental quality or pollution problems. I do not think nuclear hazards should be viewed so, anymore than Idi Amin or DNA manipulations should be viewed so—it is not sensible. In origins, kinds, and magnitudes of problems and solutions, nuclear hazards differ from environmental pollution caused by automobiles, fossil fuels, and sewage. There are tens of thousands of nuclear weapons and related nuclear minerals, facilities, and wastes in half a dozen countries. The nuclear nightmare is rooted in military and political affairs and violence, not in economic growth. The dangers, no matter whether the source of nuclear materials is weapons, power plants, research reactors, or other, are societal terrorism, violence, mass destruction, and related political problems. The solutions are not the cleansing of air and stream pollutants or the benefit–cost analysis of economics textbooks. The solutions for environmental pollution are relatively simple and at hand, even though expensive. This cannot be said of nuclear dangers.

Appendix A: Notes on Concepts

Cartel Scarcity.   The ratios

$$\frac{L_E + C_E}{O_E} \div \frac{L_N + C_N}{O_N}$$

and P_E/P_N are alternative indicators of scarcity, relevant for the weak scarcity hypothesis. But they are not equivalent or equal in magnitudes. Rather, they are substitute indicators. Each incorporates special assumptions which affect magnitude. These relate to whether the output measure is net or gross (treatment of intermediate goods used in the production), governmental tax and subsidy treatment of the industry, inflation, foreign trade, degree of competitiveness of the market, as well as other elements. One of these additional considerations relates to the fact that prices tend to indicate cost of marginal producers or supply, whereas $L + C$ tends to measure average cost over the whole product sector.

Of great importance today is the fact that prices of energy resources will immediately tend to reflect the influence of oligopoly and cartels, but the cost measure will do so less quickly, fully, and directly. The striking case is the OPEC cartel, which has imposed an international market price of about $14 a barrel on crude oil, while in the Middle East average cost measured in $L + C$ may have risen little from the pre-fall 1973 figure of much less than $1 a barrel. Even before the fall of 1973, price and cost in international markets differed because of monopoly profits and governmental levies, although the differences were far smaller than they are today.

To what extent should we let monopoly market scarcity enter into our consideration of the question of increasing scarcity? Originally, I thought it should not enter at all, but I am no longer sure of this. In the case of many minerals and even in agriculture and forestry, natural resources may be concentrated in space. They may be much more vulnerable than other sectors to monopoly action because of their concentration. The relative price measure may tend to indicate increasing scarcity resulting from monopoly markets, while an average $L + C$ cost measure would not. If the cause of a relative price rise is a condition of concentration of natural resources in specific space and limitations of resources elsewhere, we might say that monopoly of resource products should be viewed as part of the increasing scarcity question. To the extent, however, that another necessary condition was cartelization, we might hold this fact responsible for price rises and exclude such monopolies.

The consequences of monopoly market scarcity are similar to, but possibly less onerous than, "natural" scarcity. Both prompt economic, technological, and other efforts at substitution and relief from scarcity, because of higher prices. As the efforts are successful and the supply and demand curves made more elastic, the monopoly price solution will shift toward the competitive one. This can be expected in petroleum. Indeed, it is already happening, with the Middle East oil price remaining steady or increasing slightly, but being eroded by inflation since 1973.

In the United States at the national level, we have recently experienced increasing scarcity of petroleum resources. The phenomenon has been much more complicated than Malthusian and Ricardian propositions. The nation discovered and developed petroleum resources at *declining* cost in foreign places. It and other countries permitted themselves to become highly dependent on these sources. When this situation was well developed and locked in, the cartel struck. It remains to be seen, over the longer run, what will be the outcome, now that more economic resources are being devoted to energy resources, conservation, and technology development at home and elsewhere, rather than primarily to oil and gas development in the OPEC nations. Meanwhile P_E/P_N movements correctly indicate that there has been a severe and

abrupt increase in petroleum scarcity, even though the U.S. government
has moderated the increase with price ceilings.

$$\frac{L_E + C_E}{O_E} \div \frac{L_N + C_N}{O_N}$$

movements in the nation correctly indicate that petroleum scarcity has
developed. But these are average costs and the indicator has risen less
for the industry than for, say, stripper wells.

We must consider seriously whether cartel monopolization of foreign
supplies should, in some circumstances, be viewed as part of a modern-
ized Ricardian phenomenon of natural resource scarcity (see *S and G,*
chapters 1 and 11). The cost burden on the nation is real. One major
element in cartelization was concentration of the lowest cost petroleum
resources and developed supplies in one area, that is, in the Middle
East. Another major element was neglect and failure by almost all economists in the 1950s and 1960s to warn of the prospect of enormously
successful OPEC cartelization, with world scarcity effects far exceeding
$100 billion a year and U.S. scarcity effects in excess of $30 billion a
year.

The Marginal Supplier.   We should give thought to compiling $L +
C$ data on marginal suppliers of extractive products. This information
could supplement price data, which already tend to reflect costs of marginal suppliers, but which are subject to aberration and noise of various
kinds. Also, price data cannot be used to test the strong scarcity hypothesis. The marginal supplier $L + C$ data would be a more sensitive indicator of resource scarcity than average $L + C$. Such marginal data would
also reveal some of the reasons for price movements and tendencies in
resource scarcity.

A difficulty, however, is that the marginal supplier is frequently a
short-term supplier, bringing in idle, high-cost capacity in response to
short-term market imbalances. Indeed, most short-term suppliers are of
this nature. Our concern is with the marginal suppliers on a *long-run*
supply curve.

In minerals, it may be possible in some cases to distinguish marginal
suppliers on the long-run supply curves. In iron ore, taconite has been
in marginal supply for a long time and will be in the future. Compilation of taconite $L + C$ data might be possible. In copper, perhaps the
porphorys are the marginal suppliers in the long run. In aluminum, until
further development of the enormous reserves of years of highest grade
bauxite resources in West Africa, Brazil, and other places, perhaps
Australia's lower grade bauxite is the world's marginal supply. Within

our own country, various nonbauxitic ores would become the marginal supply if world supply were cut off, but none of these are presently in commercial use.

In petroleum, the present marginal supply in the United States is secondary and tertiary recovery. Such production should be viewed as marginal supply short run and also on the long-run curve. If 30 percent of an oil field is viewed as recoverable at a price of $3 a barrel, then clearly the percentage might be greatly expanded at $14 or more a barrel. Increased recovery percentages from oil pools certainly will be in the long-run supply curve, but at present prices such recovery will be planned in the development of the resource, rather than tacked on as a go-back activity. Possibly, marginal supply could be viewed as costs from fields just coming in, such as Alaska or the Atlantic Coast.

The concept of long-term marginal supply is very well known in natural gas, from the Permian Basin case and subsequent multiprice regulation activities of the U.S. Federal Power Commission. Earlier, in World War II and the Korean War, marginal supply at higher prices was used in price incentive schemes for metallic minerals; frequently short-term marginal supply was induced more than long term.

In theory, changes in long-term marginal supply cost would be a fine measure for testing both the strong and weak hypotheses of increasing resource scarcity. In practice, in a dynamic, rapidly changing world, the data problems are very great and may be insuperable. The practical difficulty may be compared with the use of economic rent as a scarcity indicator, to which the marginal supply concept is related.

Increases in Economic Rent.   It is frequently proposed that we test for increasing resource scarcity by observing changes in economic rent. The sources of the concept are Malthusian or Ricardian long-run, static theory for agricultural land, thus:

In the Malthusian case, land is of constant quality but at E_1 it is fully utilized, and beyond that point must be cultivated more and more intensively, at rising unit cost. In a Ricardian case, more land is available beyond E_1, but it is of monotonically declining economic quality, and cultivation beyond that point is at a rising unit cost for the product. (For convenience we have given the same rising cost curve to both Malthus and Ricardo; in fact they would be different. See *S and G*, chapters 3 and 5.)

At time 1 rent is zero. At time 2, demand has grown to D_2 and rent is the shaded area $p_2E_2p_1$, which measures scarcity effect. At time 3, rent has grown to $p_3E_2p_1$; the increase from time 2 is the increased scarcity effect.

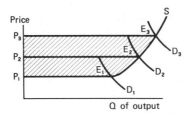

If the world conformed to the specifications of these parametrically invariant, no-depletion models, increases in economic rent would reflect increasing resource scarcity, and nothing else. Assume for example, the Ricardian model where unhomogeneous resources are free goods until productive [9]. Assume standard resources to be the highest quality ever available historically. Then their rent would always equal the marginal resource conversion cost for unhomogeneous resources of marginal quality, and would be a precise index of the increase in scarcity that had occurred from the beginning of man's economic history.

By now, however, we have recognized that there will be many types of standard resources; therefore, there will be many different figures for standard rent; and, for institutional reasons, unhomogeneous resources (including those at the margin) command a reservation price in private enterprise societies. Rent will now contain a pecuniary element that reflects, but does not measure, increasing scarcity; and there will be no single figure for rent—it will be different for each type of resource. As scarcity increases, rents will increase, and rents will also change as the result of changes in general price levels, interest rates, relative demands, and expectations concerning future resource availability. Under these conditions, advances in rent on unhomogeneous resources are an ambiguous indicator of increases in scarcity.

The inappropriateness of economic rent as an indicator of increasing scarcity is also compelling in the case of depletable mineral resources. As the best resources are used up, they disappear from the left-hand portion of the supply curves, and so do the economic rent areas. At the time that Mesabi range hematite ore is exhausted and Mesabi taconite is used, the only visible rent could be the differences among taconites.

Rent would be a useful indicator of increasing scarcity in a Ricardian no-depletion world where the resource conversion path for employment of declining quality resources stayed put, and the process of growth involved nothing more complicated than a systematic traversal of the path. But in a world of depletion, of variable reservation prices and degrees of reservation, and especially of sociotechnical change, this is no longer so. The conversion path changes shape and position, with the result that quality differences among resources, their rank in the quality spectrum, and, therefore, the rents that they earn, vary irregularly over time. Rents on different resources will disappear, decrease, or increase as a result of the depletion and economic reordering of resources, of changes in resource economizing behavior, or of changes in the technical or social parameters that determine the rank of resources in order of quality. Because of these changes in the resource quality spectrum which are induced by sociotechnical change, depletion, and so on, economic rent is a nonoperational concept in the modern world. The changes cause capital gains and losses and a variety of income elements to be blended with economic rent and make its determination impossible.

Urban land has anti-Ricardian elements of particular interest. Let us assume that rent per unit of urban land is high and increasing in the United States, even if income earned on the cost of improvements is deducted. Does this signify increasing natural resource scarcity? We think not. The emergence of urban rent does not reflect declining productivity from use at the extensive margin or inefficiencies from more intensive use in the United States. Increasing urban rent does not reflect a declining absolute quality (increasing resource conversion cost) of marginal land under the impact of growth. It reflects, on the contrary, the absolute *increase* in economic quality of intramarginal urban land due to its advancing productivity. Man's propensity to build where he has already built—his liking for crowds, together with the existence of economies of concentration—has raised the price of land in metropolitan areas. What advances the value of urban land is the fact that it offers new economies which the combination of sociotechnical advance and agglomeration create. Urban rents thus reflect the economic advantages of agglomeration, not disadvantages imposed by nature. The rents result from a *decline* in the intramarginal portion of the cost curve.

As demand rises as a result of growth and technical advance, the labor plus capital efficiency in production of the urban product increases and is supplied at a declining unit cost. The marginal productivity of strategically located blocks of land increases under these conditions, and rents rise. Urban rents have risen primarily because labor plus capital cost per unit of urban product has fallen. Thus, urban rent is not an indicator of natural resource scarcity in the classical sense. The increase in urban rent accompanies a declining cost trend for urban product that is opposite to that postulated by the classical growth doctrine of increasing resource scarcity and increasing rent. Economic rent would not be an indicator of increasing resource scarcity in our sense, even if it could be measured. Specifically, increases in urban land rent do not signify an imminent cost-increasing shortage of either land or natural resources in general.

We conclude as follows. First, Ricardian (or Malthusian) economic rent is a fine static theory. It is not a dynamic one, in a society with technical change, depletion, inflation, and great varieties of resources. Second, in general it is not practical to measure economic rent changes in order to measure or test the increasing scarcity hypotheses for various resources. Practically speaking, it is much better to measure changes in costs and prices.

Appendix B: Foreign Country and Region Time Series on Productivity, Relative Productivity, and Relative Price Regressions

CODES FOR PRODUCTS, VARIABLES,

AND COUNTRIES/REGIONS
(8 place code)

PRODUCTS (Places 1 and 2)	CODES
Agriculture	AG
Agriculture, alternative	A2
Coal	CO
Coal, Auger	CA
Coal, Ship	CS
Coal, Underground	CU
Economy	E
Economy, Alternative	E2
Industry	I
Iron Ore	IR
Iron Ore & Coal	IC
Manufacturing	MA
Metallic Minerals	MM
Minerals	MI
Mining, Energy, & Water	N
Petroleum & Gas	PG
Retail	RT
Wholesale Trade	W

VARIABLES (Places 4 and 5)	
Labor Input	L
% Labor Input of Force	LP
Output	O
Price	P
Price received ÷ Price paid	RP
Productivity	PY
Relative Productivity	RY

COUNTRY/REGION (places 7 and 8)		COUNTRY/REGION cont.	CODES
Algeria	AL	India (West Bengal)	IB
Argentina	AR	Iran	IR
Australia	AA	Iraq	IQ
Austria	A	Ireland	IL
Belgium	B	Israel	IS
Brazil	BR	Italy	I
Canada	CN	Japan	JP
Centrally Planned Economy	CP	Korea	KR
Chile	CE	Market Economies	M
Columbia	CO	Mexico	MX
Costa Rica	CR	Netherlands	NL
Czechoslovakia	CS	New Zealand	NZ
Denmark	DK	Norway	N
Developed Market Economies	DM	Phillipines	PP
Developing Market Economies	GM	Poland	P
Ecuador	EC	Portugal	PO
ECC	EE	Spain	E
Federal Republic of Germany	D	Sweden	S
Finland	SU	Switzerland	CH
France	F	Thailand	TH
Greece	GR	United Kingdom	GB
Hungary	H	United States	US
India	IN	Venezuela	VE
India (Assam)	IA	World	W
India (Punjab)	IP	Yugoslavia	YU
India (Uttar Pradest)	IU		

log time trends

```
 1 cu-py-us  time44=1       const         r/se        dw/df
ols          0.041356      1.572144      0.864646    0.000000
log tred    13.647477     29.223665      0.143660   28.000000

 2 cs-py-us  time44=1       const         r/se        dw/df
ols          0.036176      2.584150      0.953441    0.000000
log tred    24.389854     98.138855      0.070316   28.000000

 3 ca-py-us  time44=1       const         r/se        dw/df
ols          0.034578      2.829618      0.744595    0.000000
log tred     7.888243     31.479095      0.130442   20.000000

 4 co-py-us  time44=1       const         r/se        dw/df
ols          0.048680      1.668265      0.940536    0.000000
log tred    21.440306     41.388245      0.107639   28.000000

 5 co-py-gb  time44=1       const         r/se        dw/df
ols          0.034129      0.258354      0.897274    0.000000
log tred    15.946941      6.799798      0.101461   28.000000

 6 co-py-b-  time44=1       const         r/se        dw/df
ols          0.045858     -0.277905      0.971725    0.000000
log tred    31.585577    -10.781933      0.068830   28.000000

 7 co-py-f-  time44=1       const         r/se        dw/df
ols          0.041679     -0.040677      0.962628    0.000000
log tred    27.349289     -1.503521      0.072247   28.000000

 8 co-py-nl  time44=1       const         r/se        dw/df
ols          0.025868      0.351459      0.744314    0.000000
log tred     9.242305      7.073358      0.132687   28.000000

 9 co-py-d-  time44=1       const         r/se        dw/df
ols          0.051594     -0.013058      0.965301    0.000000
log tred    26.912653     -0.364247      0.077589   25.000000

10 co-py-p-  time44=1       const         r/se        dw/df
ols          0.020716      0.433913      0.706689    0.000000
log tred     7.511003      8.431286      0.103934   22.000000

11 mi-py-w-  time44=1       const         r/se        dw/df
ols          0.044261     -1.198902      0.993539    0.000000
log tred    30.391232    -35.147858      0.019694    5.000000

12 co-py-w-  time44=1       const         r/se        dw/df
ols          0.037325     -1.021738      0.981183    0.000000
log tred    17.716257    -20.705931      0.028489    5.000000

13 pg-py-w-  time44=1       const         r/se        dw/df
ols          0.059213     -1.614774      0.993935    0.000000
log tred    31.373508    -36.529228      0.025522    5.000000

14 mm-py-w-  time44=1       const         r/se        dw/df
ols          0.041358     -1.121608      0.950970    0.000000
log tred    10.833899    -12.544446      0.051621    5.000000
```

continued-log time trends

```
15 ma-py-w-   time44=1      const        r/se        dw/df
   ols        0.037885     -1.021943    0.996345    0.000000
   log tred  40.455555    -46.592659    0.012663    5.000000

16 mi-py-cp   time44=1      const        r/se        dw/df
   ols        0.044540     -1.193449    0.991702    0.000000
   log tred  28.940407    -31.857979    0.023213    6.000000

17 co-py-cp   time44=1      const        r/se        dw/df
   ols        0.036279     -0.978449    0.988019    0.000000
   log tred  24.046745    -26.643608    0.022756    6.000000

18 pg-py-cp   time44=1      const        r/se        dw/df
   ols        0.067557     -1.824031    0.982308    0.000000
   log tred  19.739670    -21.895712    0.051620    6.000000

19 mm-py-cp   time44=1      const        r/se        dw/df
   ols        0.065963     -1.768069    0.997614    0.000000
   log tred  54.107224    -59.581596    0.018388    6.000000

20 ma-py-cp   time44=1      const        r/se        dw/df
   ols        0.052146     -1.399343    0.994349    0.000000
   log tred  35.110645    -38.707981    0.022401    6.000000

21 mi-py-m-   time44=1      const        r/se        dw/df
   ols        0.044938     -1.218694    0.977205    0.000000
   log tred  16.069048    -18.606010    0.037816    5.000000

22 co-py-m-   time44=1      const        r/se        dw/df
   ols        0.037508     -1.040128    0.931637    0.000000
   log tred   9.097634    -10.771440    0.055751    5.000000

23 pg-py-m-   time44=1      const        r/se        dw/df
   ols        0.063597     -1.737559    0.981229    0.000000
   log tred  17.737984    -20.691511    0.048483    5.000000

24 mm-py-m-   time44=1      const        r/se        dw/df
   ols        0.037892     -1.030951    0.927648    0.000000
   log tred   8.827659    -10.254536    0.058045    5.000000

25 ma-py-m-   time44=1      const        r/se        dw/df
   ols        0.034302     -0.925322    0.997700    0.000000
   log tred  51.021683    -58.764652    0.009091    5.000000

26 mi-py-dm   time44=1      const        r/se        dw/df
   ols        0.045133     -1.257720    0.981112    0.000000
   log tred  19.094748    -21.860647    0.035651    6.000000

27 co-py-dm   time44=1      const        r/se        dw/df
   ols        0.032394     -0.932738    0.897997    0.000000
   log tred   7.913613     -9.361102    0.061742    6.000000

28 pg-py-dm   time44=1      const        r/se        dw/df
   ols        0.055844     -1.542553    0.995873    0.000000
   log tred  41.113274    -46.655052    0.020487    6.000000
```

log time trends

```
29 mm-py-dm  time44=1       const        r/se        dw/df
ols          0.041999     -1.178717    0.948386    0.000000
log tred    11.385123    -13.126996    0.055641    6.000000

30 ma-py-dm  time44=1       const        r/se        dw/df
ols          0.041832     -1.120172    0.996113    0.000000
log tred    42.367138    -46.608089    0.014893    6.000000

31 mi-py-gm  time44=1       const        r/se        dw/df
ols          0.044325     -1.169400    0.960901    0.000000
log tred    12.184214    -13.724585    0.049193    5.000000

32 co-py-gm  time44=1       const        r/se        dw/df
ols          0.046783     -1.270374    0.943644    0.000000
log tred    10.073006    -11.678428    0.062804    5.000000

33 pg-py-gm  time44=1       const        r/se        dw/df
ols          0.079246     -2.149493    0.950459    0.000000
log tred    10.775532    -12.478989    0.099448    5.000000

34 mm-py-gm  time44=1       const        r/se        dw/df
ols          0.032277     -0.867715    0.831203    0.000000
log tred     5.526822     -6.343762    0.078971    5.000000

35 ma-py-gm  time44=1       const        r/se        dw/df
ols          0.022833     -0.630921    0.984610    0.000000
log tred    19.617771    -23.144156    0.015739    5.000000

36 co-py-ee  time44=1       const        r/se        dw/df
ols          0.087790     -0.692818    0.865198    0.000000
log tred     6.285708     -2.467947    0.073905    5.000000

143 ag-rp-aa time44=1       const        r/se        dw/df
ols         -0.037299      0.394641    0.713697    0.000000
log tred    -5.779826      4.340480    0.097336   12.000000

144 ag-rp-a- time44=1       const        r/se        dw/df
ols         -0.010587      0.145832    0.630319    0.000000
log tred    -4.444706      4.107432    0.028485   10.000000

145 ag-rp-b- time44=1       const        r/se        dw/df
ols         -0.026772      0.183012    0.886423    0.000000
log tred   -10.122259      4.911243    0.039893   12.000000

147 ag-rp-cn time44=1       const        r/se        dw/df
ols         -0.023774      0.383495    0.718453    0.000000
log tred    -5.845803      6.693031    0.061341   12.000000

148 ag-rp-ct time44=1       const        r/se        dw/df
ols          0.008933     -0.118951    0.760874    0.000000
log tred     6.000068     -6.161269    0.017803   10.000000

151 ag-rp-d- time44=1       const        r/se        dw/df
ols         -0.004658      0.053609    0.148857    0.000000
log tred    -1.604374      1.188775    0.033467    8.000000
```

```
continued-log time trends

152 ag-rp-gr  time44=1        const        r/se        dw/df
     ols       0.005652     -0.092059     0.104288     0.000000
     log tred  1.303296     -1.240157     0.022948     5.000000

153 ag-rp-ia  time44=1        const        r/se        dw/df
     ols       0.003941     -0.011498    -0.046304     0.000000
     log tred  0.651676     -0.134938     0.091220    12.000000

154 ag-rp-ip  time44=1        const        r/se        dw/df
     ols      -0.005581      0.016785     0.054112     0.000000
     log tred -1.320491      0.281872     0.063750    12.000000

155 ag-rp-ib  time44=1        const        r/se        dw/df
     ols       0.019588     -0.087005     0.228040     0.000000
     log tred  1.833908     -0.535187     0.082733     7.000000

158 ag-rp-jp  time44=1        const        r/se        dw/df
     ols       0.007611     -0.071033     0.211555     0.000000
     log tred  2.054223     -1.322979     0.049984    11.000000

159 ag-rp-nl  time44=1        const        r/se        dw/df
     ols      -0.039894      0.332979     0.966214     0.000000
     log tred -19.307499    11.438099     0.031165    12.000000

160 ag-rp-n-  time44=1        const        r/se        dw/df
     ols      -0.006082      0.054456     0.195021     0.000000
     log tred -1.850049      1.080507     0.034481     9.000000

163 ag-rp-ch  time44=1        const        r/se        dw/df
     ols      -0.009628      0.026867     0.806804     0.000000
     log tred -7.435678      1.472754     0.019530    12.000000

164 ag-rp-us  time44=1        const        r/se        dw/df
     ols      -0.022631      0.316638     0.813191     0.000000
     log tred -7.588789      7.536225     0.044980    12.000000

165 ag-rp-cn  time44=1        const        r/se        dw/df
     ols      -0.008819      4.746822     0.337977     0.000000
     log tred -2.364023     51.580559     0.033885     8.000000

166 ag-rp-us  time44=1        const        r/se        dw/df
     ols      -0.010055      4.559631     0.523947     0.000000
     log tred -3.298093     60.631462     0.027690     8.000000

167 ag-rp-ia  time44=1        const        r/se        dw/df
     ols       0.031898      4.024894     0.727560     0.000000
     log tred  4.729650     24.723330     0.052241     7.000000

168 ag-rp-ip  time44=1        const        r/se        dw/df
     ols      -0.032330      5.454360     0.490970     0.000000
     log tred -2.413751     16.581160     0.056031     4.000000

169 ag-rp-iu  time44=1        const        r/se        dw/df
     ols       0.004793      4.612051    -0.221213     0.000000
     log tred  0.309084     13.181527     0.064866     4.000000
```

log time trends

```
170 ag-rp-ib   time44=1        const         r/se          dw/df
    ols        -0.031960      5.408308      0.348371      0.000000
    log tred   -1.435156     11.556107      0.031493      1.000000

171 ag-rp-is   time44=1        const         r/se          dw/df
    ols         0.000424      4.532634     -0.153333      0.000000
    log tred    0.130957     59.312439      0.020975      6.000000

172 ag-rp-jp   time44=1        const         r/se          dw/df
    ols         0.013475      4.236064      0.479019      0.000000
    log tred    3.045040     38.806290      0.040194      8.000000

173 ag-rp-kr   time44=1        const         r/se          dw/df
    ols        -0.001494      4.661682     -0.120587      0.000000
    log tred   -0.171060     21.632227      0.079348      8.000000

174 ag-rp-pp   time44=1        const         r/se          dw/df
    ols        -0.013006      4.992368      0.560957      0.000000
    log tred   -3.536418     55.031330      0.033404      8.000000

175 ag-rp-a-   time44=1        const         r/se          dw/df
    ols        -0.006043      4.664383      0.248742      0.000000
    log tred   -1.992247     62.335293      0.027552      8.000000

176 ag-rp-b-   time44=1        const         r/se          dw/df
    ols        -0.013464      4.908550      0.663867      0.000000
    log tred   -4.331133     64.009789      0.028236      8.000000

177 ag-rp-cs   time44=1        const         r/se          dw/df
    ols         0.014178      4.251705      0.835526      0.000000
    log tred    5.132826     57.966038      0.011555      4.000000

178 ag-rp-dk   time44=1        const         r/se          dw/df
    ols         0.008012      4.415236      0.369318      0.000000
    log tred    2.500812     55.865509      0.029101      8.000000

179 ag-rp-su   time44=1        const         r/se          dw/df
    ols         0.001123      4.970140     -0.103155      0.000000
    log tred    0.424268     76.125237      0.024040      8.000000

181 ag-rp-d-   time44=1        const         r/se          dw/df
    ols        -0.014029      4.924053      0.498438      0.000000
    log tred   -3.153552     44.871151      0.040407      8.000000

182 ag-rp-h-   time44=1        const         r/se          dw/df
    ols        -0.002250      4.796964     -0.123084      0.000000
    log tred   -0.499576     41.600239      0.029188      6.000000

183 ag-rp-ir   time44=1        const         r/se          dw/df
    ols         0.013741      4.494890      0.377021      0.000000
    log tred    2.538894     33.667591      0.049159      8.000000

184 ag-rp-i-   time44=1        const         r/se          dw/df
    ols        -0.013628      5.004635      0.348734      0.000000
    log tred   -2.410138     35.879196      0.051360      8.000000
```

continued-log time trends

```
185 ag-rp-n-  time44=1       const         r/se        dw/df
     ols      -0.007994     4.784759     0.750000     0.000000
     log tred -4.688795   109.620354     0.011049     6.000000

186 ag-rp-p-  time44=1       const         r/se        dw/df
     ols       0.020159     4.212204     0.795950     0.000000
     log tred  6.007713    50.889275     0.030478     8.000000

187 ag-rp-e-  time44=1       const         r/se        dw/df
     ols       0.015283     4.340639     0.473976     0.000000
     log tred  2.867272    32.401951     0.041287     7.000000

188 ag-rp-s-  time44=1       const         r/se        dw/df
     ols      -0.000551     4.595370    -0.200000     0.000000
     log tred -0.106999    34.242546     0.027232     5.000000

189 ag-rp-ch  time44=1       const         r/se        dw/df
     ols      -0.022163     4.882158     0.928968     0.000000
     log tred -10.894522   97.289658     0.018477     8.000000

191 ag-rp-aa  time44=1       const         r/se        dw/df
     ols      -0.026463     5.169402     0.396913     0.000000
     log tred -2.630939    20.834494     0.091359     8.000000

192 ic-py-d   time44=1       const         r/se        dw/df
     ols       0.051635    -0.711510     0.964533     0.000000
     log tred 10.477617   -17.771471     0.015584     3.000000

193 co-py-d   time44=1       const         r/se        dw/df
     ols       0.031683    -0.655029     0.885094     0.000000
     log tred  5.640169   -14.353466     0.017764     3.000000

194 ir-py-d   time44=1       const         r/se        dw/df
     ols       0.082698    -0.640232     0.735031     0.000000
     log tred  3.477947    -3.314326     0.075192     3.000000

195 ma-py-d   time44=1       const         r/se        dw/df
     ols       0.078423    -0.604122     0.941753     0.000000
     log tred  8.103927    -7.684351     0.030602     3.000000

196 ag-o--d-  time44=1       const         r/se        dw/df
     ols       0.020235    -0.223351     0.770667     0.000000
     log tred  5.882573    -4.524014     0.036077     9.000000

197 ag-o--d-  time44=1       const         r/se        dw/df
     ols       0.015406    -0.279842     0.585873     0.000000
     log tred  4.069629    -2.987724     0.045270    10.000000

198 mi-o--d   time44=1       const         r/se        dw/df
     ols       0.007753     4.413868     0.366087     0.000000
     log tred  3.623535   110.816940     0.063673    20.000000

199 i--o--d   time44=1       const         r/se        dw/df
     ols       0.066204     3.289886     0.972737     0.000000
     log tred 27.391510    73.124619     0.071922    20.000000
```

```
             log time trends

200 i--py-d   time44=1      const        r/se       dw/df
   ols         0.045467   -0.841110    0.991859    0.000000
   log tred   50.591499  -50.278332    0.026743   20.000000

201 ag-l--d   time44=1      const        r/se       dw/df
   ols        -0.045788    0.911351    0.944733    0.000000
   log tred  -16.044062   15.197762    0.052624   14.000000

202 a2-l--d   time44=1      const        r/se       dw/df
   ols        -0.042206    0.827853    0.987149    0.000000
   log tred  -32.809040   30.015823    0.021526   13.000000

203 ag-lp-d   time44=1      const        r/se       dw/df
   ols        -0.050595    3.516257    0.909349    0.000000
   log tred  -12.307386   40.707188    0.075803   14.000000

204 n--l--d   time44=1      const        r/se       dw/df
   ols        -0.044222    0.847547    0.978719    0.000000
   log tred  -25.394140   22.700449    0.029140   13.000000

205 e--l--d   time44=1      const        r/se       dw/df
   ols         0.003969   -0.090430    0.259162    0.000000
   log tred    2.499471   -2.710137    0.029282   14.000000

206 e2-l--d   time44=1      const        r/se       dw/df
   ols         0.001483   -0.035322    0.122989    0.000000
   log tred    1.721429   -1.912748    0.014413   13.000000

207 rm-p-d    time44=1      const        r/se       dw/df
   ols         0.008355    4.450535    0.505882    0.000000
   log tred    4.743849  135.755844    0.052408   20.000000

208 mi-p-d    time44=1      const        r/se       dw/df
   ols         0.027190    4.066377    0.759351    0.000000
   log tred    8.391692   68.773643    0.103075   21.000000

209 ma-p-d    time44=1      const        r/se       dw/df
   ols         0.008330    4.445939    0.666102    0.000000
   log tred    6.701231  196.001816    0.039543   21.000000

210 w--p-d    time44=1      const        r/se       dw/df
   ols         0.006121    4.485813    0.354460    0.000000
   log tred    2.649790   85.315834    0.027621   10.000000

211 rt-p-d    time44=1      const        r/se       dw/df
   ols         0.012295    4.374485    0.862557    0.000000
   log tred   11.792424  229.922684    0.033168   21.000000

212 co-py-gb  time44=1      const        r/se       dw/df
   ols         0.027202    3.007384    0.728941    0.000000
   log tred    5.020041   21.628185    0.049217    8.000000

213 mimapy-w  time44=1      const        r/se       dw/df
   ols         0.006338   -0.176021    0.697765    0.000000
   log tred    3.853840   -4.569756    0.022239    5.000000
```

continued-log time trends

```
214 comapy-w  time44=1        const        r/se        dw/df
    ols       -0.000527     -0.000749    -0.189706    0.000000
    log tred  -0.208000     -0.012632     0.034234    5.000000

215 pgmapy-w  time44=1        const        r/se        dw/df
    ols        0.021340     -0.593080     0.937886    0.000000
    log tred   9.570629    -11.356465     0.030152    5.000000

216 mmmapy-w  time44=1        const        r/se        dw/df
    ols        0.003494     -0.100053    -0.035686    0.000000
    log tred   0.890651     -1.089060     0.053042    5.000000

218 mimapycp  time44=1        const        r/se        dw/df
    ols       -0.007620      0.206300     0.984668    0.000000
    log tred -21.226696     23.607830     0.005415    6.000000

219 comapycp  time44=1        const        r/se        dw/df
    ols       -0.015858      0.420807     0.985854    0.000000
    log tred -22.109550     24.103689     0.010818    6.000000

220 pgmapycp  time44=1        const        r/se        dw/df
    ols        0.015432     -0.425462     0.674146    0.000000
    log tred   3.934723     -4.456561     0.059157    6.000000

221 mmmapycp  time44=1        const        r/se        dw/df
    ols        0.013859     -0.369666     0.896206    0.000000
    log tred   7.838451     -8.589347     0.026668    6.000000

223 mimapy-m  time44=1        const        r/se        dw/df
    ols        0.010647     -0.293652     0.672382    0.000000
    log tred   3.648833     -4.296928     0.039456    5.000000

224 comapy-m  time44=1        const        r/se        dw/df
    ols        0.003188     -0.114292    -0.082796    0.000000
    log tred   0.735672     -1.126216     0.058591    5.000000

225 pgmapy-m  time44=1        const        r/se        dw/df
    ols        0.029284     -0.811999     0.901511    0.000000
    log tred   7.477985     -8.853021     0.052955    5.000000

226 mmmapy-m  time44=1        const        r/se        dw/df
    ols        0.003588     -0.105620    -0.052266    0.000000
    log tred   0.837842     -1.053003     0.057910    5.000000

228 mimapydm  time44=1        const        r/se        dw/df
    ols        0.003361     -0.138877     0.080576    0.000000
    log tred   1.270222     -2.156084     0.039913    6.000000

229 comapydm  time44=1        const        r/se        dw/df
    ols       -0.009445      0.187645     0.340651    0.000000
    log tred  -2.148613      1.753740     0.066301    6.000000

230 pgmapydm  time44=1        const        r/se        dw/df
    ols        0.014016     -0.422463     0.838672    0.000000
    log tred   6.114716     -7.571801     0.034573    6.000000
```

log time trends

```
231 mmmapydm   time44=1       const         r/se          dw/df
    ols        0.000176      -0.058617     -0.166310     0.000000
    log tred   0.042841      -0.585683      0.062017     6.000000

233 mimapygm   time44=1       const         r/se          dw/df
    ols        0.021480      -0.538271      0.828723     0.000000
    log tred   5.480044      -5.863317      0.053003     5.000000

234 comapygm   time44=1       const         r/se          dw/df
    ols        0.023968      -0.639837      0.776074     0.000000
    log tred   4.668461      -5.321057      0.069424     5.000000

235 pgmapygm   time44=1       const         r/se          dw/df
    ols        0.056387      -1.517945      0.889287     0.000000
    log tred   7.013851      -8.061581      0.108711     5.000000

236 mmmapygm   time44=1       const         r/se          dw/df
    ols        0.009449      -0.236851      0.197914     0.000000
    log tred   1.574960      -1.685626      0.081125     5.000000

238 icmapy-d   time44=1       const         r/se          dw/df
    ols       -0.026771      -0.107409      0.846153     0.000000
    log tred  -4.795828      -2.368505      0.017652     3.000000

239 comapy-d   time44=1       const         r/se          dw/df
    ols       -0.046653      -0.051564      0.949660     0.000000
    log tred  -8.744099      -1.189620      0.016872     3.000000

240 irmapy-d   time44=1       const         r/se          dw/df
    ols        0.004244      -0.036057     -0.299148     0.000000
    log tred   0.280963      -0.293801      0.047771     3.000000

242 ag-py-d    time44=1       const         r/se          dw/df
    ols        0.086238      -1.455256      0.776050     0.000000
    log tred   4.668157      -4.885415      0.097753     5.000000

243 ag-py-d    time44=1       const         r/se          dw/df
    ols        0.060560      -1.169290      0.922263     0.000000
    log tred  10.381453      -8.466550      0.052985     8.000000

245 mi-py-d    time44=1       const         r/se          dw/df
    ols        0.042878       3.767149      0.968275     0.000000
    log tred  20.695358      84.807014      0.034669    13.000000

247 agi-py-d   time44=1       const         r/se          dw/df
    ols        0.043445      -5.254023      0.271288     0.000000
    log tred   1.798619     -13.489925      0.127813     5.000000

248 agi-py-d   time44=1       const         r/se          dw/df
    ols        0.041922      -0.614627      0.345650     0.000000
    log tred   2.041913      -1.856622      0.108637     5.000000

249 agi-py-d   time44=1       const         r/se          dw/df
    ols        0.008482      -0.173063      0.045545     0.000000
    log tred   1.195601      -1.030455      0.064434     8.000000
```

continued-log time trends

```
250 mii-py-d  time44=1       const         r/se         dw/df
    ols       -0.006734     4.702411     0.401709     0.000000
    log tred  -3.225191   105.044388     0.034939    13.000000

252 rmma-p-d  time44=1       const         r/se         dw/df
    ols        0.000745    -0.010600    -0.030751     0.000000
    log tred   0.611142    -0.467060     0.036281    20.000000

254 rmw-p-d   time44=1       const         r/se         dw/df
    ols       -0.002241     0.061244     0.070604     0.000000
    log tred  -1.354861     1.626908     0.019776    10.000000

256 rmrt-p-d  time44=1       const         r/se         dw/df
    ols       -0.005146     0.101270     0.219049     0.000000
    log tred  -2.624936     2.775120     0.058337    20.000000

258 mima-p-d  time44=1       const         r/se         dw/df
    ols        0.018862    -0.379550     0.656948     0.000000
    log tred   6.567353    -7.241822     0.091367    21.000000

260 miw-p-d   time44=1       const         r/se         dw/df
    ols        0.011057    -0.211062     0.550354     0.000000
    log tred   3.803112    -3.189260     0.034766    10.000000

262 mirt-p-d  time44=1       const         r/se         dw/df
    ols        0.014890    -0.308048     0.383731     0.000000
    log tred   3.833890    -4.346382     0.123554    21.000000

264 agw-p-b   time44=1       const         r/se         dw/df
    ols       -0.004550     0.067088     0.130474     0.000000
    log tred  -1.673506     1.823983     0.036680    11.000000

265 agw-p-f   time44=1       const         r/se         dw/df
    ols        0.004272    -0.115940     0.193694     0.000000
    log tred   1.970456    -3.953066     0.029249    11.000000

266 agw-p-d   time44=1       const         r/se         dw/df
    ols        0.008737    -0.133254     0.550177     0.000000
    log tred   3.284016    -3.290655     0.020608     7.000000

267 agw-p-ir  time44=1       const         r/se         dw/df
    ols       -0.018571     0.290347     0.839130     0.000000
    log tred  -6.924278     7.323632     0.024361     8.000000

268 agw-p-i   time44=1       const         r/se         dw/df
    ols        0.005759    -0.105450     0.250452     0.000000
    log tred   2.001810    -2.479642     0.026131     8.000000

269 agw-p-nl  time44=1       const         r/se         dw/df
    ols       -0.005974     0.114503     0.315830     0.000000
    log tred  -2.557245     3.623381     0.031515    11.000000

270 agw-p-po  time44=1       const         r/se         dw/df
    ols        0.000288     0.004019    -0.089659     0.000000
    log tred   0.112355     0.115836     0.034603    11.000000
```

                 log time trends

```
271 agw-p-e    time44=1      const         r/se         dw/df
   ols         0.007075     -0.106284     0.633671     0.000000
   log tred    2.814097     -2.550146     0.013586     3.000000

272 agw-p-s    time44=1      const         r/se         dw/df
   ols         0.011505     -0.153560     0.636831     0.000000
   log tred    4.504324     -4.314540     0.030544     10.000000

273 agw-p-yu   time44=1      const         r/se         dw/df
   ols         0.037378     -0.526620     0.571274     0.000000
   log tred    2.768116     -2.500996     0.056487     4.000000

274 agw-p-cn   time44=1      const         r/se         dw/df
   ols        -0.010619      0.166949     0.401971     0.000000
   log tred   -3.010965      3.499194     0.047580     11.000000

275 agw-p-cr   time44=1      const         r/se         dw/df
   ols        -0.002941      0.046410     0.001349     0.000000
   log tred   -1.006060      1.074196     0.026548     8.000000

276 agw-p-mx   time44=1      const         r/se         dw/df
   ols         0.006792     -0.135851     0.462842     0.000000
   log tred    3.367463     -4.979258     0.027209     11.000000

277 agw-p-us   time44=1      const         r/se         dw/df
   ols        -0.025162      0.362218     0.853998     0.000000
   log tred   -8.437472      8.978766     0.040231     11.000000

278 agw-p-ar   time44=1      const         r/se         dw/df
   ols         0.013880     -0.195632     0.550235     0.000000
   log tred    2.887959     -2.524448     0.025431     5.000000

279 agw-p-br   time44=1      const         r/se         dw/df
   ols        -0.010162      0.184314     0.534254     0.000000
   log tred   -3.842540      5.151968     0.035678     11.000000

280 agw-p-ce   time44=1      const         r/se         dw/df
   ols        -0.014235      0.401283     0.198631     0.000000
   log tred   -1.993582      4.154287     0.096331     11.000000

281 agw-p-ec   time44=1      const         r/se         dw/df
   ols        -0.008270      0.121694     0.904319     0.000000
   log tred   -8.752765      8.461636     0.007319     7.000000

282 agw-p-pr   time44=1      const         r/se         dw/df
   ols         0.006477     -0.023816     0.053170     0.000000
   log tred    1.271893     -0.360621     0.060901     10.000000

283 agw-p-ve   time44=1      const         r/se         dw/df
   ols        -0.002424      0.032924    -0.040897     0.000000
   log tred   -0.726990      0.729835     0.044988     11.000000

284 agw-p-ir   time44=1      const         r/se         dw/df
   ols         0.002484     -0.027100     0.005250     0.000000
   log tred    1.031181     -0.831769     0.032492     11.000000
```

continued-log time trends

```
285 agw-p-jp  time44=1      const        r/se        dw/df
    ols        0.017516   -0.326239    0.513501    0.000000
    log tred   3.399270   -4.411177    0.054044    9.000000

286 agw-p-al  time44=1      const        r/se        dw/df
    ols       -0.008211    0.169698    0.399981    0.000000
    log tred  -1.732007    1.662627    0.010601    2.000000

287 agw-p-cn  time44=1      const        r/se        dw/df
    ols       -0.006050    0.147397    0.370595    0.000000
    log tred  -2.734379    2.804737    0.026458   10.000000

288 agw-p-cr  time44=1      const        r/se        dw/df
    ols        0.012837   -0.261464    0.723486    0.000000
    log tred   5.457200   -4.679581    0.028130   10.000000

289 agw-p-mx  time44=1      const        r/se        dw/df
    ols        0.007334   -0.128911    0.722846    0.000000
    log tred   5.448776   -4.032402    0.016095   10.000000

290 agw-p-us  time44=1      const        r/se        dw/df
    ols       -0.000393    0.012088   -0.093424    0.000000
    log tred  -0.245233    0.317160    0.019188   10.000000

291 agw-p-ar  time44=1      const        r/se        dw/df
    ols        0.006687   -0.204800    0.059226    0.000000
    log tred   1.300963   -1.677529    0.061464   10.000000

292 agw-p-br  time44=1      const        r/se        dw/df
    ols        0.002662   -0.045842   -0.035721    0.000000
    log tred   0.787798   -0.571257    0.040402   10.000000

293 agw-p-ce  time44=1      const        r/se        dw/df
    ols        0.009262   -0.140263    0.326191    0.000000
    log tred   2.416813   -1.576532    0.040192    9.000000

294 agw-p-co  time44=1      const        r/se        dw/df
    ols       -0.000411    0.037285   -0.095147    0.000000
    log tred  -0.210514    0.804245    0.023341   10.000000

295 agw-p-ec  time44=1      const        r/se        dw/df
    ols        0.007523   -0.142998    0.778409    0.000000
    log tred   5.394677   -4.629351    0.010802    7.000000

296 agw-p-ve  time44=1      const        r/se        dw/df
    ols       -0.010150    0.251273    0.641709    0.000000
    log tred  -4.549865    4.741961    0.026678   10.000000

297 agw-p-in  time44=1      const        r/se        dw/df
    ols        0.012290   -0.217693    0.442642    0.000000
    log tred   3.120252   -2.326892    0.047101   10.000000

298 agw-p-ir  time44=1      const        r/se        dw/df
    ols        0.011206   -0.208064    0.533450    0.000000
    log tred   3.684742   -2.880275    0.036369   10.000000
```

        log time trends

299 agw-p-iq	time44=1	const	r/se	dw/df
ols	0.001454	-0.047374	-0.057063	0.000000
log tred	0.678359	-0.912881	0.022484	9.000000

300 agw-p-jp	time44=1	const	r/se	dw/df
ols	0.032899	-0.649446	0.862475	0.000000
log tred	8.365743	-6.952824	0.047027	10.000000

301 agw-p-kr	time44=1	const	r/se	dw/df
ols	0.035486	-0.881507	0.513151	0.000000
log tred	3.071191	-3.046515	0.095902	7.000000

302 agw-p-pp	time44=1	const	r/se	dw/df
ols	0.010766	-0.213938	0.677242	0.000000
log tred	4.688603	-4.013283	0.024082	9.000000

303 agw-p-th	time44=1	const	r/se	dw/df
ols	0.020363	-0.589875	-0.207097	0.000000
log tred	0.696633	-0.760815	0.065364	2.000000

304 agw-p-a	time44=1	const	r/se	dw/df
ols	-0.003774	0.092731	0.216680	0.000000
log tred	-2.010669	2.079720	0.022448	10.000000

305 agw-p-b	time44=1	const	r/se	dw/df
ols	0.006608	-0.156643	0.311503	0.000000
log tred	2.444758	-2.439856	0.032323	10.000000

306 aga-p-f	time44=1	const	r/se	dw/df
ols	0.006174	-0.141045	0.551731	0.000000
log tred	3.293392	-3.396643	0.014521	7.000000

307 agw-p-d	time44=1	const	r/se	dw/df
ols	-0.007505	0.153821	0.120173	0.000000
log tred	-1.538141	1.357924	0.051173	9.000000

308 agw-p-gr	time44=1	const	r/se	dw/df
ols	0.010231	-0.208961	0.715281	0.000000
log tred	5.111006	-4.324562	0.022012	9.000000

309 agw-p-ir	time44=1	const	r/se	dw/df
ols	0.000369	0.009708	-0.096820	0.000000
log tred	0.170284	0.188661	0.025906	10.000000

310 agw-p-i	time44=1	const	r/se	dw/df
ols	0.002488	-0.065103	0.075634	0.000000
log tred	1.317725	-1.397906	0.017148	8.000000

311 agw-p-nl	time44=1	const	r/se	dw/df
ols	0.008394	-0.176855	0.428060	0.000000
log tred	3.038552	-2.695397	0.033034	10.000000

312 agw-p-po	time44=1	const	r/se	dw/df
ols	0.002212	-0.047557	0.040255	0.000000
log tred	1.208873	-1.094171	0.021882	10.000000

continued-log time trends

```
313 agw-p-e   time44=1        const       r/se        dw/df
   ols        0.004019     -0.082755    0.230155     0.000000
   log tred   2.070890     -1.795274    0.023207    10.000000

314 agw-p-s   time44=1        const       r/se        dw/df
   ols        0.003387     -0.086435    0.130237     0.000000
   log tred   1.626999     -1.748179    0.024893    10.000000

315 agw-p-gb  time44=1        const       r/se        dw/df
   ols        0.066561     -1.274024    0.815910     0.000000
   log tred   7.053606     -5.684109    0.112844    10.000000

316 agw-p-nz  time44=1        const       r/se        dw/df
   ols       -0.019689      0.425144    0.684707     0.000000
   log tred  -4.286399      3.696080    0.038124     7.000000
%
```

variables in data ban

1	cu-py-us	56	w--p--yu	111	ag-p--kr	166	ag-rp-us
2	cs-py-us	57	ag-p--cn	112	w--p--kp	167	ag-rp-ia
3	ca-py-us	58	w--p--cn	113	ag-p--pp	168	ag-rp-ip
4	co-py-us	59	ag-p--cr	114	w--p--pp	169	ag-rp-iu
5	co-py-gb	60	w--p--cr	115	ag-p--th	170	ag-rp-ib
6	co-py-b-	61	ag-p--mx	116	w--p--th	171	ag-rp-is
7	co-py-f-	62	w--p--mx	117	ag-p--a-	172	ag-rp-jp
8	co-py-nl	63	ag-p--us	118	w--p--a-	173	ag-rp-kr
9	co-py-d-	64	w--p--us	119	ag-p--b-	174	ag-rp-pp
10	co-py-p-	65	ag-p--ar	120	w--p--b-	175	ag-rp-a-
11	mi-py-w-	66	w--p--ar	121	ag-p--f-	176	ag-rp-b-
12	co-py-w-	67	ag-p--br	122	w--p--f-	177	ag-rp-cs
13	pg-py-w-	68	w--p--br	123	ag-p--d-	178	ag-rp-dk
14	mm-py-w-	69	ag-p--ce	124	w--p--d-	179	ag-rp-su
15	ma-py-w-	70	w--p--ce	125	ag-p--gr	180	ag-rp-f-
16	mi-py-cp	71	ag-p--ec	126	w--p--gr	181	ag-rp-d-
17	co-py-cp	72	w--p--ec	127	ag-p--il	182	ag-rp-h-
18	pg-py-cp	73	ag-p--pr	128	w--p--il	183	ag-rp-ir
19	mm-py-cp	74	w--p--pr	129	ag-p--i-	184	ag-rp-i-
20	ma-py-cp	75	ag-p--ve	130	w--d--i-	185	ag-rp-n-
21	mi-py-m-	76	w--p--ve	131	ag-p--nl	186	ag-rp-p-
22	co-py-m-	77	ag-p--ir	132	w--p--nl	187	ag-rp-e-
23	pg-py-m-	78	w--p--ir	133	ag-p--po	188	ag-rp-s-
24	mm-py-m-	79	ag-p--jp	134	w--p--po	189	ag-rp-ch
25	ma-py-m-	80	w--p--jp	135	ag-p--e-	190	ag-rp-gb
26	mi-py-dm	81	ag-p--al	136	w--p--e-	191	ag-rp-aa
27	co-py-dm	82	w--p--al	137	ag-p--s-	192	ic-py-d
28	pg-py-dm	83	ag-p--cn	138	w--p--s-	193	co-py-d
29	mm-py-dm	84	w--p--cn	139	ag-p--gb	194	ir-py-d
30	ma-py-dm	85	ag-p--cr	140	w--p--gb	195	ma-py-d
31	mi-py-gm	86	w--p--cr	141	ag-p--nz	196	ag-o--d-
32	co-py-gm	87	ag-p--mx	142	w--p--nz	197	ag-o--d-
33	pg-py-gm	88	w--p--mx	143	ag-rp-aa	198	mi-o--d
34	mm-py-gm	89	ag-p--us	144	ag-rp-a-	199	i--o--d
35	ma-py-gm	90	w--p--us	145	ag-rp-b-	200	i--py-d
36	co-py-ee	91	ag-p--ar	146	ag-rp-br	201	ag-l--d
37	ag-p--b-	92	w--p--ar	147	ag-rp-cn	202	a2-1--d
38	w--p--b-	93	ag-p--br	148	ag-rp-ct	203	ag-lp-d
39	ag-p--f-	94	w--p--br	149	ag-rp-su	204	n--l--d
40	w--p--f-	95	ag-p--ce	150	ag-rp-f-	205	e--l--d
41	ag-p--d-	96	w--p--ce	151	ag-rp-d-	206	e2-1--d
42	w--p--d-	97	ag-p--co	152	ag-rp-gr	207	rm-p-d
43	ag-p--ir	98	w--p--co	153	ag-rp-ia	208	mi-p-d
44	w--p--ir	99	ag-p--ec	154	ag-rp-ip	209	ma-p-d
45	ag-p--i-	100	w--p--ec	155	ag-rp-ib	210	w--p-d
46	w--p--i-	101	ag-p--ve	156	ag-rp-ir	211	rt-p-d
47	ag-p--nl	102	w--p--ve	157	ag-rp-i-	212	co-py-gb
48	w--p--nl	103	ag-p--in	158	ag-rp-jp	213	mimapy-w
49	ag-p--po	104	w--p--in	159	ag-rp-nl	214	comapy-w
50	w--p--po	105	ag-p--ir	160	ag-rp-n-	215	pgmapy-w
51	ag-p--e-	106	w--p--ir	161	ag-rp-pr	216	mmmapy-w
52	w--p--e-	107	ag-p--ia	162	ag-rp-po	217	mamapy-w
53	ag-p--s-	108	w--p--ia	163	ag-rp-ch	218	mimapycp
54	w--p--s-	109	ag-p--jp	164	ag-rp-us	219	comapycp
55	ag-p--yu	110	w--p--jp	165	ag-rp-cn	220	pgmapycp

variables in data bank

221	mmmapycp	276	agw-p-mx
222	mamapycp	277	agw-p-us
223	mimapy-m	278	agw-p-ar
224	comapy-m	279	agw-p-br
225	pgmapy-m	280	agw-p-ce
226	mmmapy-m	281	agw-p-ec
227	mamapy-m	282	agw-p-pr
228	mimapydm	283	agw-p-ve
229	comapydm	284	agw-p-ir
230	pgmapydm	285	agw-p-jp
231	mmmapydm	286	agw-p-al
232	mamapydm	287	agw-p-cn
233	mimapygm	288	agw-p-cr
234	comapygm	289	agw-p-mx
235	pgmapygm	290	agw-p-us
236	mmmapygm	291	agw-p-ar
237	mamapygm	292	agw-p-br
238	icmapy-d	293	agw-p-ce
239	comapy-d	294	agw-p-co
240	irmapy-d	295	agw-p-ec
241	mamapy-d	296	agw-p-ve
242	ag-py-d	297	agw-p-in
243	ag-py-d	298	agw-p-ir
244	ag-ll-d	299	agw-p-iq
245	mi-py-d	300	agw-p-jp
246	n-ll-d	301	agw-p-kr
247	agi-py-d	302	agw-p-pp
248	agi-py-d	303	agw-p-th
249	agi-py-d	304	agw-p-a
250	mii-py-d	305	agw-p-b
251	ii--py-d	306	aga-p-f
252	rmma-p-d	307	agw-p-d
253	mama-p-d	308	agw-p-gr
254	rmw-p-d	309	agw-p-il
255	ww-p-d	310	agw-p-i
256	rmrt-p-d	311	agw-p-nl
257	rtrt-p-d	312	agw-p-po
258	mima-p-d	313	agw-p-e
259		314	agw-p-s
260	miw-p-d	315	agw-p-gb
261	ww-p-d	316	agw-p-nz
262	mirt-p-d		
263	rtrt-p-d		
264	agw-p-b		
265	agw-p-f		
266	agw-p-d		
267	agw-p-ir		
268	agw-p-i		
269	agw-p-nl		
270	agw-p-po		
271	agw-p-e		
272	agw-p-s		
273	agw-p-yu		
274	agw-p-cn		
275	agw-p-cr		

variables in data bank

259		63	ag-p--us	166	ag-rp-us	296	agw-p-ve
202	a2-1--d	89	ag-p--us	306	aga-p-f	273	agw-p-yu
201	ag-1--d	75	ag-p--ve	247	agi-py-d	3	ca-py-us
244	ag-11-d	101	ag-p--ve	248	agi-py-d	6	co-py-b-
203	ag-1p-d	55	ag-p--yu	249	agi-py-d	17	co-py-cp
196	ag-o--d-	242	ag-py-d	304	agw-p-a	193	co-py-d
197	ag-o--d-	243	ag-py-d	286	agw-p-al	9	co-py-d-
117	ag-p--a-	144	ag-rp-a-	278	agw-p-ar	27	co-py-dm
81	ag-p--al	175	ag-rp-a-	291	agw-p-ar	36	co-py-ee
65	ag-p--ar	143	ag-rp-aa	264	agw-p-b	7	co-py-f-
91	ag-p--ar	191	ag-rp-aa	305	agw-p-b	5	co-py-gb
37	ag-p--b-	145	ag-rp-b-	279	agw-p-br	212	co-py-gb
119	ag-p--b-	176	ag-rp-b-	292	agw-p-br	32	co-py-gm
67	ag-p--br	146	ag-rp-br	280	agw-p-ce	22	co-py-m-
93	ag-p--br	163	ag-rp-ch	293	agw-p-ce	8	co-py-nl
69	ag-p--ce	189	ag-rp-ch	274	agw-p-cn	10	co-py-p-
95	ag-p--ce	147	ag-rp-cn	287	agw-p-cn	4	co-py-us
57	ag-p--cn	165	ag-rp-cn	294	agw-p-co	12	co-py-w-
83	ag-p--cn	177	ag-rp-cs	275	agw-p-cr	239	comapy-d
97	ag-p--co	148	ag-rp-ct	288	agw-p-cr	224	comapy-m
59	ag-p--cr	151	ag-rp-d-	266	agw-p-d	214	comapy-w
85	ag-p--cr	181	ag-rp-d-	307	agw-p-d	219	comapycp
41	ag-p--d-	178	ag-rp-dk	271	agw-p-e	229	comapydm
123	ag-p--d-	187	ag-rp-e-	313	agw-p-e	234	comapygm
51	ag-p--e-	150	ag-rp-f-	281	agw-p-ec	2	cs-py-us
135	ag-p--e-	180	ag-rp-f-	295	agw-p-ec	1	cu-py-us
71	ag-p--ec	190	ag-rp-gb	265	agw-p-f	205	e--1--d
99	ag-p--ec	152	ag-rp-gr	315	agw-p-gb	206	e2-1--d
39	ag-p--f-	182	ag-rp-h-	308	agw-p-gr	199	i--o--d
121	ag-p--f-	157	ag-rp-i-	268	agw-p-i	200	i--py-d
139	ag-p--gb	184	ag-rp-i-	310	agw-p-i	192	ic-py-d
125	ag-p--gr	153	ag-rp-ia	309	agw-p-il	238	icmapy-d
45	ag-p--i-	167	ag-rp-ia	297	agw-p-in	251	ii--py-d
129	ag-p--i-	155	ag-rp-ib	299	agw-p-iq	194	ir-py-d
127	ag-p--il	170	ag-rp-ib	267	agw-p-ir	240	irmapy-d
103	ag-p--in	154	ag-rp-ip	284	agw-p-ir	209	ma-p-d
107	ag-p--iq	168	ag-rp-ip	298	agw-p-ir	20	ma-py-cp
43	ag-p--ir	156	ag-rp-ir	285	agw-p-jp	195	ma-py-d
77	ag-p--ir	183	ag-rp-ir	300	agw-p-jp	30	ma-py-dm
105	ag-p--ir	171	ag-rp-is	301	agw-p-kr	35	ma-py-gm
79	ag-p--jp	169	ag-rp-iu	276	agw-p-mx	25	ma-py-m-
109	ag-p--jp	158	ag-rp-jp	289	agw-p-mx	15	ma-py-w-
111	ag-p--kr	172	ag-rp-jp	269	agw-p-nl	253	mama-p-d
61	aq-p--mx	173	aq-rp-kr	311	aqw-p-nl	241	mamapy-d
87	ag-p--mx	160	ag-rp-n-	316	agw-p-nz	227	mamapy-m
47	ag-p--nl	185	ag-rp-n-	270	agw-p-po	217	mamapy-w
131	ag-p--nl	159	ag-rp-nl	312	agw-p-po	222	mamapycp
141	ag-p--nz	186	ag-rp-p-	302	agw-p-pp	232	mamapydm
49	ag-p--po	162	ag-rp-po	282	agw-p-pr	237	mamapygm
133	ag-p--po	174	ag-rp-pp	272	agw-p-s	198	mi-o--d
113	ag-p--pp	161	ag-rp-pr	314	agw-p-s	208	mi-p-d
73	ag-p--pr	188	ag-rp-s-	303	agw-p-th	16	mi-py-cp
53	ag-p--s-	149	ag-rp-su	277	agw-p-us	245	mi-py-d
137	ag-p--s-	179	ag-rp-su	290	agw-p-us	26	mi-py-dm
115	ag-p--th	164	ag-rp-us	283	agw-p-ve	31	mi-py-gm

variables in data bank

21	mi-py-m-	86	w--p--cr
11	mi-py-w-	42	w--p--d-
250	mii-py-d	124	w--p--d-
258	mima-p-d	52	w--p--e-
223	mimapy-m	136	w--p--e-
213	mimapy-w	72	w--p--ec
218	mimapycp	100	w--p--ec
228	mimapydm	40	w--p--f-
233	mimapygm	122	w--p--f-
262	mirt-p-d	140	w--p--gb
260	miw-p-d	126	w--p--gr
19	mm-py-cp	46	w--p--i-
29	mm-py-dm	128	w--p--il
34	mm-py-gm	104	w--p--in
24	mm-py-m-	108	w--p--iq
14	mm-py-w-	44	w--p--ir
226	mmmapy-m	78	w--p--ir
216	mmmapy-w	106	w--p--ir
221	mmmapycp	80	w--p--jp
231	mmmapydm	110	w--p--jp
236	mmmapygm	112	w--p--kp
204	n--l--d	62	w--p--mx
246	n-ll-d	88	w--p--mx
18	pg-py-cp	48	w--p--nl
28	pg-py-dm	132	w--p--nl
33	pg-py-gm	142	w--p--nz
23	pg-py-m-	50	w--p--po
13	pg-py-w-	134	w--p--po
225	pgmapy-m	114	w--p--pp
215	pgmapy-w	74	w--p--pr
220	pgmapycp	54	w--p--s-
230	pgmapydm	138	w--p--s-
235	pgmapygm	116	w--p--th
207	rm-p-d	64	w--p--us
252	rmma-p-d	90	w--p--us
256	rmrt-p-d	76	w--p--ve
254	rmw-p-d	102	w--p--ve
211	rt-p-d	56	w--p--yu
257	rtrt-p-d	210	w--p-d
263	rtrt-p-d	255	ww-p-d
130	w--d--i-	261	ww-p-d
118	w--p--a-		
82	w--p--al		
66	w--p--ar		
92	w--p--ar		
38	w--p--b-		
120	w--p--b-		
68	w--p--br		
94	w--p--br		
70	w--p--ce		
96	w--p--ce		
58	w--p--cn		
84	w--p--cn		
98	w--p--co		
60	w--p--cr		

References

1. H. J. Barnett and Chandler Morse, *Scarcity and Growth: The Economics of Natural Resource Availability* (Baltimore, Johns Hopkins University Press for Resources for the Future, 1963).
2. ———, "Population Change and Resources: Malthusianism and Conservation," in *Demographic and Economic Change in Developed Countries*. Conference of the Universities—National Bureau Committee for Economic Research, 1958 (Princeton, N.J., Princeton University Press, 1960).
3. ———, "The Measurement of Change in Natural Resource Economic Scarcity," in *Output, Input, and Productivity Measurement*, 1958 NBER Conference on Income and Wealth (Princeton, N.J., Princeton University Press, 1961).
4. D. H. Meadows, D. L. Meadows, J. Randers, and W. W. Behrens III, *The Limits to Growth* (New York, Universe Books, 1972).
5. P. R. Ehrlich, *The Population Bomb* (New York, Ballantine, 1968).
6. Garrett Hardin, "The Tragedy of the Commons," *Science* vol. 162 (December 13, 1968) pp. 1243–1248.
7. V. Kerry Smith, "Measuring Natural Resource Scarcity: Theory and Practice," *Journal of Environmental Economics and Management* vol. 5 (June 1978) pp. 150–171.
8. R. G. Ridker, "Resource and Environmental Consequences of Population Growth in the United States: A Summary," in R. G. Ridker, ed., *Population, Resources and the Environment*, The Commission on Population Growth and the American Future Research Reports, vol. 3 (Washington, GPO, 1972).
9. David Ricardo, *Principles of Political Economy and Taxation* (London, 1926).

9

The Adequacy of Measures for Signaling
The Scarcity of Natural Resources

Gardner M. Brown, Jr. and Barry Field

I
Overview

Are natural resources, collectively or individually, growing more scarce in an economic sense? The answer to this question requires an index or indicator that will register scarcity accurately, when it occurs. There are several candidates for such an indicator and disagreement about which is best. We have concentrated on the three most common measures:[1] unit cost, omitting the cost of natural resources, as developed by Barnettt and Morse in their widely referenced work;[2] extractive natural resource product price; and[3] natural resource rental rate. We conclude that each of these measures has flaws.

In the first part of the paper each index is defined and illustrations of its use are cited from the literature. In some cases the indexes have been updated, amended, and revised. Then the scarcity indicators are compared and evaluated.

The elasticity of substitution between natural resources and other inputs is discussed in the second part of the paper. The elasticity of substitution, while not a scarcity indicator itself, gives some feeling for the difficulty of adjusting for growing natural resource scarcity.

In the final section, a menu of topics for future research is provided. A summary of our conclusions follows.

1. The unit cost measure of Barnett and Morse, the most commonly cited index of scarcity among economists, is an ambiguous indicator of scarcity for the following reasons.

This paper is an outgrowth of a research project (SIA 75-15189) sponsored by National Science Foundation in 1975. A distilled version was presented at the American Economics Association Meetings in Atlantic City, N.J., September 1976. In addition to being a substantial embellishment, the present piece discusses future research directions. We would like to acknowledge the helpful contributions made by Charles Grebenstein, Richard Hartman, and Ron Johnson.

a. In a dynamic world the unit cost measure mistakes certain types of technological progress for growing natural resource scarcity.
b. Under all conditions the unit cost measure mistakes ease of adjustment to increasing scarcity (which we should welcome) for increasing scarcity itself (which is not desired).
c. The unit cost measure is a lagging, not a leading, indicator. Expected future costs of extraction are not contained in this measure.
d. The unit cost measure does not warn us of impending physical exhaustion.
e. Unit cost is a difficult index to measure precisely.

2. The real price of natural resource-intensive products is relatively superior to unit cost as an indicator of scarcity.

a. The real price of the resource-intensive product is forward looking insofar as it reflects the expected future cost of exploration, discovery, and extraction.
b. Technical progress distorts the scarcity signal provided by real price. Timber became more scarce in the late nineteenth century but technological progress was responsible for maintaining stable product prices.
c. Real price does not presage impending exhaustion for resources which have close substitutes. The passenger pigeon became extinct with hardly a ripple in its commercial price.
d. The real price of a resource can rise or fall, indicating increasing or decreasing scarcity, depending upon which particular price deflator is used to adjust the nominal resource price. Therefore, this measure gives mixed scarcity signals.

3. The rental rate of natural resources, or the value of resources *in situ,* is a third measure of scarcity. Rental rates may indicate scarcity while the other indexes do not. The rental rate on timber generally rose during the past sixty years; the unit cost generally fell during this period while the product price (lumber) fell relative to the rental rate.

a. So little data are available, however, that often the rental rate is not a practical measure in the short run.
b. The rental rate anticipates growing scarcity in an economic sense, but impending physical exhaustion is compatible with any prior path and level of the rental rate.

All of the above indexes may be biased because futures markets don't really exist and because they fail to reflect the pressure of non-market demands associated with environmental quality. For these reasons the search for exact measures of scarcity may be frustrated. Nevertheless, we feel that continued effort is yet justified. There appear to be a few opportunities to study rental rates, as in the case of public oil leases, and rather more options for looking at the paths of discovery costs as a proxy for rental rates. Applied research incorporating the effect of uncertainty on rates of extraction is overdue.

Efforts should be directed at devising new measures of scarcity. One of these would be to focus on the extent of economic disruption that would result from scarcities of particular natural resources. The elasticity of substitution is a measure that takes this perspective, since it indicates the ease with which other inputs may be substituted for scarce natural resources. It is feasible to apply modern techniques to estimate the elasticity of substitution between conventional inputs (labor and capital) and individual natural resources. This is especially true for such widely used resources as steel, aluminum, copper, and pulp and paper; we sketch our preliminary results for these resources. We also propose further studies; however, small sample size may lead to poor estimates of substitutability when it comes to such resources as zinc, lead, mercury, silver, tin, and uranium, whose physical supplies, some believe, are inadequate.

Finally, we suggest that it would be very useful to investigate how responsive and extensive institutional change has been to changing availability of natural resources.

II
Unit Costs of Extractive Output

Probably the most common source of empirical conclusions about natural resources scarcity cited by economists is the work of Barnett and Morse [1]. Their principal measure of scarcity is the "unit cost of extractive output," defined as $(\alpha L + \beta K)/Q$ where L is labor, K is reproducible capital, and Q is the output of extractive industries. The factors α and β are weights for aggregating inputs. Data on L and Q were derived from Potter and Christy [2] while Barnett and Morse obtained estimates of K, α, and β directly from Kendrick [3]. It needs to be stressed that the capital measure includes only reproducible capital, and does not include the value of natural resources.

Unit cost, as Barnett and Morse define it, is not the common garden variety unit cost one would construct to include the cost of all inputs per unit of output. Nevertheless, the Barnett and Morse measure is the empirically relevant one. It is the one cited in many references, including [4–8], whereas the all-inclusive measure of unit cost has not, to our knowledge, been referenced at all in the professional literature.[1]

[1] Note that the inclusive measure of unit cost is simply product price in a competitive environment and where economists customarily limit production functions to be homogeneous of degree one.

Table 9-1. Indexes of Labor-Capital Input per Unit of Extractive Output, as Given in *Scarcity and Growth*

	Total extractive		Agriculture		Minerals		Forestry		Fishing
	A	B	A	B	A	B	A	B	A
1870–1900	134	99	132	97	210	154	59	37	200
1919	122	103	114	97	164	139	106	84	100
1957	60	87	61	89	47	68	90	130	18

Source: H. J. Barnett and C. Morse, *Scarcity and Growth: The Economics of Natural Resource Availability* (Baltimore, Johns Hopkins University Press for Resources for the Future, 1963) pp. 8, 9, 172.
Key: A, indexes of direct unit extraction costs.
   B, indexes of unit extraction costs relative to nonextractive goods.

Barnett and Morse reasoned in support of their unit cost measure as follows. Imagine that a dose of constant quality capital and labor combine with a dose of constant quality natural resources to produce a given amount of output. As natural resources grow more scarce, lower quality resources are drawn into the production process; it takes more than a dose of capital and labor to produce the same output as previously. Thus the unit cost of extractive output must rise through time. Barnett and Morse's empirical results are summarized in table 9-1. In most industries the unit cost of extractive output generally fell at an increasing rate from 1870 to 1950, thus signifying that natural resources were growing more plentiful, not more scarce. Forestry in the United States was a major exception.

The advantages claimed for unit cost are summed up as follows: it is the only measure "capable of reflecting and netting out the effects of (a) all resource constraints, (b) all offsets to (and reversals of) these constraints, and (c) the real costs of developing and effectuating these offsets and reversals" [9, p. 127]. In other words, the primary advantage of unit extraction cost is that it includes the effects of technological changes in the extractive sector, which are conceived of as serving to relax natural resource constraints. This approach to the problem may create more difficulties than it solves, for technological progress in extraction may be only one, and not even the most important, source of the escape from scarcity. Clearly, under static conditions it can be shown that an increase in unit extraction cost as defined by Barnett and Morse is associated with a decrease in aggregate per capita output, hence a decline in measured consumption (welfare) per capita. But in a world enriched throughout by technical progress, this could be an ambiguous scarcity indicator, as Barnett and Morse see: "the unit cost of aggregate social output, therefore, may . . . decrease (social welfare is improving) even if the unit cost of extractive output rises continuously." They conclude that it therefore is "virtually impossible to postulate a realistic set of conditions that would yield either generally increasing natural resource scarcity or diminishing returns in the social production process" [7, p. 7]. If unit extraction cost may go up without implying diminishing returns, it is also true that it may stay steady or decline without implying reduced scarcity of a natural resource.

We are concerned with economic scarcity, not physical scarcity—the actual reduction of the number of units left of a particular natural resource. In some sense physical exhaustion may be considered the terminal phenomenon in a course of rising economic scarcity. At any rate, there seems to be implicit faith that Barnett and Morse's unit extraction costs will signal imminent exhaustion. Herfindahl [10, p. 1] says that long before exhaustion occurs "difficulties will arise in the form of persistently increasing cost because new deposits are becoming harder to find or because the quality of the new deposits found is deteriorating." But as exhaustion is approached, there is every reason to expect the search for, discovery, and introduction of various technological developments in extraction that will lower unit cost. The path of unit cost would be related to these changes in technique and could show almost any pattern. Since unit cost reflects current resource costs associated with extraction, it says nothing about costs of future extraction. A vivid example recently has been uncovered by Norgaard [11]. He found that technological change in oil well drilling has been sufficiently strong to offset a substantial part of the large decline in resource quality. As a result, unit costs have increased far less than they would have had technology been constant.

There is another important conceptual problem with using unit cost, so defined, as a scarcity measure. Suppose that the price (rental rate) of a natural resource increases and induces producers of extractive output to substitute out of natural resources and into relatively lower cost factors. This substitution clearly increases the unit cost of extractive output as defined by Barnett and Morse, but the magnitude of increase depends on the ease of substituting capital and labor for natural resources. Assume for example, that the extractive sector is characterized by the CES production function:

$$Q = (aL^{-\beta} + bR^{-\beta})^{-1/\beta}, \qquad \frac{1}{1 + \beta} = \sigma; \qquad \beta > -1 \qquad (1)$$

where L is a composite labor-capital input, R is a natural resource input, and σ is the elasticity of substitution. In competitive factor markets the ratio of the marginal product of each factor equals the factor price ratio.

Letting w be the price of the labor-capital input and λ that of the natural resource, we have

$$\frac{aL^{-\beta-1}}{bR^{-\beta-1}} = \frac{w}{\lambda} \tag{2}$$

or

$$\frac{R}{L} = \left(\frac{wb}{\lambda a}\right)^{\sigma} \tag{3}$$

Since (1) is constant returns to scale, (3) can be substituted into (1) after expressing (1) as labor/capital per unit of output, giving

$$\frac{L}{Q} = \left[a + b\left(\frac{\lambda a}{wb}\right)^{\beta\sigma}\right]^{1/\beta} \tag{4}$$

Relationship (4) has its most dramatic interpretation if, eschewing subscripts, we imagine instead that it describes production relations for two separate outputs. All parameters are alike except that the elasticity of substitution differs in the two hypothesized cases. Suppose the price of the natural resource input (λ) common to both outputs rises relative to w. Then (5) says that unit cost registers the greatest increase in the case where substitution is easiest! That is,

$$\frac{\partial(L/Q)}{\partial\lambda} > 0 \quad \text{and} \quad \frac{\partial^2(L/Q)}{\partial\lambda\partial\sigma} > 0$$

This is perverse.[2] The unit cost of extractive output alarms us with signs of dramatically increasing scarcity when, in fact, technology has made it easy to decrease the use of natural resources. As steamships became better substitutes for sailing craft, followers of the unit cost measure of scarcity would have grown even more strident in their demand to preserve the tall pole timber for masts.

Unit extraction costs have important practical difficulties as well. There is the problem of measuring the inputs, particularly capital, and combining them into a meaningful aggregate. Because of a poor data base, Barnett and Morse were forced to draw statistics from different stages of the total manufacturing process. Whereas the metals output series appears to be at the extractive level [2, p. 368ff.], the metals employment data include some undetermined fractions of workers in the separate processing sectors. There is the further problem of developing a valid index of aggregate inputs, particularly capital. Usually a substantial proportion of capital investment is devoted to finding new deposits of

---

[2] We are grateful to John Moroney for pointing out an error in an earlier formulation of this argument.

minerals and ought not to be, but frequently is, attributed to the cost of producing current output [10, pp. 5–6].

III
Real Price of Natural Resource Products

The most readily computed measure of natural resource scarcity in economics is the real price of extractive products. This is the price of a natural resource *after* it has been extracted and perhaps also after some amount of processing or fabrication. Clearly, a complete natural resource-using cycle could be subdivided into many steps. Perhaps the simplest is a breakdown of the following sort:

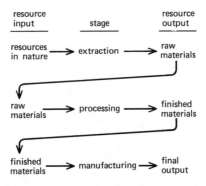

In terms of the schema, our reference to the "real price of natural resource products" relates to the price of "raw materials," the output of the extractive sector, or sometimes "finished materials," the output of the processing sector.

Barnett and Morse calculated extractive output prices relative to a GNP deflator, concluding that "where the trend of relative price is upward—certainly forestry and possibly in fishing—there is support for . . . the natural resource scarcity hypothesis. Where the trend is approximately horizontal—in agriculture, minerals and total extraction—the scarcity hypothesis fails" [1, p. 211].

V. Kerry Smith [12], analyzing the updated time paths of natural resources prices, finds that the rate of decline has diminished in the real prices of metals and fuels, two resources untouched by any scarcity effects in the Barnett and Morse analysis. Smith concludes that this implies the presence of persistent, though disguised, scarcity effects. However, in agriculture and forestry the rate of price increase has been diminishing.

Herfindahl [4] appraised the scarcity of copper in terms of the price

Table 9-2. Relative Price of Minerals to Labor
(1900 = 100)

	1900	1920	1940	1950	1960	1970
Coal	459	451	189	208	111	100
Copper	785	226	121	99	82	100
Iron	620	287	144	112	120	100
Phosphorus	—	—	—	130	120	100
Molybdenum	—	—	—	142	108	100
Lead	788	388	204	228	114	100
Zinc	794	400	272	256	125	100
Sulfur	—	—	—	215	145	100
Aluminum	3,150	859	287	166	134	100
Gold	—	—	595	258	143	100
Crude petroleum	1,034	726	198	213	135	100

Source: From W. D. Nordhaus, "The Allocation of Energy Resources," *Brookings Papers on Economic Activity*, no. 3 (1973) pp. 529–570.
Note: Values are price per ton of mineral divided by hourly wage rate in manufacturing.

of refined copper relative to the wholesale price index of the Bureau of Labor Statistics. His main results indicate a decline until about the 1920s but relative stability from then until 1957. On this basis Herfindahl concludes that there is no evidence for increasing scarcity in copper.

Ruttan and Callahan [13] follow Herfindahl's approach in their study of scarcity in forestry and agriculture, as does Irland [14] in his study of forestry. Irland concludes that on the whole, "the statistical record of real prices for lumber and plywood sheds considerable doubt on the hypothesis that sawtimber is a scarce resource" [14, p. 23]. He finds general support for this conclusion in the real prices of major paper products.

Real prices were also used by Nordhaus [15]. For eleven minerals he took the price of refined output relative to manufacturing wage rate for selected years during the period 1900–70. The results are presented in table 9-2. In all eleven cases the trend of this index was downward, but with a few temporary reversals.

Real prices are meant to reflect relative costs. All users agree that the sectors being studied and compared have to exhibit the same degree of competition in product and factor markets. Changes in the degree of monopoly, level of unionization, and in taxes and subsidies between the extractive and nonextractive sectors could drive up the relative price of extractive output. This would erroneously indicate increasing natural resource scarcity, according to many authors. Accordingly, they must believe that changes in market structure and government policies should be thought to be fundamentally different from other causes of price increase.

Table 9-3. Real Price of Selected Minerals Using Price of Capital as Numeraire, Selected Years, 1920–50

	1920	1940	1950
Coal	340	195	413
Copper	170	125	129
Iron	216	149	146
Phosphorus	—	141	170
Molybdenum	—	—	186
Lead	292	211	298
Zinc	301	281	335
Sulfur	—	—	281
Aluminum	647	297	217
Gold	—	615	337
Crude petroleum	547	205	278

Source: Taken from D. Jorgenson and Z. Griliches, "The Explanation of Productivity Change,"*Review of Economic Studies*, vol. 34 (July 1967) pp. 250–282; U.S. Bureau of Census, *Historical Statistics of the United States, 1789–1945* (Washington, GPO, 1949); U.S. Bureau of Census, *Long-Term Economic Growth 1860–1965* (Washington, GPO, 1966); and U.S. Bureau of Census, *Statistical Abstracts of the United States, 1974* (Washington, GPO, 1974).

There is agreement that *relative* prices are the appropriate measures of scarcity because changes in natural resource product prices by themselves mean nothing. There is less agreement on what natural resources product prices should be compared with. We think there is no one correct answer. A consumer probably should be interested in the price of resource products relative to other products he purchases and would therefore use a retail price index or the equivalent. A firm using a resource product as an input should be interested in the price of other inputs, such as labor or capital, or an index of other factor prices.

The choice of the numeraire point of reference is crucial. For example, if one computes for the minerals selected by Nordhaus, the prices of minerals relative to the price of capital, as measured by Jorgenson and Griliches [16], four of the indexes show increasing scarcity of minerals (see table 9-3), even though the mineral price relative to wage rate fell for all eleven minerals, according to Nordhaus. The other seven mineral prices fall relatively more slowly when the price of capital replaces the wage rate as the numeraire.

There is a less dramatic comparison when Denison's [17, 18] quality adjusted wage rate is used. As shown in figures 9-1 to 9-4 the minerals exhibit a fall in relative price from 1920 to 1970, but using the quality adjusted wage dampens the price decrease by roughly 25 percent.[3] The constant quality wage rate is the proper wage rate to use because the

[3] Denison's index is used because it is available for more years, making it particularly useful for the comparison in trends for Douglas fir below.

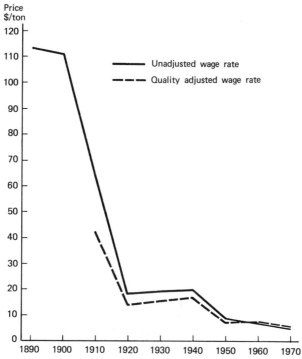

Figure 9-1. Price of all metals, as adjusted by two difference numeraires. (Figures 9-1 through 9-4 derived from E. F. Denison, *The Sources of Economic Growth in the United States and the Alternatives Before Us,* Supplementary paper 13, Committee for Economic Development, 1962; *Accounting for U.S. Economic Growth, 1929–1969,* Washington, D.C. Brookings Institution, 1974; and R. S. Manthy, *Natural Resource Commodities, 1870–1973: Prices, Output, Consumption, and Employment,* Baltimore, Johns Hopkins University Press for Resources for the Future, 1978.)

numerator is the price of a mineral whose quality has been held constant at a given concentrate over the time period in question. The price of a natural resource product is clearly an ambiguous indicator of the scarcity of the underlying natural resources.

IV
Rental Rates on Natural Resources

The conceptually ideal measure of economic scarcity is price. If something is not scarce, it has an exchange value of zero. When more is wanted than is available at a zero price, the exchange value ultimately

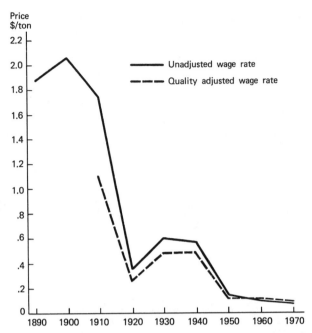

Figure 9-2. Price of bauxite as adjusted by two different numeraires. (See figure 9-1 for sources.)

must become positive. And if something is more scarce in one place than in another, or at one time compared with another, we would know this because its price is greater in the more scarce circumstance. This argument, so fundamental to economics, applies to natural resources. Natural resources are said to be growing more scarce if their relative price is rising over time.

By relative resource price, or rental rate, we refer to the price of the resource in nature. There has been a fair amount of confusion in the past over the proper relationship of natural resources rents, royalties, user costs, net prices, and the like.[4] We do not propose here to sift through this literature, except to say that what we have in mind is the price that a rational individual would pay to have available today one more unit of the natural resource in question. This is applicable to both renewable and nonrenewable resources.

Not everyone agrees that rents are useful scarcity measures. Barnett and Morse argue that rent is not a useful measure of scarcity "in a world of depletion, . . . [or] of sociotechnological change" [1, pp. 225–226]. An increasing rent will reflect increasing scarcity, but increases in rent

[4] For a discussion of some of these concepts see [19].

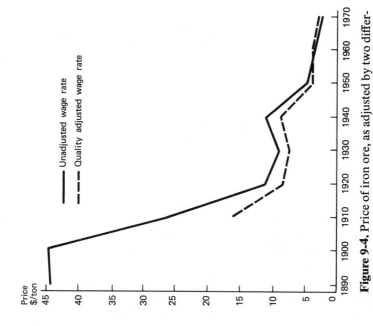

Figure 9-4. Price of iron ore, as adjusted by two different numeraires. (See figure 9-1 for sources.)

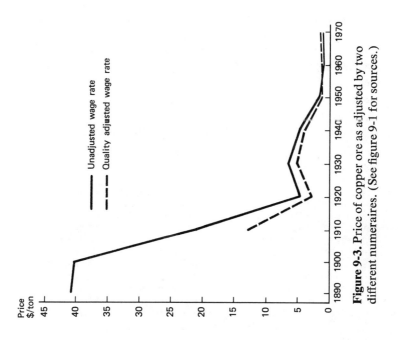

Figure 9-3. Price of copper ore as adjusted by two different numeraires. (See figure 9-1 for sources.)

may also be due to "changes in interest rates, relative demand, and expectations concerning future resource availability. Under these conditions, advances in rent on unhomogeneous resources are an ambiguous indicator of increases in scarcity" [1, p. 225].[5] But it is important that a scarcity indicator *does* pick up the influence of these factors. Whether a resource is becoming more scarce or not, for example, ought to depend in part on "expectations about future supplies." We see no economic reason for ranking sources of changes in rental rates, rejecting some and accepting others.[6] It may be that some of the changes are more readily countermanded by public policy than others. This is a quite separate issue. But even if these influences on rental rates are thought to bias this index of scarcity, critics still must show that a fall in interest rates or a rise in tax rates or a change in the structure of competition due to corporate, labor union, or public sector activity, imparts a smaller bias to the index of their choosing. We know of no suggestive evidence, much less substantive research results, to support such a view.

Some question arises over the relation of resource rental rates as defined above and Ricardian rents as measures of scarcity. There is reluctance to view Ricardian rents, such as rents on location or input quality, as valid measures of scarcity. According to Barnett and Morse, for example, the price of urban land may rise, not because of "intrinsic" physical and locational qualities which advance the value of urban land, but because of the fact that man has a "propensity to build where he has already built. . . . Urban rents thus reflect the economic advantages of agglomeration, not disadvantages imposed by nature" [1, p. 226].[7] But the scarcity of any resource is a reflection of the interacting effects of the physical supplies cast up by nature and the demands made on these supplies by man. If people choose to live in cities, then desirable location or accessibility will become a scarce resource. Thus there is no reason to discount changes in urban land rent as a scarcity index. Nevertheless, it is certainly true that the rental rates with which we primarily concern

---

[5] Barnett and Morse appear to believe that rent as a measure of scarcity requires an assumption of homogeneous land. Marshall argued that "all rents are scarcity rents" [20, p. 351].

[6] The distinguishing feature cannot be degree of permanence. Wars consume vast quantities of natural resources and are more irreversible than government policies in general. Changes in taste which shift demand are not decidedly more or less irrevocable than changes in market structure.

[7] Marshall [20] differentiated among the causes of urban land rent and further distinguished between public and private sources of increased rental values. The private part of land rent stems from the "work and outlay of its individual holders." The public value arises from such factors as the growth of an industrial population near it [21, p. 360]. This part of land rent Barnett and Morse say is unrelated to true scarcity. In contradistinction, Marshall argues that the industrial demand for land is *in all respects* parallel to the agricultural demand [20, p. 373].

ourselves in this paper refer to rents on conventional types of extractive natural resources.

V

Comparisons Among Rival Scarcity Measures

The different scarcity measures can be compared on both conceptual and empirical grounds. Owing to data problems, it is usually easier to do the former than the latter.

Unit Cost and Price. Price data are generally available for specific resources such as copper, bauxite, and the like. Unit cost data are not, however, nor can they be easily constructed from secondary information.

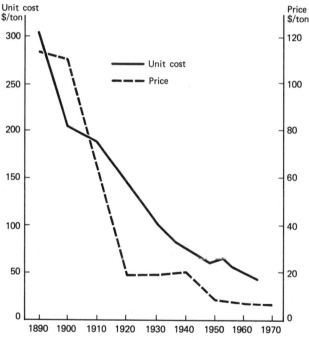

Figure 9-5. Price and unit cost for all metals, 1890–1970. (From L. C. Irland, "Is Timber Scarce? The Economics of a Renewable Resource," Bulletin 83, New Haven, Yale University School of Forestry and Environmental Studies, 1974; J. W. Kendrick, *Postwar Productivity Trends in the United States, 1948–1969,* Washington, D.C., National Bureau of Economic Research, 1973; and R. S. Manthy, *Natural Resource Commodities, 1870–1973: Prices, Output, Consumption, and Employment,* Baltimore, Johns Hopkins University Press for Resources for the Future, 1978.)

Unit cost data have been worked out by Kendrick [3, 22] for natural resource aggregates, "all metals," "all mining," "forestry," and the like, and these may be compared with updated price series for the same aggregates developed by Manthy [23]. Figure 9-5 shows a comparison of unit extraction cost and price for all metals over the past century.

The superiority of price over unit cost as a measure of scarcity is frequently stated in terms of its higher degree of inclusiveness: "The cost that is reflected in price movements over long periods . . . includes not only the cost of mining and processing copper ore, but also the cost of finding and developing deposits" [10, p. 7]. In a variety of circumstances relative price can give a different impression of scarcity than unit extraction costs. If, for example, the elements in price excluded by unit cost are changing over time, there will be a discrepancy. It very well could be the case, as observed by Solow [24] and Schulze [25], that the cost of labor and capital per unit of output is falling, owing to technological progress, but the cost of the natural resource is rising, with a result that product price is constant or falling.[8] The empirical point is made by Irland: "From the Civil War to about 1900, lumber prices were stable while timber prices rose. Prominent forces were the decline in real transport costs and improvements in milling" [14, p. 13]. It is this fact that technological change can intervene and present us with misleading trends in prices of natural resource products which makes this index so problematic. This phenomenon is very likely to happen in resources that are held in common and receive no rent. Then technological change need only keep up with the tendency for capital and labor costs to rise, in order for output price to remain constant. A particularly vivid example is the passenger pigeon, first harvested commercially in about 1840. Tober presents evidence suggesting that the market price for wild pigeons fluctuated, with little tendency to increase, right up until they became effectively extinct in the 1890s [26, p. 181ff.]. A major, though not the sole, reason for this was the development of improved methods for catching the birds.

Passenger pigeons probably had good substitutes in demand, and this illustrates another problem with using price as a scarcity indicator when resource values are observed at early stages of production. A highly elastic demand curve for the private good may permit no scope for substantial and obvious price increases to reflect the social value of preserving a species. Of course the presence of close substitutes casts doubt on the whole notion of what is meant by "scarcity" and "running

---

[8] The Barnett and Morse relative price test for agriculture shows little change in scarcity, while their unit cost test shows a marked decrease in agricultural scarcity.

out" of a particular resource, at least for those who believe that "running out" is not good.

Price and Rental Rate.   The explicit relationship between the rental rate of the natural resources (R) and the natural resource extractive product price (P) is easy to establish. R is simply P weighted by the contribution of natural resources to extractive output (the marginal product of natural resources).

Suppose there are reserves of natural resources, S_t, which can be depleted by use, denoted by R_t, and augmented by a discovery process, denoted by $D(E, t)$ where E is some input. At all times,

$$S_t = S_{t-1} + D(E, t) - R_t \tag{5}$$

Production of final output is governed by a constant returns-to-scale production function,

$$Q = F(L, R, t) \tag{6}$$

where L represents labor or some composite input. Time subscripts are added only when necessary to avoid possible confusion. We have specified a very simple relationship between the natural resource (R) and final output Q. There is, however, no reason why (6) cannot represent a compact way of writing a production process which includes extractive, processing, . . . and final product production. L can then be thought of as a vector. The objective function for the owner of natural resources with profit-maximizing motives is

$$W(L, E, R) = \sum_t \{PQ - P_E E - WL + \lambda_t[-S_t + S_{t-1} + D(E, t) - R_t]\}\theta^t \tag{7}$$

where the discount factor, $\theta^t = 1/(1 + r)^t$, λ_t is a Langrangian, and the cost of variable factors, W and P_E are parametric.

Anticipating only interior solutions, the necessary conditions for a maximization of $W(\cdot)$ yield[9]

$$PF_L = W \tag{8a}$$

$$PF_R = \lambda \text{ and} \tag{8b}$$

$$\lambda D_E = P_E \tag{8c}$$

Equation (8a) says quite simply that in every period natural resources should be used in amounts which equalize the shadow price (λ)

[9] When discovery is not possible, our model, adjusted for a boundary value solution, readily yields the standard result that the price of natural resources rises at the rate of discount. From (7)

$$\frac{\partial W}{\partial S_t} = \theta^{t+1} \lambda_{t+1} + \theta^t \lambda_t = 0, \text{ whence } \lambda_{t+1} = \lambda_t \theta^{-1} = \lambda_t(1 + r)$$

or rental rate of the natural resource with the value of its marginal product. It shows clearly the relationship between product price and rental rate: these two measures of scarcity differ by the marginal product of natural resources, bearing a constant relationship to each other only in the unlikely case that F_R is constant through time.[10] Rearranging (8b) and differentiating with respect to time yields

$$\frac{\dot{P}}{P} = \frac{\dot{\lambda}}{\lambda} - \frac{\dot{F}_R}{F_R} \tag{9}$$

The last term in this expression can be put into more familiar terms, using the assumption of constant returns to scale and the standard expression for σ, the elasticity of substitution. Letting r be the resource-labor ratio, (9) becomes

$$\frac{\dot{P}}{P} = \frac{\dot{\lambda}}{\lambda} + \frac{\alpha}{\sigma}\left(\frac{\dot{r}}{r}\right) \tag{10}$$

where α is the share of nonresource inputs in total output.[11]

When substitution is possible, product price underestimates the seriousness of growing natural resource scarcity because price rises less rapidly than the rental rate of natural resources. Second, the magnitude of this bias varies directly with the share of output going to factors other than natural resources. This is a particularly serious criticism since it is widely believed, and there is supporting empirical evidence that the share of natural resources in production is small [28, 29]. Our research corroborates this finding with respect to pulp and paper, steel, aluminum, and copper. It is also true that neutral and capital- or labor-augmenting technological progress drives down the cost of production and product price, movements unrelated to changing natural resource prices.

The connection between these two measures of scarcity and the unit cost of extraction output is not drawn as easily. Still, these measures can be compared under a special case when substitution is not possible between natural resources and other inputs in the production of natural

[10] Suppose a more elaborate production process was specified

$Q = h(L, I)$

$I = g(L, E)$

$E = \psi(L, R)$

where I is intermediate product and E is extractive output. Then (8.2) becomes

$$p\,\frac{\partial Q}{\partial I}\frac{\partial I}{\partial E}\frac{\partial E}{\partial R} = \lambda$$

It is still true that product price and rental rate differ by the marginal product of natural resources, but its computation is just a bit more roundabout.

[11] This result is more general than that of Dasgupta and Heal [27, p. 11] which holds when $\dot{\lambda}/\lambda$ is rising at the rate of discount.

resource-intensive extractive products. In this case, the extractive product price will change by the absolute amount of any change in the rental rate, as long as the prices of other inputs aren't changing and output expands at the rate inputs increase. Under these conditions, the unit cost of extractive output remains constant, wrongly signifying no changes in scarcity, while the two other indexes are signaling increasing scarcity when the prices of natural resources are rising. The fixed coefficient assumption lets the natural resource cost component move separately from the unit cost element which, in turn, is changed by technological progress affecting capital, labor, and so forth. Thus, the *path* of the unit cost of extractive output will bear no necessary relationship to increasing natural resource scarcity or impending exhaustion. This may be an empirically uninteresting case because it is unlikely that fixed coefficients will occur in practice. But its consideration is useful because it shows us what is going on and helps us see an important point: owners of natural resources express their best guess about the future prospects for discovery and avoidance of exhaustion through changes in the rental rate. Such forward-looking adjustments occur quite independently of present changes in the unit cost of extractive output.

A rising rental rate always portends increasing scarcity and eventual exhaustion, unless there is a "backstop technology" [as in, e.g., 30]. A rising unit cost or price of extractive output gives an ambiguous signal. However, a rental rate increasing at a given rate provides no information about the date of resource exhaustion. On the other hand, the *price level* of the natural resource relative to correctly measured other prices is a measure of scarcity and an indication of the perceived consequence of exhaustion. The indicator is accurate insofar as the markets are competitive and those bearing the burden of exhaustion can express their preferences or, if they are future generations, have their preferences accurately expressed by present traders.

Rental rates have been rejected on practical grounds because they are not readily available. There is some truth in this. Rental rates for minerals are the prices of given deposits that hold, with some probabilities, prospective quantities and qualities of ore. Companies engaged in exploiting these deposits, or in looking for new deposits, are loath to make public the sort of price information that might put them at a competitive disadvantage. Given the fact that each deposit has its own unique characteristics, the motive of profit maximization is likely to be better served if full price information does not become widespread. To this must be coupled the fact that valuation of deposits usually has enormous tax implications for the people who own them.

There is one important exception to the paucity of data on rental

Figure 9-6. Douglas fir stumpage price relative to Douglas fir lumber price. (Taken from USDA Forest Service, "The Demand and Price Situation for Forest Prices, 1972," Washington, GPO, 1972; U.S. Bureau of Census, *Historical Statistics of the United States, 1789–1945*, Washington, GPO, 1949; *Long-Term Economic Growth, 1860–1945*, Washington, GPO, 1966; and *Statistical Abstracts of the United States 1974*, Washington, GPO, 1974.)

rates. The U.S. Forest Service manages a significant fraction of this nation's timber supply. The technical term for the rental value of standing timber is the stumpage price. It can be seen (figure 9-6) that the stumpage price of Douglas fir relative to Douglas fir lumber price has risen rather sharply through time, while the "unit cost of extractive output" has fallen (figure 9-7).[12] For the past fifty years, the "unit cost" halved but the stumpage price (relative to extractive product price) increased by about a factor of four. Note also that the two indexes move in opposite fashion. Whenever the stumpage prices increase within a decade, the unit cost falls, and vice versa. Figure 9-8 shows that the stumpage price of Douglas fir relative to the quality adjusted wage rate

[12] Douglas fir stumpage prices and lumber prices were obtained from the U.S. Forest Service [31]. Employment data came from Potter and Christy [2] and the U.S. Bureau of Census [32, 33, 34].

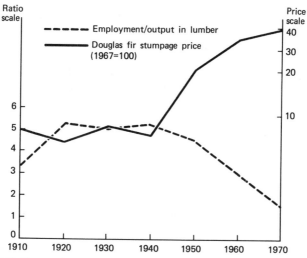

Figure 9-7. Comparison of unit cost and stumpage price. (Taken from
N. Potter and F. T. Christy Jr., *Trends in Natural Resource Commodities:
Statistics of Prices, Output, Consumption, Foreign Trade and Employment in the United States, 1860–1959*, Baltimore, Johns Hopkins University Press for Resources for the Future, 1962; see figure 9-6 for other
sources.)

has increased since about 1920. The increase is comparable to the rise
when the numeraire is the unadjusted wage rate.[13]

VI
When Conventional Scarcity Indicators May Fail

There are four reasons why rental rates and product price poorly
measure increasing natural resource scarcity. First, many valuable resources such as passenger pigeons, whales, salmon, and migratory water-
fowl are common property resources. No spot markets post daily or
annual prices for these resources. In the absence of public intervention,
harvesters will make decisions on the assumption that the stock has zero
value. Thus, actual rental rates are not good measures of scarcity in
this instance, and resources are depleted at too fast a rate.

[13] The conclusion of increasing scarcity from these data very likely is unaffected
by observations [35] that the private timber companies do not pay competitive
stumpage values. Even if the accusations are true, they bear on level of stumpage
values, not the path over time.

Second, in the absence of forward markets, traders in natural resources have to form their own expectations about future prices. Geoffrey Heal [36] has shown that the assumptions about how expectations
are formed and the value economic parameters take on, can produce a
full range of rates of extraction relative to an optimal rate. Therefore,
formal analysis or intuition can lead reasonable men to become alarmed
about the propriety of using current rental rates (or product price) as
valid measures of scarcity.

Third, much has been written about the misallocation of resources
which arises when there are no markets for contingent commodities.
Heal's helpful discussion of the problem in the context of natural resources makes it unnecessary to dwell on the subject. It is sufficient to
note that depletion proceeds too rapidly and consumption shifts to the
more certain present if traders are risk averse on balance. Since simple
and complex forward markets are virtually nonexistent, it is no wonder
that prudent men doubt the accuracy of actual prices or rental rates as
scarcity measures.

Finally, spot and futures markets may exist but their prices may fail
to reflect the existence of aggregate demand for the public goods aspects
of natural resources. Although it is difficult to quantify, a broad spectrum
of people believe there is economic value in such nonexclusory services

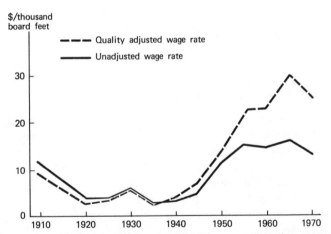

Figure 9-8. Douglas fir stumpage price relative to unadjusted wage rates.
(Taken from E. F. Denison, *The Sources of Economic Growth in the
United States and the Alternatives Before Us,* Supplementary paper 13,
Committee for Economic Development, 1962; *Accounting for U.S.
Economic Growth,* 1929–1969, Washington, D.C., Brookings Institution,
1974; for other sources see figure 9-7.)

as maintaining the gene pool, preserving species diversity, and knowing that a particularly wondrous natural setting will remain undeveloped. Yet it is difficult for these demands to find accurate expression in markets, most of which don't even exist. S. V. Ciriacy-Wantrup [37] spoke persuasively about this general point twenty-five years ago, recommending the adoption of a safe minimum standard which would prohibit extinction of species; and John Krutilla [38] a decade ago expressed his case for less depletion in terms of the potential contribution of a species or botanical specimen to scientific discovery in general and to modern medicine in particular. The passenger pigeon again provides an example. The path or rental rates did not rise because improved methods of harvest were developed. None of the scarcity measures was a harbinger of extinction. But even if the passenger pigeon was not a common property resource, it would have been extremely difficult to express future certain private demands and future certain and uncertain demands for nonconsumptive (public) uses in markets that did not exist.

VII
Other Scarcity Indicators

While work ought to continue on the comparative evaluation of conventional scarcity indicators, the search should also be pressed for appropriate modifications of these indexes and development of new indexes. In this section we discuss some new directions in natural resource scarcity measures.

Modification of Conventional Measures. With the rising interest in environmental quality, it has become common to point out that conventional scarcity indicators do not take environmental costs into account. Should these costs actually be going up through time, the conventional indexes may be giving us misleading signals regarding natural resources scarcity, broadly considered. We need to consider two things: (1) Of the three conventional indexes, unit cost, output price, and rent, is there any reason to suspect that one may be more sensitive than the others in terms of environmental impacts? (2) What feasible modifications might be made in the conventional indexes to heighten their environmental sensitivity?

Regarding question (1), the most interesting subquestion is whether rents might be more effective in picking up the effects of environmental scarcity than would unit extraction costs. It seems clear that unit extraction costs, defined so as to exclude the value of the natural resource, will never be able to pick up environmental costs unless regulations or taxes are instituted to cause these costs to be internalized. On the other hand, we think it barely possible that rental rates might be sensitive to entrepreneurial expectations regarding the likelihood of being forced to undertake environmental costs in the future. We know of nobody who has tried to model this phenomenon, and suggest that it might be worthwhile for someone to do so, at least on the strictly theoretical level.

The other part of this question concerns the possibility of developing something like environmental impact shadow prices that might be used to adjust conventional scarcity indexes. Take, for example, the unit cost of extracting copper ore as it has behaved through recent history. Might it be possible to adjust this cost to reflect the amount of environmental damage attributable to copper mining during this period?

Elasticities of Substitution. Perhaps the search for exact measures of natural resource scarcity is misguided owing both to conceptual and to empirical difficulties. Attention might better be redirected from trying to determine if we are running out of particular resources to the question of the ability of the economic system to adjust and accommodate to increasing resource scarcities if and when they occur.

The process of "running out" of a natural resource need not cause much alarm if it is easy to substitute conventional inputs or more plentiful natural resources for the scarce natural resource. A resource is not scarce, in this sense, as long as it is easy to find substitutes. This suggests that a useful scarcity index might be the elasticity of substitution, which depicts the responsiveness of changes in the use of natural resources and conventional inputs to changes in their prices. To our knowledge only two studies [28, 39] present estimates of elasticities of substitution involving natural resources. The resource commodity in the study by Humphrey and Moroney is an aggregate of nineteen resources.[14]

We have explored, on the other hand, the possibility of estimating elasticities of substitution for individual resources such as copper, aluminum, pulp and paper, and steel.[15] Our estimates indicate that technology

[14] There are several very recent studies dealing exclusively with energy and the substitutability of conventional inputs for energy inputs [see 40, 41, 42, 43].

[15] We used a translog production function specification, which does not require an assumption that the elasticity of substitution is constant over the full range of input combinations. The translog function has been discussed at length elsewhere [44, 45] so we need not go into details here. Briefly, for an n-input translog function, we have

$$\ln Q = \ln \alpha_0 + \sum_j \alpha_j \ln X_j + \tfrac{1}{2} \sum_j \sum_k \gamma_{jk} \ln X_j \ln X_k$$

$$j, k = 1, \ldots, n,$$

Table 9-4. Measures of Responsiveness for Selected Natural Resources, 1967

Elasticity of substitution between:	Steel	Aluminum	Copper[a]	Pulp and paper
Labor and natural resources	4.5	3.0	15.1	1.9
Capital and labor	1.0	1.4	0.6	0.8
Capital and natural resources	3.0	3.4	9.4	6.0

Source: See footnote 14.
[a] Estimates are for 1963.

favors users of pulp and paper and that it is very easy to use capital and labor in place of pulp and paper in the production of goods using these services (table 9-4). It is only slightly more difficult to make substitutions between capital and labor in the pulp and paper-using sectors. A case in point has been the recent increase in the use of mechanical wood chippers for converting formerly nonusable logging residue into a readily usable form as an input into paper and building board manufacturing.

The conclusion that the natural resource input has good substitutes also holds for steel, copper, and aluminum. In the first two cases, however, labor is a more facile substitute for the resource than is capital, while for aluminum the opposite is the case.

VIII
Further Research Directions

We thought it would be useful to have a look at contemporary research on this topic to jog our imagination about future research directions. The results are hardly electrifying as judged by what the Smithsonian Science Information Exchange spewed forth under the subject of "The Economics of Natural Resources Scarcity." Of about fifty entries for the recent year, one-third were devoted to studies of energy resources; 15 percent pertained to increasing the efficiency of processes related to coal and oil development and use; three focused on geothermal

---

where Q is output and the X's are inputs. The coefficients are estimated by using the first-order conditions:

$$M_j = \alpha_j + \sum_k \gamma_{jk} \ln X_k$$

where M_j is the share of the jth input in total cost. Estimation was done by means of iterative Zellner-efficient estimation. After estimating the γ_{jk} we use these, together with the M_j, to construct estimates of the Allen partial elasticities of substitution. Data were gathered from publications of the departments of agriculture [31] and commerce [46–50]. For steel, aluminum, and copper the data refer to fabrication processes, in which processed metal is combined with other inputs to produce final output; for pulp and paper the data refer to all four-digit industries consuming pulp and paper in significant quantities.

resources; 20 percent were resource (or residuals) specific such as zinc, sand, and gravel, forests and water (four); about 20 percent seemed to have been misfiled or the grant jargon made them impenetrable ("explore and adopt new computational tools . . . for rapid processing"). Only about 10 percent of the projects (most of whose project investigators are at this conference) seemed interesting. Frankly, the compilation dulled our senses.

Obtaining Better Estimates of Elasticities of Substitution. Since elasticities of substitution warn us about how difficult it will be to substitute other inputs for natural resources if they grow more scarce, it makes sense to pursue this kind of research in a number of ways. First, studies should be expanded to cover more individual natural resources such as lumber, lead, zinc, and so forth.

Second, for some natural resources such as mercury (based on the information available for deliveries of resources to purchasing SIC sectors) there may be too few observations. Thus the statistical precision of the estimates using such data is questionable. Some of these resources having few entries also are in short physical supply. It would be productive to explore the possibility of estimating elasticities of substitution by using cross-section data across states.

Third, another way to expand sample size is to conduct the analysis using cross-section data obtained from different countries. Sufficient data are available to study ferrous and nonferrous metals in this fashion.

Fourth, it would be desirable to adduce empirical evidence to test the analytical proposition that changes in the Barnett and Morse measure of unit cost of extractive output, instead of signaling decreasing natural resource scarcity, may simply be revealing that substitution possibilities are diminishing over time. To test this hypothesis, investigations should be undertaken of the trend in elasticities of substitution through time and/or for different time periods.

The analytical and estimation procedures we used to estimate elasticities of substitution are so new that there remain many snags to be worked out. We are particularly concerned about the sensitivity of our results to changes in definitions of capital and labor; inclusion or exclusion of intermediate goods in the analysis; and related definitional matters. Some of our estimates do not seem completely reasonable and work ought to be carried out to develop more accurate measures in these cases.

The elasticity of substitution provides relative information about ease of substituting other inputs for natural resources. The analysis leaves out a major source of adjustment, the possibility of substituting away from natural resource-intensive products and into other goods. On the one hand, the concept of the price elasticity of demand for a natural resource captures explicit the two major adjustment possibilities resulting from increasing scarcity of natural resources: the adjustment from one natural resource-intensive product to another product and from one natural resource input to other inputs. On the other hand, the general unavailability of rental rates on natural resources has precluded estimation of the price elasticity of demand for natural resources by other investigators. Now, however, the price elasticity of demand for natural resources can be estimated by combining separate estimates of the elasticity of substitution which we have begun to obtain and estimates of output elasticities which remain to be done.

Analysis of Rental Rates.   Rental rates for natural resources are not readily available. We have uncovered one important exception. Offshore or onshore oil leases periodically are auctioned off at public sales. Successful bid prices are published. The U.S. Geological Survey makes estimates of the oil and gas supplies on these properties and these data are available in field offices. It should be possible to construct an index of the price of oil *in situ* during the past two decades or so.

We are not optimistic that rental rates for various minerals can be obtained by searching through the trade journals and publications. One finds sales prices occasionally posted but mineral quantities rarely, if ever, are mentioned. On the other hand, earlier we showed the connection between rental rates and discovery costs. Discovery costs may be fairly good proxies for rental rates. In real life, the exploration and discovery processes are quite complicated, therefore more sophisticated models are appropriate before large-scale empirical work is undertaken. The fact that exploration is subject to uncertainty, for example, may drive a wedge between rents and marginal exploration costs, depending on such factors as prospectors' attitudes toward risk. It may also be necessary to adjust here, as always, for market structure effects that can lead to exploration becoming a tool for "market control, price maintenance, preclusive aggrandizement, perpetuation of management, premature acquisitiveness under conditions of imperfect tenure, etc." [19, p. 356]. Furthermore, information externalities may be an important distorting factor in the discovery process, as analyzed by Peterson [51]. Nevertheless, for those willing to make a perfectly competitive "leap of faith," comparing the trend in discovery costs over time (as a proxy for rental rates) with product price and unit cost may be a tractable exercise.

Special Studies of Renewable Resources.   We are struck by public concern that we are running out of nonrenewable resources such as oil.

Yet the most famous cases of resource exhaustion or truly threatened exhaustion are all drawn from the renewable category. Instances of near exhaustion caused by commercial harvest are easy to find and include the beaver, buffalo, Alaskan fur seal, and most recently, the blue whale. Some people recently have gone so far as to conclude that many of our "nonrenewable" resources are, for all practical purposes, available without limit, as new technology becomes available to exploit lower quality stocks and as substitution phenomena continue. This implies that more of our attention ought to be devoted to "renewable" resources, particularly those that have run out, or nearly so. It would be very instructive to establish, for a number of these renewable resources, how the different scarcity indexes performed as the resources approached exhaustion. It would also be valuable to identify those social mechanisms through which exhaustion was averted (in those cases where it actually was). One of those mechanisms undoubtedly would be substitution in production, similar to the process covered in detail above for "nonrenewable" resources. But there may be more potent social processes at work and available for public policy. In the case of renewable resources, the most effective way of dealing with threatening exhaustion (extinction) may be changes in the social institutions which determine the rate at which particular natural resources are exploited. More needs to be done along the lines of careful case studies of renewable resources to identify how public policy and economic institutions changed (or did not change) in response to scarcity situations, and how these changes affected the resources in question.

Incorporating Uncertainty. We have mentioned that the lack of forward markets and markets for contingent commodities casts doubt on the accuracy of conventional natural resource scarcity indicators. It would be very useful to derive accurate indicators of natural resource scarcity given that these futures markets do not exist. There may even be some plausible adjustments to apply to one or more of the conventional measures. It seems reasonable to believe that the failure of the futures markets has tilted consumption of natural resources toward the more certain present. Is this bias most pronounced in those resources about which there is most uncertainty? Since there is so much uncertainty surrounding the available quantity of natural resources *in situ* and regarding future demand, it makes a good deal of sense to encourage applied research to stem from models in which the variables take on a stochastic character.

Thomas Tietenberg made a similar point at the Conference on the Political Economy of Depletable Resources [21]. A proceedings document with the same name contains useful ideas for future research. Some of them sounded nonoperational, a number were tied specifically to energy research, and others are not amenable to easy summarization. But a few should be mentioned: (1) ideal institutional and policy arrangements for dealing with depletion should be compared with the actual; (2) principles for evaluating resource management and using institutions should be formulated and tested; (3) the formation and behavior of cartels, particularly international ones, was thought to be an attractive subject, not surprisingly, in light of OPEC's evident ability to flex its profitable muscles.

Research about the optimal size of the genetic reservoir and the distribution of its components provides a fine opportunity for an interdisciplinary endeavor containing applied and empirical content as well as having a heavy component of uncertainty. Only a little work has been done (namely, Myers [52]) on this most basic natural resource of all.

IX
Concluding Remarks

Controversial issues are seldom resolved by one study or by one conference. Our more modest hope is that this paper increases the reluctance of investigators to conclude from trends in unit cost and product price that natural resources are growing more or less scarce through time. It may be too much to expect that vast sums of money now will be devoted to the estimation of time series data on natural resource rental rates, a superior measure of scarcity. But the identification of growing natural resource scarcity in an economic sense would be facilitated if public agencies began to assemble data on the costs of discovering selected natural resources over time. A time series begun this year soon would have merit for indicating where we are going, even if it is silent about historical scarcity.

References

1. H. J. Barnett and C. Morse, *Scarcity and Growth: The Economics of Natural Resource Availability* (Baltimore, Johns Hopkins University Press for Resources for the Future, 1963).
2. N. Potter and F. T. Christy, Jr., *Trends in Natural Resource Commodities: Statistics of Prices, Output, Consumption, Foreign Trade and Employment in the United States 1860–1957* (Baltimore, Johns Hopkins University Press for Resources for the Future, 1962).
3. J. W. Kendrick, *Productivity Trends in the United States* (Princeton, N. J., Princeton University Press, 1961).

4. P. Bradley, "Increasing Scarcity: The Case of Energy Resources," *American Economic Review* vol. 63 (May 1973) pp. 119–125.
5. A. C. Fisher, J. V. Krutilla, and C. Cicchetti, "The Economics of Environmental Preservation: A Theoretical and Empirical Analysis," *American Economic Review* vol. 62 (September 1972) pp. 605–619.
6. E. J. Mishan, "Ills, Bads, and Disamenities: The Wages of Growth," in M. Olson and H. Landsberg, eds., *The No-Growth Society* (New York Norton, 1973) pp. 63–87.
7. M. Roberts, "On Reforming Economic Growth," in M. Olson and H. Landsberg, eds., *The No-Growth Society* (New York, Norton, 1973) pp. 119–139.
8. V. Kerry Smith, "The Effect of Technological Change on Different Uses of Environmental Resources," in J. V. Krutilla, ed., *Natural Environments* (Baltimore, Johns Hopkins University Press for Resources for the Future, 1972).
9. C. Morse, "Discussion," *American Economic Review* vol. 63 (May 1973) pp. 126–128.
10. O. C. Herfindahl, *Copper Costs and Prices: 1870–1957* (Baltimore, Johns Hopkins University Press for Resources for the Future, 1959).
11. R. B. Norgaard, "Resource Scarcity and New Technology in U. S. Petroleum Development," *Natural Resources Journal* vol. 15 (April 1975) pp. 265–295.
12. V. Kerry Smith, "A Re-Evaluation of the Natural Resource Scarcity Hypothesis," Paper presented at the meetings of the Western Economic Association, June 25, 1975.
13. V. W. Ruttan and J. C. Callahan, "Resource Inputs and Output Growth: Comparison Between Agriculture and Forestry," *Forest Science* vol. 8 (March 1962) pp. 68–82.
14. L. C. Irland, *Is Timber Scarce: The Economics of a Renewable Resource.* Bulletin no. 83 (New Haven, Yale University School of Forestry and Environmental Studies, 1974).
15. W. D. Nordhaus, "Resources as a Constraint on Growth," *American Economic Review* vol. 64 (May 1974) pp. 22–26.
16. D. Jorgenson and Z. Griliches, "The Explanation of Productivity Change," *Review of Economic Studies* vol. 34 (July 1967) pp. 250–282.
17. E. F. Denison, *The Sources of Economic Growth in the United States and the Alternatives Before Us.* Supplementary Paper 13, Committee for Economic Development, 1962 (Reprinted 1973).
18. E. F. Denison, *Accounting for U. S. Economic Growth 1929–1969* (Washington, D.C., Brookings Institution, 1974).
19. M. Gaffney, ed., *Extractive Resources and Taxation* (Madison, University of Wisconsin Press, 1967).
20. A. Marshall, *Principles of Economics* (London, Macmillan, 1959).
21. A. C. Fisher (Conference Organizer), Conference on the Political Economy of Depletable Resources, sponsored by National Science Foundation at Brookings Institution, June 9–10, 1975.

22. J. W. Kendrick, *Postwar Productivity Trends in the United States 1948–1969* (Washington, D.C., National Bureau of Economic Research, 1973).
23. R. S. Manthy, *Natural Resource Commodities 1870–1973: Prices, Output, Consumption, and Employment* (Baltimore, Johns Hopkins University Press for Resources for the Future, 1978).
24. R. M. Solow, "Richard T. Ely Lecture: The Economics of Resources or the Resources of Economics," *American Economic Review* vol. 64 (May 1974) pp. 1–14.
25. W. D. Schulze, "The Optimal Use of Non-Renewable Resources: The Theory of Extraction," *Journal of Environmental Economics and Management* vol. 1 (May 1974) pp. 53–73.
26. James A. Tober, "The Allocation of Wildlife Resources in the United States, 1850–1900." Unpublished Ph.D. dissertation, Yale University, 1974.
27. P. Dasgupta and G. Heal, "The Optimal Depletion of Exhaustible Resources," *Review of Economic Studies* Symposium Issue (1974) pp. 3–28.
28. H. Binswanger, "The Measurement of Technical Change Biases with Many Factors of Production," *American Economic Review* vol. 64 (December 1974) pp. 964–976.
29. T. Schultz, *The Economic Organization of Agriculture* (New York, McGraw-Hill, 1953).
30. W. D. Nordhaus, "The Allocation of Energy Resources," *Brookings Papers on Economic Activity* no. 3 (Washington, D.C., Brookings Institution, 1973) pp. 529–570.
31. U.S. Department of Agriculture, Forest Service. *The Demand and Price Situation for Forest Products, 1972* (Washington, GPO, 1972).
32. U.S. Department of Commerce, Bureau of the Census, *Historical Statistics of the United States 1789–1945* (Washington, GPO, 1949).
33. U.S. Department of Commerce, Bureau of the Census, *Long-Term Economic Growth 1860–1965* (Washington, GPO, 1966).
34. U.S. Department of Commerce, Bureau of the Census, *Statistical Abstract of the United States 1974* (Washington, GPO, 1974).
35. W. J. Mead, "Natural Resources Disposal Policy—Oral Auction versus Sealed Bids," *Natural Resources Journal* vol. 7 (April 1967) pp. 194–224.
36. G. Heal, "Economic Aspects of Natural Resource Depletion," in D. W. Pearce and J. Rose, eds., *The Economics of Natural Resource Depletion* (New York, Wiley, 1975) pp. 118–139.
37. S. V. Ciriacy-Wantrup, *Resource Conservation* (Berkeley, University of California, 1952).
38. J. V. Krutilla, "Conservation Reconsidered," *American Economic Review* vol. 57 (September 1967) pp. 777–786.
39. D. B. Humphrey and J. R. Moroney, "Substitution Among Capital, Labor and Natural Resource Products in American Manufacturing," *Journal of Political Economy* vol. 83 (February 1975) pp. 57–82.
40. S. E. Atkinson and R. E. Halvorsen, "Interfuel Substitution in Steam

Electric Power Generation," *Journal of Political Economy* vol. 84 (October 1976) pp. 959–978.

41. E. R. Berndt and D. O. Wood, "Technology, Prices and the Derived Demand for Energy," *Review of Economic Statistics* vol. 57 (August 1975) pp. 259–268.

42. M. Fuss, "The Demand for Energy in Canadian Manufacturing: An Example of the Estimation of Production Structures with Many Inputs," *Journal of Econometrics* vol. 5 (January 1977) pp. 89–116.

43. J. M. Griffin and P. R. Gregory, "An Inter-Country Translog Model of Energy Substitution Responses," *American Economic Review* vol. 66 (December 1976) pp. 845–857.

44. E. R. Berndt and L. R. Christensen, "The Translog Function and the Substitution of Equipment, Structures and Labor in U.S. Manufacturing 1929–68," *Journal of Econometrics* vol. 1 (March 1973) pp. 81–114.

45. L. R. Christensen, D. W. Jorgenson, and L. J. Lau, "Transcendental Logarithmic Production Frontiers," *Review of Economic Statistics* vol. 60 (February 1973) pp. 28–45.

46. U.S. Department of Commerce, Bureau of the Census, *Census of Manufacturers, 1963,* vol. 1, *Summary and Subject Statistics* (Washington, GPO, 1966).

47. U.S. Department of Commerce, Bureau of the Census, *Annual Survey of Manufacturers, 1964 and 1965* (Washington, GPO, 1968).

48. U.S. Department of Commerce, Bureau of the Census, *Census of Manufacturers, 1967,* vol. 1, *Summary and Subject Statistics* (Washington, GPO, 1971).

49. U.S. Department of Commerce, Bureau of the Census. *Annual Survey of Manufacturers, 1968 and 1969* (Washington, GPO, 1973).

50. U.S. Department of Commerce, Office of Business Economics. *Input–Output Structure of the U.S. Economy, 1967,* 3 vols (Washington, GPO, 1974).

51. F. M. Peterson, "The Theory of Exhaustible Natural Resources: A Classical Variational Approach," Unpublished Ph.D. dissertation, Princeton University, 1972.

52. N. Myers, "An Expanded Approach to the Problem of Disappearing Species," *Science* vol. 193 (July 16, 1976) pp. 198–202.

10

Measures of Natural Resource Scarcity

Anthony C. Fisher

I
Introduction: Physical and Economic Scarcity

The widely publicized predictions of impending scarcity and even exhaustion of extractive natural resources such as metals and fuels, in the Club of Rome study *The Limits to Growth,* and the less widely publicized rebuttals (see, for example, Beckerman [1], Nordhaus [2], and Kay and Mirrlees [3]) suggest that a careful analysis of what is meant by resource scarcity, and of how it is measured or indicated, might be worthwhile. This paper is intended to provide such an analysis. Specifically, in this section I consider the meaning of scarcity, and in subsequent sections a number of proposed measures, their properties, and their behavior as a resource stock is depleted or augmented over time.

Perhaps the question, "What is scarcity?" is too simple for economists, or at any rate, too simple to be made explicit. We ordinarily say a good—or a resource—is scarce if the quantity demanded exceeds the quantity supplied at some benchmark price, such as the prevailing one, so that in a competitive market there is an upward pressure on the price. As a special case, goods are sometimes considered scarce, or "economic," as opposed to "free," if this excess demand is positive at a *zero* price. But much of the current debate about natural resource scarcity focuses on *physical* measures, such as the stock of reserves. To obtain some idea of the economic implications of an estimated reserve base, it is typically compared with another physical quantity, projected consumption, giving rise to conclusions on how many years' worth of coal, or iron, or whatever is left at current or projected rates of consumption.[1]

Now, a physical measure such as reserves makes no sense for a non-

I am grateful to Bengt Hansson, Geoffrey Heal, Alvin Klevorick, Harvey Lapan, and Karl-Göran Mäler for helpful discussions and comments on an earlier draft.

[1] One of the best examples of this type of analysis is *Population, Resources, and Environment,* a report of the (U.S.) Commission on Population Growth and the American Future [4].

extractive commodity, since we can, at a cost, produce as much as we want. Except in the very short run, "reserves" are not important. But looking more closely at extractive resources, the simple distinction begins to blur. That is, it is not clear that there really is a limited stock, at least one corresponding to reserves. Reserves are defined as the known amounts of a mineral that can be profitably recovered at current prices for the mineral and the inputs used in extracting and processing it.[2] Obviously, then, reserves can be expanded by, among other things, discoveries of new deposits or technical changes which convert formerly uneconomic materials, such as ores with low metal content, into "reserves." We might say that the stock of an extractive resource can be augmented by investing in information, just as the number of effective units of labor can be augmented by human capital formation—or for that matter, the supply of any nonextractive commodity. But if this is true, then the economic concept of scarcity, rising price, becomes significant for extractive natural resources as well as these other items. The point is that for most, if not all, resources it is difficult to speak precisely about physical scarcity, either because we are uncertain about the extent, location, and quality of deposits, or because of ambiguities in the definition of ultimately recoverable reserves. Coal deposits, for example, though subject to less uncertainty than those of oil and gas, and most metallic minerals, are (necessarily) rather arbitrarily reckoned as consisting only of a given thickness of seam, and at most a given overburden of soil.[3] The economic measure, price, then, is a kind of summary statistic, reflecting a precise outcome of conflicting influences on an unknown and perhaps unknowable physical magnitude.

The similarity of extractive and nonextractive resources may be a bit overdrawn. One could object that in the long run extraction is bound by the finite stocks of minerals in the earth's crust. Long before these limits are reached, it is likely that the incremental energy and environmental costs of extraction would become prohibitive. In the next section I shall set out a fairly traditional model of competitive extraction under certainty, that is, a model which does not explicitly include investment in augmenting the resource stock. But later on I consider, less formally, how results might be affected by such augmentation. In succeeding sections investment in creating reserves by exploration is made endogenous to the model.

The purpose of the model in the next section is to bring out the relationships between a number of different economic scarcity measures

---

[2] This is the generally accepted definition, as explained in greater detail by Schanz [5], drawing on U.S. Geological Survey publications and practice.

[3] For precise specifications, see Darmstadter [6].

that have been proposed for resources. I have referred to rising price as "the" measure of scarcity, but as we shall see, resources *are* different. There are at least two candidates for price measures: the ordinary market price, and something that might be called a pure scarcity rent, the value of a unit of the resource "in the ground." Further, in the most influential study to date, that by Barnett and Morse [7], still another measure, the unit cost of extractive output, is emphasized. This in fact derives from perhaps the earliest scarcity theorist, Malthus, who believed that increasing agricultural output would require ever-increasing "doses" of labor and capital, and also from Ricardo, who extended this conclusion to mineral output.[4] A simple model of optimal extraction by a competitive firm will not only bring out the relationships between these measures, but will shed some light on how each is affected by changes in the resource stock.

Broadly speaking, the conclusion is that each is well behaved, in the sense that it is generally (though not always, as we shall see) negatively related to the size of the stock. That is, the smaller the stock, the higher the price (rent, cost), and the larger the stock, the lower the price (rent, cost). But it does not follow that all three are equally sensitive or accurate measures of scarcity. This raises the question of what properties such a measure should have. In the remainder of this section I propose an answer that enables us to discriminate at least between cost, price, and rent. Also, I attempt to justify briefly the statement made at the outset that an inquiry into the meaning and measurement of scarcity may be worthwhile.

Perhaps the two key questions about natural resource use that have emerged in the recent theoretical literature are (1) whether the time pattern of extraction produced by a competitive market is socially efficient and (2) how various sources of market imperfection—monopoly, externalities, etc.—distort the competitive pattern.[5] Implicit in these questions is the possibility that market-determined rates of extraction could be too slow, as well as too rapid. So in a sense my concern with scarcity is a restricted one. It assumes that the underconsumption of resource stocks is less of a problem than overconsumption. Two things can be said about this. First, there is no presumption that (existing) markets do, on balance, overconsume; this has not been demonstrated in the literature.

---

[4] For a clear and informative discussion of the views of the classical economists, see Barnett and Morse [7, pp. 51–71].

[5] See the several studies in the *Review of Economic Studies Symposium on the Economics of Exhaustible Resources*. Resource market imperfections are also classified and analyzed by Sweeney [8], and Kay and Mirrlees [3]. Nordhaus [9], Solow [10], and Heal [11] consider in particular the problems caused by the lack of futures markets.

Second, however, it seems reasonable to worry more about the consequences of this possibility. As Common [12] has put it:

Depleting finite stocks of fossil fuels closes our future options in a way that depreciating a capital stock does not, in that the former is irreversible while the latter is not. Given labour and natural resources, capital equipment can be created from scratch: if, today, the world's entire capital stock were destroyed, it could be recreated. Given labour and capital equipment, natural resources cannot be created: if, today, the world's entire stock of fossil fuels were destroyed, it could not be recreated. [12, p. 8].

I have suggested that natural resource stocks can, in a sense, be augmented, but that does not really counter Common's point. It is precisely the possibility of substituting producible capital, such as machines or knowledge, for nonproducible materials, such as highly concentrated ores, that allows us to effectively augment resource stocks. For some types of resources, such as unique natural environments, even this may not be possible. Once the redwood forests or the Grand Canyon are gone, they are gone; they are irreplaceable.[6] The point is that a concern with natural resource scarcity, which seems to be shared by a wide segment of the general public, is not entirely irrational, however irrational some of the arguments motivated by this concern appear to be. I need hardly add that this does not imply that investigations into possible sources of over-conservation should not be undertaken. But in this paper I am simply trying to respond to the concern about impending exhaustion by indicating how it might be reflected in some alternative measures.

If it is agreed that a measure of scarcity may be of interest, what properties should it have? Let me propose a very simple answer. A measure of a resource's scarcity should have just one essential property: it should summarize the sacrifices, direct *and indirect,* made to obtain a unit of the resource. This appears to concentrate on the supply side, to the exclusion of demand, but in fact it does not. First, note the operative word, "made"; this implies a willingness to pay. Second, note the emphasis on indirect cost. In general, consumption of a unit of a resource today will have a direct cost, the labor and capital (and other resource) inputs required to extract and convert it, and an indirect cost, the value of future consumption forgone. After describing the relationships between cost, price, and rent with the aid of the model in the next section, I shall argue that the unit cost of extractive output is, in *theory,* deficient as an indicator of scarcity because it does not capture this indirect component. Price is the preferred measure, though there is something to be said for

---

[6] A substantial literature on the economics of natural environments, which emphasizes the implications of the irreversibility of their consumption, has recently emerged. For perhaps the most complete statement, see Krutilla and Fisher [13].

rent. Even unit cost comes back into the picture because, though it does not reflect the demand for, and value of, future output forgone, it typically moves in the right direction (increases) as a stock is depleted.

There is in fact, as I shall show in sections III and IV, an interesting duality between cost and rent. Where production conditions are such that cost increases with depletion, rent behaves erratically, and if cost increases sufficiently, rent ultimately falls to zero. On the other hand, where cost does not increase with depletion, rent rises smoothly. Once again, then, price is the preferred measure, since it is in both cases negatively related to stock size. This suggests one other desirable property, hinted at earlier, for an economic measure: that it be related to stock changes in an intuitively plausible way. The plan of the paper is as follows. In the next section, some elements of a model of optimal extraction are set out. Section III focuses on the much-discussed unit cost measure, noting its advantages and disadvantages. Section IV takes up the behavior of resource rents and prices over time, and their relationships to stock changes. Finally, in section V investment in stock-augmenting exploration is introduced into the model. This has the advantage of leading to a practical proposal for estimating rent, though it also raises some troubling questions of market failure.

II
Optimal Extraction and the Relationship Between Scarcity Measures

In order to discuss sensibly the advantages and disadvantages of the alternative cost, price, and rent measures of scarcity, we need a clear idea of how these measures are related to each other. A simple model of optimal extraction by a competitive firm can provide this.[7] Further, it can be extended to show how they behave as a resource stock is depleted— or augmented, as through exploration—and how rent, ordinarily very difficult to observe, might be estimated. Now, if we are interested in social scarcity, that is, scarcity to society, not just to a single firm, it might seem preferable to model extraction to maximize an (social) objective such as discounted aggregate consumers' plus producers' surplus from the resource. But as the necessary conditions which delineate the relations between cost, price, and rent are the same in either case, under standard assumptions, it will do just as well to analyze the slightly more convenient case of the firm.[8] On the other hand, when it becomes important to

---

[7] The model is based in part on one in Peterson and Fisher [14].

[8] The original proof of something like this proposition is in Hotelling [15]. More recently, it has been extended by Schulze [16] and Sweeney [8], among others.

broaden the focus to economy-wide depletion, I shall do this explicitly, as in parts of section IV.

A key construct in the model is an extraction production function,

$$Y = f(E, X, t) \tag{1}$$

where Y is extractive output, E is effort (an index of labor and capital) devoted to extraction, X is the resource stock, and t is time. The function is assumed to have the normal concavity in E, that is,

$$f_E > 0, \qquad f_{EE} < 0$$

Also, and very importantly, I assume a positive "stock effect" on output, that is, $f_X > 0$ and $f_{EX} > 0$. In other words, with a larger stock, more output is obtained for a given effort and also for a given increment of effort. It is in fact this stock effect that drives costs up as a resource is depleted. It is possible to think of processes that do not exhibit the property—for example, the extraction of salts from sea water—but they are not typical. As John Stuart Mill observed, mineral extraction costs rise because "shafts must be sunk deeper, galleries driven further," and so on.[9] Similarly, for one of the most valuable resources, oil, the decrease in pressure as a well is depleted requires increasing inputs of effort. I emphasize all this because many, if not most, of the recent contributions to the theoretical literature on natural resource depletion assume, explicitly or otherwise, no such stock effect—in terms of our model, $f_X \equiv f_{EX} \equiv 0$. This in turn has, as we shall see, implications for the behavior of rents and prices, as well as costs, as a resource is depleted.

The firm's objective is to maximize the present discounted value of its profits from sales of the resource. It does this by choosing a path of extraction subject to nonnegativity restrictions on effort, $E \geq 0$, and to the finite stock constraint,

$$X(t) = X(0) - \int_0^t Y(\tau) \, d\tau, \qquad X(t) \geq 0 \tag{2}$$

where $X(0)$ is the initial stock.[10] Differentiating equation (2) with respect to time, we obtain the system equation for the state variable X,

$$\frac{dX}{dt} = -Y(t) \tag{3}$$

The formal statement of the firm's problem is:

$$\max \int_0^\infty [Pf(E, X, t) - WE]e^{-rt} \, dt \tag{4}$$

[9] The quotation from Mill is taken from Barnett and Morse [7, p. 67].
[10] For the time being I assume a known, initial stock to be depleted, with no possibility of augmentation as through exploration.

subject to the nonnegativity restrictions and the system equation (3), where P is the price of the resource (a parameter to the competitive firm), W is the wage of effort, and r is the rate of discount.

The problem is now in a form suited to the application of the maximum principle of Pontryagin and coauthors [17]. The Hamiltonian equation is

$$H = [Pf(E, X, t) - WE - qY]e^{-rt} \tag{5}$$

where q is the costate variable attached to the constraint on the state variable X. It may be interpreted, as in other constrained maximization problems, as the change in the optimal value of the objective function resulting from a small change in the constraint. *In particular in this problem $q(t)$ is the effect on (discounted) future profits of removing a unit of the resource from the stock at time t.*[11] The maximum principle states that the control variable E must be chosen to maximize H. Differentiating H with respect to E we obtain

$$H_E = PY_E - W - qY_E \tag{6}$$

and, ignoring corner solutions and setting the result equal to zero,

$$P = \frac{W}{Y_E} + q \tag{7}$$

This is an important result, but before I discuss it let me briefly say something about the technique used to obtain it.[12] The basic principle is that we solve a complicated problem—choosing an entire time path of a variable—by breaking it down into a series of simple ones—choosing, in each short interval of time, a desired level for the variable.

The net return or profit to the resource-extracting firm, in a short interval dt, is $(PY - WE)dt$. The choice of E in the interval should obviously be influenced by its impact on this quantity. But it should not be influenced *solely* by this, because it also has an impact, as seen from equations (1) and (3), on depletion of the stock. This is essentially what equation (5), the Hamiltonian, suggests. The right-hand side of equation (5), $(PY - WE - qY)e^{-rt}$ is just the (rate of) flow of profit due to current extraction $(PY - WE)$, plus the (negative) value, in terms of the objective function, of depletion of the stock due to current extraction, qY— all appropriately discounted back to $t = 0$. Central to this explanation is of course the interpretation of q as the effect on the objective

---

[11] For an interpretation of dual variables as shadow prices in nonlinear programming, see Balinski and Baumol [18].

[12] For further details, see the intuitive development of Dorfman [19] and the more rigorous one of Arrow and Kurz [20].

function of removing a unit of the resource from the stock, where Y represents the number of units removed.

Now let us return to equation (7). What it tells us is that, at all points along the firm's optimal extraction path, the market price P is equated to the sum of the *marginal cost of current extraction, W/Y_E,* and the marginal loss in profit from future extraction, q. Note that had we assumed the firm to choose E to maximize current return, the resulting necessary condition would have been the conventional $P = W/Y_E$, or price equals marginal cost. Note also that the divergence of price from marginal cost in a resource market does not arise from any market imperfection.

I have already given a couple of interpretations of the costate variable q. Now let me give another: q is the *rent* to a unit of the resource, the difference between what is received by the resource owner, P, and what is paid out to contractual inputs, W/Y_E.[13] So we have the following simple relationship between cost, price, and rent: price equals marginal cost plus rent, where q, the rent, is our desired measure of the indirect or opportunity cost of resource extraction.

This seems to settle the question of which measure of scarcity is "best." Price, which reflects both the direct and indirect sacrifices required to obtain a unit of the resource, would seem to fit the bill. But here I am going to get very slippery and suggest that it depends on what one means by "resource." Is a resource the raw material in the ground? Or is it the extracted, or extracted and converted, product? If the latter, then price is the appropriate measure of scarcity. But if the former, as Brown and Field (chapter 9) argue, the extraction cost component of price is not relevant and rent is the appropriate measure.[14]

However one views this matter, rent clearly has a role in any assessment of scarcity. But as I shall show in section IV, rent as an indicator of scarcity has the disturbing property of sometimes decreasing as the resource stock decreases. In section IV I spell out the circumstances in which this can occur. But first, I consider some problems with the unit cost measure.

III
Problems with the Unit Cost Measure

Before turning to the problems with unit cost, let me start on a positive note. This measure, as Morse has observed,[15] is suggested by the

[13] Still another term for q is marginal user cost, due to Scott [21]. It corresponds also to Nordhaus's [9] royalty, and Solow's [22] net price.

[14] This distinction is drawn also by Smith [24].

[15] Forum on the Economics of Natural Resource Scarcity, Resources for the Future, Washington, D.C., October 18–19, 1976.

classical economists' concern that the natural resource sector would draw ever-increasing amounts of labor and capital from other sectors, exerting a drag on growth. This seems to me a reasonable concern, and sufficient motivation for the cost calculations reported by Barnett and Morse [7] and Barnett (chapter 8, this volume). It is true, as Brown and Field (chapter 9) point out, that as richer deposits of a mineral are depleted, technical change in methods of extraction and conversion can offset the tendency to higher costs that would otherwise result from the movement to thinner deposits. The same sort of offsetting effect has probably also been produced by economies of scale in working the thinner deposits, which typically occur in larger concentrations. But in any event, it seems legitimate to try to sort out these several effects. *Ceteris paribus,* it should be true that depletion of higher grade ores leads to a rise in the unit cost of mineral production. The potential for technical change and economies of scale is not inconsistent with this proposition, and indeed is worth exploring, not only for the purpose of interpreting our cost data, but also for what it can tell us about these processes in the natural resource sector and in the economy generally.

I do, however, see a number of theoretical and empirical difficulties with the unit cost measure. One is that unit costs of production (or extraction) do not reflect anticipated future scarcity. It is perfectly possible, in theory, for unit costs to remain stable—and at a very low level—as a resource approaches exhaustion. Now it must be noted that this phenomenon is more a feature of highly simplified neoclassical models of optimal extraction than it is of extraction in the real world. There, as I have suggested earlier, following Mill, a positive stock effect ($f_x > 0$, $f_{EX} > 0$) means that costs will rise as the stock is depleted. To see how this works, recall that marginal extraction cost is given in our model by the expression W/f_E. Now, as X decreases, f_E decreases

$$\left[\frac{\partial \left(\frac{\partial f}{\partial E} \right)}{\partial X} > 0 \right]$$

so the marginal cost is driven up. Conversely, an increase in X caused, for example, by new information suggesting that a resource deposit is larger than originally believed, or by technical change that creates reserves out of formerly uneconomic materials, results in an increase in f_E and consequently a decrease in marginal cost W/f_E. But it must be acknowledged that future scarcity is not *explicitly* captured by any measure of current extraction costs. A positive stock effect merely pushes it in the right direction.

Another difficulty with unit cost, an empirical one, is that it is not readily observed. It must be constructed, as Barnett and Morse [7] have done, from series on labor and capital inputs and extractive outputs. This gives rise to problems of aggregation. One problem well known from investigations in another branch of economics is how heterogenous capital is to be aggregated into a single input series. Another, noted by Brown and Field (chapter 9), has to do with the aggregation of the various input series: "whereas the metals output series [in Barnett and Morse] appears to be at the extractive level, the metals employment data include some undetermined fractions of workers in the separate processing sectors" (p. 223). These are serious problems. The moral, I think, is not that we should abandon cost estimation, simply that we must recognize that it may not be a straightforward procedure.

Resource Scarcity and the Environment. Perhaps the most serious difficulty with this measure, and one that was emphasized at the recent Resources for the Future Forum on the Economics of Natural Resource Scarcity,[15] is that it does not fully reflect the effects of resource use on the environment. This is not a new point. Barnett and Morse [7] in their pathbreaking study of trends in unit costs and prices observed that the effects of landscape disfigurement were not reflected in their calculations. If, as many people believe—though the time series evidence is scanty— such disruptions of the environment have been growing over time, then results like those of Barnett and Morse, which indicate a relative *decline* in the unit cost or price of extractive output, need to be reconsidered. That is, although the private cost has declined, the social cost may not have. Note, by the way, that failure to reflect environmental effects is a problem for any conventional measure of scarcity. I discuss it here because it has recently (at the RFF forum) received attention with respect to cost measures.

Barnett (chapter 8, this volume) has in fact reconsidered this question, and provides a partial answer to the concern about environmental cost. Recognizing the difficulty of estimating pollution damages, he looks at current and projected future costs of abatement implied by the recent clean air and water standards of the U.S. Environmental Protection Agency. Of course, even with these standards there will remain some pollution and other environmental disruption. But laying these aside for the moment, what can be said about the costs of achieving the standards? It turns out that, although these costs are growing both absolutely (in 1974 dollars) and relatively (to GNP), they are still quite small (3 percent of GNP) by the year 2000. Put another way, "we would have to

---

[15] Forum on the Economics of Natural Resource Scarcity, Resources for the Future, Washington, D.C., October 18–19, 1976.

give up less than a tenth of one percentage point in annual growth of national output to pay for this active abatement policy" (p. 187, this volume). This relatively complacent view can be challenged on a number of grounds. The basic problem, as it has been stated by Krutilla,[16] is that to use an extractive natural resource such as coal, say, it is generally also necessary to use a common property resource, such as air or water. Implicit in Barnett's calculations is the possibility of uncoupling these joint products. That is, the idea is that it should be possible to produce and consume increasing tonnage of coal without at the same time "consuming" increasing amounts of clean air. This seems plausible with respect to many conventional pollutants, such as, for example, large particulates from coal burning power plants. But if Krutilla's point has any force, it is precisely that there may be a rather rigid relationship between goods and *some* bads. Again taking coal as our our example, the buildup of carbon dioxide in the atmosphere that results from the combustion of coal (and other fossil fuels) may be a problem that cannot be dealt with by any conceivable abatement technology because it proceeds from the basic chemistry of combustion.[17] In fact, this is recognized by Barnett, along with radiation and nuclear waste storage, as a possible exception to his broad conclusion that pollution can be taken care of by a growing gross national product.

Mention of radiation and nuclear waste suggests a more general point. Technical change, which as documented by Barnett and Morse and others, has played such an important role in relaxing natural resource constraints, has in some ways put more of a burden on the environment. We are now becoming concerned, for example, about trace metals and other new and exotic chemical contaminants or carcinogens in drinking water and some agricultural products, as stressed by Page.[18] Some of these substances may be sufficiently toxic that virtually complete abatement, or prohibition of discharge, will be required. Complete abatement can of course be very costly. A closely related point has to do with threshold levels for various pollutants. As suggested by Mishan,[19] ozone depletion and oil spills in the oceans, to take two examples, may not register until critical accumulations have been reached. Neither the damages nor the costs of preventing them will be taken into account by calculations like those presented earlier in this section.

Barnett has suggested an answer to the concerns about increasing

[16] Ibid.

[17] For a discussion of relationships between fossil fuel combustion, carbon dioxide in the atmosphere, and global climate, see Nordhaus [25].

[18] Forum on the Economics of Natural Resource Scarcity, Resources for the Future, Washington, D.C., October 18–19, 1976.

[19] Ibid.

amounts of conventional pollution which may be applicable to the newer, more exotic forms as well. It is that just as substitution in production and consumption, and technical change, have prevented the unit costs of extractive output from rising, they may do the same for pollution abatement. In order to meet a given air quality standard, for example, it will not be necessary to remove an ever-increasing proportion of the sulfur from coal. Instead, cleaner sources of power may be substituted for coal over time, a less energy-intensive mix of goods may be consumed, or perhaps the sulfur can be removed cheaply from the coal with the aid of a new technology developed for the purpose.

A resource optimist would emphasize this line of reasoning, along with the relatively modest costs of achieving a substantial degree of cleanup even with currently known technologies. A resource pessimist, on the other hand, would perhaps be impressed by the difficulty in breaking the historical links between consumption of extractive and common property resources, and also with the dangers posed by some of the newer pollutants, which may be highly toxic even in minute quantities. It seems fair to say that in determining to what extent conventional measures of the cost of extractive output may need to be modified to reflect environmental concerns, we are confronted with a major research task. I think the key question—and it is an empirical one—is, to what extent processes generating the "new pollution" can be modified through substitution, technical change, or other methods.

IV
The Behavior of Rents and Prices over Time

Consider the equation for the evolution of the shadow price or rent, q, in the model.[20] The result that rent need not rise at the rate of interest, or even monotonically as a resource is depleted follows almost immediately:

$$\dot{q} = rq - \hat{H}_X \tag{8}$$

Substituting for $\hat{H}_X$, the partial derivative of $\hat{H}$ (where $\hat{H} = He^{rt}$) with respect to X, and rearranging terms, we obtain

$$\frac{\dot{q}}{q} = r + \left(1 - \frac{P}{q}\right)Y_X \tag{9}$$

In other words, the rate of change of rent, $\dot{q}/q$, is equal to the rate of interest, r, only if there is no stock effect, that is, only if $Y_X = 0$, or there is no marginal extraction cost, that is, $P = q$. In the general case in

[20] Again, see Arrow and Kurz [20] for a derivation of this equation.

which these conditions do not hold, what does equation (9) tell us about the behavior of rent over time? Assuming $Y_x > 0$, and since $P > q$, the right-hand side of equation (9) must be less than r. The pure return to holding a unit of the resource in the stock over a short interval of time, $\dot{q}/q$, is less than the return on an alternative investment, given by r, because there is value, in the form of reduced extraction costs, to holding a unit "in the ground." Note that not only is the rate of change of q not equal to r, in general, it may even become negative.

I think these results are worth emphasizing because they run counter to a fairly commonly held notion that in an optimal program, rent, or the shadow price of an exhaustible resource, rises over time as the resource is depleted, and moreover rises at precisely the rate of interest. As I have shown, the latter will occur only in the special case in which there is no stock effect. As for the possibility that rent as an indicator of scarcity is not well behaved, that is, does not rise as the stock shrinks, this can be demonstrated more strikingly with the aid of a slightly different model, and different definitions of resource and rent.

Let me start by recalling the classic concept of a resource rent as described by David Ricardo. Ricardo argued, in essence, that rent was just the difference between the payment to some resource input, such as a parcel of good agricultural land, and the (labor and capital) costs of producing from it. Rent could persist, even in a competitive equilibrium, if the good land was in limited supply relative to demand. That is, if demand were sufficient to call into production poor land as well, the cost of production and hence the price of the product would be above the cost of production from the good land, the difference constituting a rent to the land. Although agricultural land is generally used to illustrate this concept, Ricardo noted that it applied to mineral resources as well. These too vary in "fertility," some being richer or more accessible than others. But as Barnett and Morse [7, p. 64] also observe, the Ricardian rent to a mineral, or the land on which it is found, is *not* a payment for the exhaustion of the mineral. After all, even if it were replenishable, like agricultural land, Ricardian rent would arise as long as market demand in any period could not be met by production from the richest and most accessible units alone. Conversely, as we shall see, even where production in any period depends only on a single (large) deposit, with constant marginal and average costs of extraction, so that there is no Ricardian rent, a scarcity rent like q in our model will exist.

A couple of simple diagrams will bring out these distinctions more clearly. In figure 10-1, the equilibrium relationship $P = W/f_E + q$ is illustrated by the intersection of the price line (P) with the curve ($W/f_E + q$). At the equilibrium output $Y = Y^*$, there is, in general, a

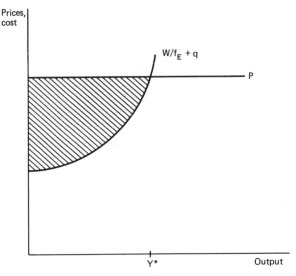

Figure 10-1.

positive scarcity rent q. But on all of the inframarginal units, there is also a Ricardian rent, the shaded difference between price and cost, where q is regarded as a part of the cost, which of course it is, whether paid by the producer to the owner of the resource rights, or simply imputed if producer and owner are one and the same. Now consider a somewhat different case, in which all of the economy's production of a resource, in any period, is at constant marginal and average costs, from a deposit or deposits of constant quality. The necessary conditions, namely

$$P = W/f_E + q \qquad (W/f_E = \text{constant}) \tag{i}$$

and

$$\frac{\dot{q}}{q} = r \qquad \qquad (\text{no stock effects}) \tag{ii}$$

continue to hold, though the demand price P is now $P = P(Y)$, where Y is total output in the period, so condition (i) describes the intersection of a downward sloping demand $(\partial P/\partial Y < 0)$ with a horizontal line.[21] Just above I suggested that production at constant costs will entail no rent in the sense of Ricardo, but it will entail a scarcity rent like q. The

---

[21] In all of this I am abstracting from the problem of monopoly. If the deposit is privately owned, I assume the owner is a discriminating monopolist. If publicly owned, I assume optimization of something like producer's plus consumers' surplus. In either case, as I noted earlier, the necessary conditions are like (i) and (ii), and price does not include any element of monopoly rent.

proof of the first part of this proposition is obvious. But what is the nature of the scarcity rent? Suppose, following Nordhaus [9], there exists some substitute for the resource—a "backstop," such as nuclear fusion reactors for fossil fuels—which produces the same final services as the resource, but at higher cost. Then, as Nordhaus also shows, the resource is used first, and its shadow price or scarcity rent—or royalty, as he calls it—is just equal to the difference between the cost or price of producing from the backstop (P^B) and the cost of producing from the resource (C), at the switch date (T) from resource to backstop. At any time, t, $0 \leq t \leq T$, the royalty, equivalent to our q, is $(P^B - C)e^{-r(T-t)}$. That is, in the absence of stock effects, the royalty grows at the rate r as the resource is depleted. So far, so good; as the stock shrinks, the rent rises. Note, by the way, that this rent in fact looks rather Ricardian. That is, although there is no true Ricardian rent, all production in any period coming from a constant quality deposit, the rent does reflect a cost difference.

But now suppose there is a second quality of deposit, poorer than the first, but still more economical than the backstop. In this case, which is realistic certainly for most resources, it is easy to show that the rent or royalty does not rise monotonically as the resource is depleted. Starting from the switch date from the first, good quality deposit to the second, poor quality one, the analysis is exactly as above. The royalty on the second deposit is $(P^B - C_2)e^{-r(T_2-T_1)}$, where T_1 is the switch date from the first to the second deposit, T_2 is the switch date from the second to the backstop, and C_2 is the (constant) cost of producing from the second. The royalty rises at the rate r to $(P^B - C_2)$ at T_2. The price of the second deposit at T_1, when it enters production, is again the sum of marginal extraction cost and royalty, or $C_2 + (P^B - C_2)e^{-r(T_2-T_1)}$. This price, call it P_2, plays the same role, in turn, in the determination of the royalty on the first deposit as the price of the backstop plays in the determination of the royalty on the second. Thus the royalty on the first deposit is initially, at $t = 0$, $(P_2 - C_1)e^{-rT_1}$, where C_1 is the (constant) cost of producing from the first deposit, and it rises to $(P_2 - C_1)$ at $t = T_1$. At this point, where the resource price is P_2, and recalling that $C_1 < C_2$, the royalty must fall, to $(P_2 - C_2)$, on the second deposit. So the scarcity rent on the *resource* must fall.

Of course, one could take the view that the different quality deposits are different resources. In the absence of stock effects, the rent or royalty on each must rise—at the rate of interest. This is what I meant, earlier, in suggesting that whether rent rises monotonically as a resource stock is depleted depends on the definition of "resource." But my impression is that the same word—"copper," or "oil," or whatever, is commonly used to describe deposits of varying quality, so the result is not trivial. The

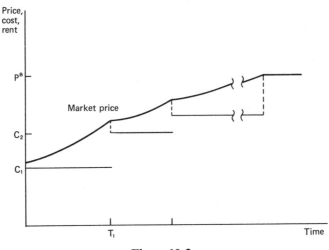

Figure 10-2.

analysis is easily extended from two to many different qualities of a resource, with each transition to a lower quality as the higher is depleted leading to a fall in the rent. Recalling the old distinction between intensive and extensive margins, as applied to agricultural land, we might say that the resource rent rises on the intensive margin and falls on the extensive. If and when resource extraction costs reach P^B, the price of the backstop, the rent falls to zero. All of this is represented in figure 10-2. Market price always rises as the resource is depleted, cost rises in discrete jumps, and rent rises and falls, ultimately falling to zero when the market price reaches P^B.[22] Another way of interpreting the result that rent vanishes is to consider the backstop as "average rock," instead of a new technology that substitutes for the resource. That is, ultimately all of the above-average concentrations of the resource are exhausted, and it is extracted from a virtually limitless supply of material in the earth's crust.[23] It is intuitively plausible that, in this situation, there will be no rent, Ricardian or other, accruing for any unit, since one is as good, or as bad, as another now and forever (almost).

Finally, note that we can approximate the continuous case described in the model of the preceding section, and equations (8) and (9), by letting the time between cost jumps approach zero. Although the analysis there was for a single firm, and we are now talking about the resource

[22] This diagram, and the related analysis, are essentially the same as in Herfindahl and Kneese [26], one difference being that there the ultimate price, P^B, is the price at which demand for the resource equals zero.

[23] A similar model is considered by Heal [27].

industry, the result is the same. Rent evolves smoothly over time, according to an equation like (9), either rising or falling, but ultimately falling to zero if stock effects push up extraction costs indefinitely.

What conclusions can we draw, then, about the behavior of rent as the stock of a resource is depleted? First, the statement in the introductory section, that rent generally rises as the stock falls, is too sweeping. Where the costs of extraction are not affected by depletion, it is correct. But where they are, either in a continuous fashion as in the original model, or in a discrete fashion as in the transition to different quality deposits in this section's model, there are conflicting tendencies, and if extraction costs rise all the way to the price of the backstop, the result is that rent falls to zero. Interestingly, there is a kind of duality between rent and cost as indicators of scarcity. Where cost is not a good indicator, rent is, and vice versa. That is, where there are no stock or quality effects, cost does not rise as a stock is depleted, but rent does. On the other hand, where these effects are present, cost is driven up, and rent rises along the intensive margin but falls along the extensive, ultimately to zero.

Thus far I have considered the evolution of rent as a stock is depleted over time. Another question is, what is the effect of a stock change on the *initial* value of the rent? In other words, instead of asking how rent behaves as a resource stock is depleted over time, I am now asking the comparative statics question of how the initial value is affected by a change on the initial stock. In symbols, what is the sign of $\partial q_0 / \partial X_0$, where X_0 refers to initial stock for the economy? Notice that this introduces uncertainty. X_0 will be affected, as suggested in the introduction, by information about new deposits, or methods of producing a resource product from lower grade materials. These would be positive effects, but one can also imagine better information leading to a downward revision of an estimated stock, as has recently occurred, for example, in the case of U.S. offshore oil deposits. In any event, it is clear that the sign of $\partial q_0 / \partial X_0$ is negative, as inspection of the expression for q in this section's model of economy-wide depletion suggests.

Taking the simplest case, sufficient for our purposes, of depletion of a single grade of the resource up to replacement by a backstop, $q_0 = (P^B - C)e^{-rT}$. The only thing affected by a stock change, dX_0 is the switch date T, since P^B and C are technologically determined and r is a parameter to the resource sector. For a given pattern of demand for the resource, then, we have $T = T(X_0)$, where $dT/dX_0 > 0$. From this we obtain

$$\frac{\partial q_0}{\partial X_0} = \frac{\partial q_0}{\partial T} \frac{dT}{dX_0} = (-r)(P^B - C)(e^{-rT}) \left(\frac{dT}{dX_0}\right) \qquad (10)$$

Since $(P^B - C) > 0$, $e^{-rt} > 0$, and $dT/dX_0 > 0$, for $r > 0$ we must have $\partial q_0/\partial X_0 < 0$. A slightly more complicated analysis yields a similar but qualified result for price, as I shall presently indicate.

Now, what can be said of the relationship between stock change and price? Price appears to be generally well behaved, as seen for example in figure 10-2. The equilibrium condition for both competitive firm and social planner, that price in any period equals marginal cost plus rent, ensures that price will always move in the right direction as a stock is depleted over time, pushed up either by rising cost or rising rent. The only remaining question is, how is the current market price affected by a change in the current estimate of the stock size?

In a world without a complete set of resource futures markets, the answer is not clear. But I think there is some presumption that price will continue to be well behaved. The crucial question is, how are price expectations formed? A number of theorists have recently considered this question, with interesting but not definitive results.[24] Here I just indicate the links, as I see them, in the chain connecting stock to price changes. This will enable us to identify the conditions under which current price increases (decreases) with a decrease (increase) in the estimated initial stock.

Suppose at $t = 0$ the reserve base for a mineral resource increases, due to a new process which makes profitable the extraction and conversion of a very thin ore. This lowers the price expected to prevail in the future, when the new material will come on line—or, what is the same thing, the current rent, as indicated by equation (10). This, in turn, should lead either the public resource agency or private resource owners to expand current production, resulting (for given demand) in a fall in the current price. So, through the links of negative relations between initial stock and rent $[(\partial q_0/\partial X_0) < 0]$, and current output and price $[(\partial P/\partial Y) < 0]$, a larger initial stock is associated with a lower current price.

The difficulty, or potential difficulty, lies in the effect that a change in the current price will have on the expected future price. Let us define the elasticity of expectations as

$$\epsilon = \frac{dP_t^e}{P_t^e} \bigg/ \frac{dP_0}{P_0}$$

where P_t^e is the price expected to prevail at time $t > 0$ in the future. If $\epsilon = 0$, then the story is ended. The expected future price is determined solely by estimates of future demand and technology, which are not

[24] See, for example, Nordhaus [9], Solow [22], Stiglitz [28], Heal [11], and Mishan [29].

speculatively related to current price changes. But it is conceivable, and quite plausible, that $\epsilon > 0$. In this case, the reduction in P_0 leads to a reduction in P_l, which leads in turn to a further expansion of current output and further reduction in P_0, and so on. Whether an equilibrium is reached should depend on the size of ϵ; if it is small enough, the current price changes should approach zero. But in any event, with these speculative effects we have perhaps too much of a good thing: current price overreacts to a change in the estimated initial stock. If, finally, $\epsilon < 0$, which is conceivable, though not very plausible, then current price could react perversely, increasing with an increase in the stock.[25]

Although the possibility of speculative effects can cause problems for price as an indicator of scarcity, I don't think too much should be made of this. In the first place, the really bad result of current price varying positively with current estimated stock could occur only if there were a sufficiently strong negative elasticity of expectations. But it is hard to tell a convincing story that would produce this result. In the second place, even the more realistic positive elasticity is not likely to persist. At some point beliefs about future demand and technology will call a halt to the round of speculative price decreases. Admittedly, the net result could be some deviation from an efficient extraction path, but this is of greater relevance to the question of whether the lack of a complete set of resource futures markets will lead to inefficiency than to the narrower question of whether price is likely to reflect scarcity.

V
Exploration and Externalities

I have spoken of the possibility of augmenting a resource stock through investment devoted to this purpose, as in the exploration for new deposits. In this section such exploration is introduced into the model of section II. This is not merely a formal exercise, however, as it leads to a new insight into resource rent and a practical proposal for estimating it. The basic idea is that, once we recognize that optimal depletion is not simply a matter of using up a known stock, but involves the allocation of effort to find new sources, we might conjecture that the rent, or indirect cost of a unit extracted today, will reflect not the loss in future income from that unit, but the cost of finding another to replace it. This is precisely the result we shall obtain, as do also Brown and Field (chapter 9). There does arise, however, an interesting problem involving externalities in exploration which they do not consider.

[25] For a detailed analysis of the implications for competitive extraction paths of different expectations elasticities, though not in the context of a discussion of scarcity, see Mishan [29].

Before proceeding it is important to recognize just how strong the assumption about exploration is, and how it changes the earlier model. It makes the exhaustible resource into something like a renewable one— only more so, since the growth of a renewable resource is usually constrained by nature. And as with a renewable resource, a steady state, in which stock size and rent (the shadow price of a unit in the stock) do not change, becomes possible. In any event, the earlier criterion for judging a measure of scarcity—how it behaves as a stock is physically depleted—is no longer relevant, as the stock is potentially without limit. But effort is in fact required to extend the limit at any time, and this brings us back to the desirable property for a measure of scarcity suggested in the introduction: that it reflect the sacrifices made to obtain the resource. As we shall see, rent can be considered a good indicator in this sense, in a model with exploration—at least if one is interested in the resource in the ground.

I don't intend to consider the dynamics any further here. Instead, I shall derive an expression that can be used to estimate the rent at any point in time. No doubt the associated view of exploration is too optimistic. On the other hand, section II's model, which allows no growth in the resource stock, is probably too pessimistic. In any event, let us here develop the implications of the optimistic view. The relevance of either is of course an empirical matter.

Formally, the new element in the model is an exploration or discovery production function, $f^d(E^d, t)$, where f^d represents new discoveries, measured in units of the resource, say tons, and E^d is effort devoted to exploration. The idea is that the stock can be augmented by exploration, as well as diminished by extraction. The system equation then becomes

$$\frac{dX}{dt} = f^d(E^d, t) - f^e(E^e, X, t) \tag{11}$$

where the extraction production function is now written $f^e (E^e, X, t)$, and effort devoted to extraction E^e.

The firm maximizes the discounted present value of profits

$$\int_0^\infty [Pf^e(E^e, X, t) - W^d E^d - W^e E^e]e^{-rt}\, dt \tag{12}$$

where W^d is the wage of effort E^d, and W^e the wage of effort E^e. The necessary condition (7) is replaced by a pair of conditions corresponding to the two control variables E^d and E^e:

$$-W^d + qf_{E^d}^d = 0 \tag{13}$$

$$Pf_{E^e}^e - W^e - qf_{E^e}^e = 0 \tag{14}$$

Equation (14) is just the same as equation (7), but from equation (13), we can substitute $W^d/f_{E^d}^d$ for q. This term, $W^d/f_{E^d}^d$, is clearly the marginal cost of exploration, as $W^e/f_{E^e}^e$ is the marginal cost of extraction.

Somewhat surprisingly, complicating the optimal extraction model by introducing exploration results in a simple suggestion for estimating rent. This also has implications for efficiency if, as suggested in the preceding section, we are worried about the way in which q is determined by the expectations of agents in resource markets. Of course, an exploration cost or production function must still be estimated, but this is less of a venture into the unknown than forming an expectation of an entire price path.

The results are misleading, however, in appearing to banish uncertainty from the process of deciding how to allocate effort to exploration and extraction over time. Uncertainty is important in particular in exploration, which might in fact be viewed as fundamentally an exercise in reducing uncertainty. Two interesting strains of analysis have emerged in this area. One, following Allais [30], considers exploration formally as a problem in sampling from an incompletely known size distribution of deposits. Another, more recent, and exemplified by the work of Gilbert [31], introduces uncertainty into relatively simple versions of optimal depletion models. Though further discussion is beyond the scope of this paper, these approaches are clearly central to a better understanding of the economics of exploration.[26] But I think it is fair to say that the deterministic production function approach taken above also has a role to play.

A fruitful way to proceed here might be to introduce a stochastic term into the exploration production function. Exploration in one period could then have several effects. It would locate deposits, as in the deterministic case, but it could also reduce the effort needed to locate deposits in future periods by developing information about the geology of a region. In other words, it could shift the exploration production function —and perhaps also the extraction production function. Exploration might also result in a reduction in the variance of the stochastic term. If the agent undertaking the exploration were risk averse, such a reduction would be valuable. But in any event, a first approximation to the marginal user cost measure of rent might be obtained by looking just at exploration costs, as suggested by equations (13) and (14).

There is just one other issue I want to touch on, and that, is externalities in exploration. It is easily introduced through extension of the basic model. This will also shed some light on the effects of uncertainty.

[26] An informative presentation of recent work in probabilistic assessment of mineral prospects is found in Grenon [32].

We keep the same objective function as in equation (12), but change the system equation (11) in order to reflect the influence of past discoveries on the relationship between current exploratory effort and output. We do this by putting another argument, D, for cumulative past discoveries, into the exploration production function. In symbols, this is

$$\frac{dX}{dt} = f^d(E^d, D, t) - f^e(E^e, X, t) \tag{15}$$

I shall consider the role of past discoveries presently, but first let us complete the structure of the problem and indicate the solution.

In addition to equation (15), there is a system equation describing the change in D over time, which we write as

$$\frac{dD}{dt} = f^d(E^d, D, t) \tag{16}$$

The Hamiltonian for this problem is

$$H = [(Pf^e - W^dE^d - W^eE^e) + q(f^d - f^e) + p(f^d)] e^{-rt} \tag{17}$$

where p is the costate variable attached to the system equation for D. Differentiating H with respect to the control variables E^d and E^e respectively, and setting the resulting partial derivatives equal to zero, we obtain

$$H_{E^d} = -W^d + qf^d_{E^d} + pf^d_{E^d} = 0 \tag{18}$$

and

$$H_{E^e} = Pf^e_{E^e} - W^e - qf^e_{E^e} = 0 \tag{19}$$

Equation (19) tells us, once again, that price should be set equal to the sum of marginal extraction cost and marginal user cost, or rent. But rearranging equation (18) we have a new expression for rent,

$$q = W^d/f^d_{E^d} - p \tag{18'}$$

The first term on the right-hand side of equation (18′) is just the marginal discovery cost. The second term, p, represents the shadow price of a unit added to the stock of discovered resources, D. The sign of p will reflect the influence of D on the exploration production function, but a priori, the direction of the influence is not clear. It could be positive, in the sense that discovering another unit provides information that can reduce the effort involved in future discoveries. This is a possibility I hinted at just above in discussing a stochastic exploration production function. But it could also be negative. Suppose there is a finite number of discoverable deposits of a mineral in a region. Then one more discovered today means one less discovered tomorrow. Not only that, but to the extent that the better deposits are discovered soon, there could be a substantial opportunity loss in depleting the "stock of discoveries." The upshot of these remarks is that p could be positive or negative, and the marginal discovery cost accordingly adjusted up or down. This seems to be a question which could usefully be addressed in specific cases, depending on the geology of the mineral and region.

Where do the externalities come in? They come in with both of the effects just discussed, as noted first in a paper by Peterson [33]. Suppose a discovery does in fact provide information about where to look for further deposits and how. To the extent that this information is not kept within the firm making the discovery, it will benefit other firms, or even potential firms, searching for the mineral. The information spillover is an external economy, and if not appropriately compensated, will lead to a nonoptimal allocation of effort to exploration by decentralized decision makers. In particular, it seems likely that firms will explore too little, each sitting back and waiting for the other to provide information, as Peterson [33] and also Stiglitz [34] have suggested.

The other effect, depletion of a stock of discoveries, is a classic common property phenomenon. Clearly, it is not just the firm making the discovery whose future prospects are diminished. All others are the poorer as well—there is that much less for them to find, and it will be that much harder to find. This creates an incentive for each firm to over-explore, compared with what would be optimal if it enjoyed a secure tenure in all of the deposits of a mineral within a region. As is well known, one method of getting an individual economic agent to behave as if he were the sole owner in a common property setting, short of actually making him the owner, is to impose a tax that reflects the losses he imposes on others.

I conclude, then that the determination of p, the adjustment to the marginal cost of discovery, or something analogous to it in an appropriate multiparty setting, is still more complicated than it appeared when we were concerned only with the effects of discovery internal to the firm. This looks like a very promising area for future research—though calculations of the behavior of discovery costs as proxies for rents need not wait on its completion.

VI
Conclusions

The main point of this paper has been to examine the behavior of a number of proposed economic measures of a resource's scarcity as the resource is depleted or augmented (as through discovery of new sources) over time. A secondary point has been to examine the effect on the current value of each measure of a change in the current estimate of the resource stock. The proposed measures are price, cost, and rent. It turns out that price is preferred, always increasing (decreasing) as a stock is depleted (augmented) over time. Also, current price generally varies inversely with estimated stock at a moment in time—though this conclusion is subject to the condition that there not be a strong negative elasticity of expectations.

Cost and rent are sometimes well behaved as indicators of scarcity, sometimes not. It depends on the technology of extraction, and specifically on the strength of stock or quality effects on extraction costs. Where there are such effects, extraction cost rises as a stock or high quality deposit is depleted, but rent is erratic, rising and falling, in either discrete or continuous fashion, and ultimately falling to zero if extraction cost rises all the way to the price of the backstop for the resource. For a given quality deposit, and if there are no stock effects, cost does not rise as exhaustion nears, but rent does. So there is a kind of duality between cost and rent as measures of scarcity: where cost moves in the right direction, rent does not, and vice versa.

Another question considered in the paper is, to what extent must these conventional economic measures be adjusted to reflect the environmental effects of resource use? On the basis of currently available evidence, this remains an unresolved question. Calculations like those reported by Barnett (chapter 8), which show a very small fraction of gross national product required to attain fairly stringent air and water quality standards, suggest a modest adjustment, one that in most cases would not reverse the long-term decline in unit costs.

This finding is strengthened by theoretical arguments for substitution and technical change in pollution control, as in resource extraction. On the other hand, one cannot, it seems to me, reject the hypothesis that the costs of dealing with a variety of new and exotic pollutants may be quite high, particularly as unknown thresholds are reached. Substitution and technical change may be less effective where, as with the accumulation of carbon dioxide from the combustion of fossil fuels, the bad is difficult or impossible to separate from the good. The whole question of the adjustment of scarcity measures to reflect the consumption of common property environmental resources, and in particular of the possibilities for substitution away from these resources, seems to me deserving of further research effort.

A final question deals with behavior of rent—and one could extend the analysis to cost and price—when the resource stock can be indefinitely renewed by exploration. In this case, the relationship between rent and depletion is not particularly relevant. Complicating the formal model of optimal extraction by introducing the possibility of expanding the stock frees the economic measure from its tie to the physical. It turns out that rent on a mineral resource can be estimated, at least to a first approximation, by the marginal replacement cost, that is, the cost of discovering new deposits. This is not a bad measure of scarcity, at least of the resource "in the ground," in that it reflects the sacrifices required to obtain the resource. It also raises interesting possibilities for empirical investigation—and challenging theoretical issues—because uncertainty about the size and location of deposits, and externalities in their exploration, indicate adjustments to the discovery cost measure of rent. For example, the cost might be adjusted up or down, depending on whether a discovery carries a cost in that it depletes the "stock of discoveries" or a benefit in that it provides information about the prospects for future discoveries. Moreover, the question is complicated by the fact that neither effect is internal to the firm making the discovery.

References

1. W. Beckerman, "Economists, Scientists, and Environmental Catastrophe," *Oxford Economic Papers* vol. 24, no. 3 (November, 1972) pp. 237–244.
2. W. D. Nordhaus, "World Dynamics—Measurement Without Data," *Economic Journal* vol. 82, no. 332 (December 1973) pp. 1156–1183.
3. J. Kay and J. M. Mirrlees, "The Desirability of Natural Resource Depletion," in D. W. Pearce, ed., *Economic Aspects of Natural Resource Depletion* (London, MacMillan, 1975).
4. R. G. Ridker, ed., *Population, Resources, and the Environment*, U.S. Commission on Population Growth and the American Future (Washington, GPO, 1972).
5. J. J. Schanz, "Problems and Opportunities in Adapting USGS Terminology to Energy Resources," in M. Grenon, ed., *First IIASA Conference on Energy Resources*, International Institute for Applied Systems Analysis (Laxenburg, Austria, 1976).
6. Joel Darmstadter, *Energy in the World Economy* (Baltimore, Johns Hopkins University Press for Resources for the Future, 1971).
7. H. J. Barnett and C. Morse, *Scarcity and Growth: The Economics of Natural Resource Availability* (Baltimore, Johns Hopkins University Press for Resources for the Future, 1963).
8. J. L. Sweeney, *Economics of Depletable Resources: Market Forces and Intertemporal Bias* (Washington, D.C. Federal Energy Administration, 1976).
9. W. D. Nordhaus, "The Allocation of Energy Resources," *Brookings Papers on Economic Activity* vol. 3 (a) (1973) pp. 529–570.
10. R. M. Solow, "Intergenerational Equity and Exhaustible Resources," *Review of Economic Studies Symposium on the Economics of Exhaustible Resources* (b) (1974) pp. 29–45.

11. G. Heal, "Economic Aspects of Natural Resource Depletion," in D. W. Pearce, ed., *The Economics of Natural Resource Depletion* (London, MacMillan, 1975).

12. M. Common, "Comments on the Papers by Robinson, Surrey and Page," in D. W. Pearce, ed., *The Economics of Natural Resource Depletion* (London, MacMillan, 1975).

13. J. V. Krutilla and A. C. Fisher, *The Economics of Natural Environments: Studies in the Valuation of Commodity and Amenity Resources* (Baltimore, Johns Hopkins University Press for Resources for the Future, 1975).

14. F. M. Peterson and A. C. Fisher, "The Exploitation of Extractive Resources," *Economic Journal* vol. 87 (December 1977) pp. 681–721.

15. H. Hotelling, "The Economics of Exhaustible Resources," *Journal of Political Economy* vol. 39 (April 1931) pp. 137–175.

16. W. D. Schulze, "The Optimal Use of Non-Renewable Resources: The Theory of Extraction," *Journal of Environmental Economics and Management* vol. 1, no. 1 (May 1974) pp. 53–73.

17. L. S. Pontryagin, et al., *The Mathematical Theory of Optimal Processes,* translated by K. N. Trirogoff (New York, Wiley, 1962).

18. M. L. Balinski and W. J. Baumol, "The Dual in Nonlinear Programming and Its Economic Interpretation," *Review of Economic Studies* vol. 35, no. 3 (1968) pp. 237–256.

19. Robert Dorfman, "An Economic Interpretation of Optimal Control Theory," *American Economic Review* vol. 59, no. 5 (December 1969) pp. 817–831.

20. K. J. Arrow and M. Kurz, *Public Investment, the Rate of Return, and Optimal Fiscal Policy* (Baltimore, Johns Hopkins University Press for Resources for the Future, 1970).

21. A. D. Scott, "Notes on User Cost," *Economic Journal* vol. 63 (June 1953), pp. 368–384.

22. R. M. Solow, "The Economics of Resources or the Resources of Economics," *American Economic Review* vol. 64, no. 2a (May 1974) pp. 1–14.

23. G. M. Brown and B. Field, "The Adequacy of Measures for Signaling the Scarcity of Natural Resources," in V. Kerry Smith, ed., *Scarcity and Growth Revisited* (Baltimore, Johns Hopkins University Press, for Resources for the Future).

24. V. Kerry Smith, "Measuring Natural Resource Scarcity: Theory and Practice," *Journal of Environmental Economics and Management* vol. 5 (June 1978) pp. 150–171.

25. W. D. Nordhaus, "The Climatic Impact of Long Run Energy Growth," paper presented at American Economic Association Meetings, Atlantic City, August 16–18, 1976.

26. O. C. Herfindahl and A. V. Kneese, *Economic Theory of Natural Resources* (Columbus, Ohio, Charles E. Merrill, 1974).

27. G. Heal, "The Relationship Between Price and Extraction Cost for a

Resource with a Backstop Technology," *Bell Journal of Economics* vol. 7, no. 2 (Autumn, 1976) pp. 371–378.

28. J. E. Stiglitz, "Growth with Exhaustible Natural Resources: The Competitive Economy," *Review of Economic Studies Symposium on the Economics of Exhaustible Resources* 1974, pp. 139–152.

29. E. J. Mishan, "Does Perfect Competition in Mining Produce an Optimal Rate of Exploitation?" (London School of Economics, unpublished paper, 1977).

30. M. Allais, "A Method of Appraising Economic Prospects of Mining Exploration over Large Territories: Algerian Sahara Case Study," *Management Science* vol. 3 (July 1957) pp. 285–347.

31. R. Gilbert, "Optimal Depletion of an Uncertain Stock," Institute for Mathematical Studies in Social Sciences, Stanford University, 1976.

32. M. Grenon, ed., *First IIASA Conference on Energy Resources,* CP-76-4 International Institute for Applied Systems Analysis (Laxenburg, Austria, 1976).

33. F. M. Peterson, "Two Externalities in Petroleum Exploitation," in G. M. Brannon, ed., *Studies in Energy Tax Policy* (Cambridge, Mass., Ballinger, 1975).

34. J. E. Stiglitz, "The Efficiency of Market Prices in Long Run Allocations in the oil industry," in G. M. Brannon, ed., *Studies in Energy Tax Policy* (Cambridge, Mass., Ballinger, 1975).

11

Summary and Research Issues

V. Kerry Smith and John V. Krutilla

I
Introduction

There is a diversity of opinion, popular and professional, today over the importance of natural resources for economic growth and the maintenance of society's well-being. The papers in this volume span the whole range of positions. Such diversity in the speculation on the adequacy of natural resources is not new. Adam Smith saw limits to the possible size of a nation's industrial production which would be set by the difficulty of obtaining an expanding supply of raw materials without dramatic increases in their prices. Economic historians, notably Wrigley [1], have more recently observed that Smith failed to realize the potential powers of the natural endowments when the transition from organic to inorganic raw materials is recognized.[1] With recognition of these possibilities, many economists felt the limits to size evaporate. However, Jevons [2] warned that new limits were forthcoming, because natural resources play an essential role in production. He observed that:

Coal, in truth, stands not beside but entirely above all other commodities. It is the material energy of the country—the universal aid—the factor in everything we do. With coal almost any feat is possible or easy; without it we are thrown back in the laborious poverty of early times. [2, p. viii]

Despite the many seemingly persuasive arguments, the same concerns over a materials limit to economic activity have arisen almost invariably in association with sharp increases in the materials consumed during a given period. Thus the Paley and Cooke commissions can be considered as responses to the concern over resource availability following the heavy materials demand of World War II. Since that time, however, the

V. Kerry Smith and John Krutilla are Senior Fellows in the quality of the environment division, Resources for the Future.

[1] In this case they were not referring to the scientific definitions, but the consideration of organic as having to do with living matter and inorganic nonliving sources of raw materials.

276

work of Barnett and Morse [3] has played an important role in buoying optimism regarding natural resource availability. Their arguments are intriguing, suggesting that the very factors giving rise to heavy materials demands also provide strong incentives, through the market, to meet them. Thus they concluded that there is no resource problem in a limitational sense. Rather, they argued that the issue is best viewed:

as one of continual adjustment to an ever changing economic resource quality spectrum. The physical properties of the natural resource base impose a series of initial constraints on the growth and progress of mankind, but the resource spectrum undergoes kaleidoscopic change through time. Continual enlargement of the scope of substitutability—the result of man's technological ingenuity and organizational wisdom—offers those who are nimble a multitude of opportunities for escape. [3, p. 244]

This perspective is appealing and has remained a widely accepted conceptualization of the natural resource problem. Nonetheless, as we argued in our introductory essay, it does not address all of the significant aspects of the natural resource problem. Natural resources include more than simply the raw material inputs to production and consumption activities. They should be considered as including all the original endowments of the earth whose services may bear directly or indirectly on our ability to produce and consume utility-yielding goods and services while maintaining ambient conditions supportive of life. With this more general definition of natural resources, it seemed appropriate to reconsider the issues first advanced comprehensively in *Scarcity and Growth*. Our reevaluation does not pretend to have been comprehensive. The Barnett–Morse volume commented on the intellectual concern over the availability of natural resources and the economic modeling of their role in production. It also evaluated the trends in scarcity indexes. It was impossible in our discussion to fully reflect all the diverse views on each element of the Barnett–Morse argument, and we have implicitly reserved many for further research. The papers in this volume have focused on the divergence in views in each of three general areas: (1) the appropriate modeling of the role of natural resources in economic activity; (2) the nature of the physical (primarily geological) constraints to providing natural resources as they have conventionally been defined; and (3) the measurement of the adequacy of our stocks of natural resources for maintaining economic well-being.

The last two of these issues relate to different sources of information on the availability of natural resources. When the definition of these resources is restricted to materials exchanged on commodity markets, we can rely on well-functioning markets to provide signals on competing needs relative to available supplies for the goods exchanged. They do not necessarily provide an absolute index of resource availability. However, Barnett and Morse, as we noted at the outset, adopted a classical view of economic processes. In this framework, long-run prices tend to "natural" values determined by the real resource costs of production. While this perspective is not explicitly detailed in *Scarcity and Growth,* it seems that this is what the authors had in mind. To fully understand the framework and results, it is useful to consider Eagly's [4] recent explanation of the classical model. He observed that one must:

distinguish between the classical concepts of "market price," which is determined by cost of production. *Ricardian natural price is a cost-of-production concept in which commodities exchange with one another according to the relative quantities of inputs used in the production of each. . . .* Market price may diverge from natural price in the short run. When the two do diverge in a given industry, the profit rate in that industry diverges from the profit rate in the lead sector. In turn, it is this discrepancy in the profit rates that provides the basis for capital movements within the economy." [4, p. 51; emphasis added]

This view of the world was deemed desirable, for it was believed to provide an objective benchmark for evaluating resource availability—the natural price. While market prices would tend toward these natural levels, they could not be relied upon to accurately gauge availability in the short run. Thus in a genuine sense the philosophical issues we addressed on the meaning of scarcity and appropiate definition of society's ends did not have to be addressed within the classical model.

Unfortunately, these issues must be addressed. We recognize today that economic processes do not conform to the classical paradigm. There are no objective prices free of consumers' valuations. As a result, two difficult issues must be faced in resolving the problems associated with natural resource availability. The first of these concerns the definition of natural resources and the ability of markets to provide all of the information necessary to signal resource scarcities. The Barnett–Morse description of the natural resource problem is based on the existence of perfect markets, natural tendencies for prices, and a specific (raw materials) definition of natural resources. Even if we accept initially the presumption of perfect markets, for the sake of argument, the last two matters call for careful reconsideration. Taking the last first, the services of common property environmental resources are not exchanged or organized markets. One must ask how the information otherwise provided and transmitted by markets is to be conveyed. In order to address this issue, we explore briefly the role of other institutions in the allocation of resources and the functions we might expect them to perform in dealing with common property resources.

The second difficulty is equally important and concerns the objective appraisal of scarcity. Once we deny the existence of natural or objective signals, then prices are recognized as indexes of the social interaction postulated to be taking place in a perfect market. Thus:

neither the marginal evaluation of the demanders nor the marginal costs of suppliers . . . can be employed as a basis for determining prices. . . . There is no "theory" of normal exchange rates with positive content here. The analysis provides an "explanation of results, a logic of interaction . . . [5, pp. 85–86]

Section II discusses the role of institutions in the allocation of resources, and considers the potential information available from nonmarket institutions to assist in the efficient allocation of common property environmental resources. The third section discusses the importance of the treatment of physical or natural endowment constraints to economic activity in evaluating the adequacy of natural resources. In the last section we consider the implications of these general issues for future research.

II
Institutions and the Allocation of Resources

As we noted in the introductory essay, four reasons for the Barnett–Morse [3] findings concerning the trends in real unit costs and relative prices for extractive outputs have become a part of the conventional explanation of the factors influencing natural resource availability. We repeat them briefly below:

1. As higher grade deposits of a mineral are exhausted, lower grades are available in greater abundance.
2. With the growing scarcity of a resource, price increases induce the substitution of other resources to achieve the same ends.
3. Price increases accompanying scarcity stimulate exploratory activity and the recycling of natural resources.
4. Technical change reduces the cost of providing constant quality natural resource commodities.[2]

[2] Two points should be noted here. The literature on induced technical change was not widely accepted at the time Barnett and Morse prepared their book. Their discussion of technical change was more in terms of a description of the past patterns of technological change rather than a specific generating mechanism. Nonetheless, it seems clear from their explanations that they did consider the increasing scarcity of natural resources among the motivations for developing new technologies.

The second aspect of this discussion is what may seem a curious contradiction in the Barnett–Morse reasoning. We noted in the introductory discussion that they adopted a concept of "natural" prices which seemed to offer objective measures of resource availability independent of tastes. These were apparently the long-run tendencies of market prices. It would be difficult to envision how the long-run ad-

With the exception of the first reason, these factors rely on the functioning of perfect markets to reveal indirectly, through the process of exchange, the information necessary to assure an efficient distribution of any resource scarcities.

In evaluating these explanations, then, it is useful to recognize the influence of institutions on market and extramarket resource allocations. While there is an array of institutions which potentially influence the allocation of resources, economists have tended to focus on the market, to the exclusion of many others. The rationale for this attention probably rests with the unique character of the market as an institution for organizing the social interaction involved in the exchange of resources. Virtually all elementary economics texts acknowledge that the perfect market reveals, through the process of exchange between demanders and suppliers, the respective marginal values and costs for the last unit of the good or service exchanged. This attribute is clearly appreciated. However, the role of markets as only one of many possible institutional influences on these interactions is often overlooked. While this simple observation has long been recognized by the institutionalist school in economics, it has not been fully reflected in formal economic analysis. Randall's [6] recent review of the interrelationships between institutionalist school and contemporary economic thought supports this view. Moreover, his review of Commons' development of the role of institutions seems particularly relevant to our argument. He observed that for Commons:

Institutions are defined as collective action in control, liberation, and expansion of individual action. . . . For Commons, the basic unit of analysis is the transaction, which involves alienation and acquisition of the rights of property and liberty created by society and which therefore must be negotiated between the parties concerned before production, exchange, and consumption can take place. The institutional framework makes the transaction feasible by providing the parties with reasonably sure expectations of performance. [6, pp. 3–4]

Buchanan [5] and Mishan [7] also develop arguments which support our position. For example, in an early paper Buchanan discussed the implications of institutional constraints to the definition and use of Pareto optimal criteria. He observed that:

At any particular moment of time, there must exist a set of rules, either legally imposed and enforced by some collectively organized agency or convention-

---

justments described by Barnett–Morse in these three factors are consistent with the existence of objective natural prices existing independent of tastes. Certainly there seems to be some inconsistency in the arguments. However, in fairness to Barnett and Morse we should note that a substantial part of the discrepancy arises from the mechanism postulated to bring the market prices into equality with their natural counterparts.

ally honored, and these rules serve to constrain the behavior of the members of the group as they act in their capacities as private individuals. . . . The set of rules serves to define a "Pareto region," described as the set of all possible positions or points attainable under both these rules and the physical constraints that are present. . . . *Any change in the rules governing private behavior will change the structure of the region.* [5, pp. 342–343]

Our introductory essay and several of the papers in this volume discussed the potential for government policies, in particular the tax and subsidy treatment of the extractive sector, to influence the efficiency of a market-mediated resource allocation. Where impediments arise to the free interaction which characterizes exchange on idealized markets, we cannot claim that the allocations realized will be efficient. As a corollary to this observation, the information provided us by these markets may not reflect the equilibrium sacrifices of demanders and suppliers. There is an element of judgment which must enter any appraisal of the importance of such institutional influences on market allocations. To see this point, one need only compare Stiglitz's (chapter 2) evaluation of the importance of market imperfections for the efficiency of exhaustible resource allocation with Nordhaus' [8] evaluation for a similar set of conditions.[3]

When we turn our attention to those natural resources which do not exchange on organized markets, the services of common property environmental resources, the problems encountered are not simply issues of judgment in evaluating the relative importance of particular external influences. Markets indirectly and other institutions directly influence the allocation of these resources, and unfortunately none of these can be relied upon to provide the information on the marginal valuation of the resources involved in these allocations. Perfect markets offer effective mechanisms for transmitting information on the marginal values and costs of the goods and services exchanged on them. In order to evaluate the properties of any other means of resource allocation, we must have available or obtain an extensive set of information on tastes and technology. It seems logical to ask whether other institutions provide some of this information through their influence on the allocation patterns of common property environmental resources. That is, we noted at the outset of this section that institutions serve to set the ground rules (i.e., in Commons' terms "working rules") directly or indirectly for all allocation processes. We are implicitly asking here whether or not the processes for

---

[3] Stiglitz (chapter 2) concludes that it is unlikely that a Pareto improvement will result from government intervention. Nordhaus [8], on the other hand, concludes that a type of indicative planning is essential because the market mechanism must be regarded as an "unreliable means of pricing and allocating exhaustible appropriable natural resources" (p. 537).

defining these ground rules in a democractic society can be relied on to indirectly reveal something of the character of the population's preferences for nonmarketed goods and services, including views on ethical issues involving intergenerational equity. Randall [6] seems to argue that the Commons' work led to a model that was fundamentally insoluble. That is, he noted:

Institutions, while themselves the creation of man, tend to shape man by influencing his patterns of thought, behavior, and expectations. In aggregate, working rules establish a social framework specifying how economic, social, and spiritual life is organized. Thus, man shapes institutions and is shaped by them. [6, p. 4]

These arguments are true in degrees. There are elements of institutional quiescence which may reduce the jointness in the process of institutional formation and, in turn, the effects of established institutions on individual behavior. Thus Randall's arguments on the ability of institutions to function as mechanisms for recording the collective sentiment may be overly pessimistic.

The principal institutions we can look to for such information are the legislative, public administrative, and judicial systems. One need only look at the legislation concerning air and water pollution to be convinced that the legislative process along with EPA rule making does play a central role in the allocation of environmental common property resources.[4] Unfortunately, social sciences devoted to the study of political processes and budgetary allocations to implement policies have not, as yet, been able to characterize in a very discriminating way the relationship (if any) between the political outcomes represented by a given set of regulations implementing legislation and the underlying preferences of the populace. Thus the information offered by these institutions does not seem to extend beyond a signaling of concern and an attendant need to distribute real (or perceived) scarcities among individuals or groups, and perhaps generations.

An equally important institutional mechanism for allocating common property resources seems to fall to the judicial system. Here again, however, the objectives of the courts tend to limit the information on values and costs obtained through the allocation process. Rosenblum's [11] recent overview of the courts' role in allocating common property resources makes this point clearly. He concluded that:

This scanning of typical cases in which courts make and find law through constitutional and statutory construction and through monitoring the actions

[4] For a convenient summary of this legislation, see Kneese and Schultze [9] and Freeman [10].

of administrative bodies evinces an aura of judicial thoroughness and integrity, but *it does not produce uniform policies in the allocation of common property resources . . . the most definitive assertions of role have centered on the essentials of process and methodology to be observed by decision makers. How allocative policies are made more than their goodness or badness is of primary judicial concern.* [11, pp. 141–142; emphasis added]

Thus we are forced to the conclusion that while nonmarket institutions do offer a means for allocating resources, we cannot expect that they will provide the informational signals that are by-products of the exchange activities that a perfect market would. Accordingly, we must consider the kind of information necessary for an efficient allocation of the services of common property environmental resources, and second, the appropriate way to obtain such information, if possible, or to reach prudent decisions in its absence if it is impossible to obtain such information.

III
Potential Physical Constraints on Improvement in Material Well-Being

Our introductory essay described the conventional view of constraints on economic activity. We identified a basic assumption common to most economic analyses of the resource adequacy/stringency issue. This conventional view maintained a specific type of distribution and set of characteristics for the occurrence of mineral elements. We indicated that evidence from the work of geologists and geophysicists suggests there is a question about the reliability of this hypothesis, which holds that as higher grade deposits are exhausted, lower grades are available in greater abundance (Barnett and Morse). This is an area that deserves careful attention in both earth and social science research. Somewhat related to this issue is the fact that some rare elements with peculiar geochemical properties indispensable to advanced technologies (e.g., niobium in prospective fusion reactor technology, helium in cryogenics) are severely limited in supply and lack adequate substitutes.[5]

This leads to the issue of the actual existence of microtechnologies which are assumed to exist when we posit implied substitution for scarce materials on an aggregate scale. That is, given the likelihood of relatively low total capacity for such limitational inputs, there may be significant reasons for doubting the ability of an anticipated backstop technology to attain the level of use implied by substitution in the aggregate. This is an area that requires a much more extensive and intensive exchange

[5] This view of such resource limitations argues that the very attributes which make a particular resource essential in a given use include a geochemistry of resource occurrences that makes substitutes (with similar characteristics) correspondingly rare.

among the scientific, engineering, and economic communities to enhance the realism and relevance of the working assumptions and information that are used in assessing resource adequacy.

In the past, physical constraints were treated as synonymous with materials constraints, so that natural resource availability was gauged only in terms of the goods which exchanged on primary commodity markets. It may be useful to relate the restricted nature of this conceptualization to the prevailing view of the normative significance of price and cost signals flowing from market transactions of only a quarter of a century ago. The effect of market transactions on third parties external to the exchange was considered largely insubstantial and of no practical significance.[6] Today external effects are a pervasive concern and play a central role in a substantial portion of policy applications of microeconomic analysis.

The importance of explicitly treating the external effects of market transactions of individual economic agents exchanging private goods is perhaps best illustrated by a comparison with the conditions required for such actions taken in the aggregate to produce outcomes consistent with a socially optimal set of results. In those cases where there are mechanisms which do take account of such externalities in some fashion, and they are not incorporated in a model of decentralized decision-making affecting resource allocations, we know that the two outcomes will diverge. That is, in the absence of a market or an equivalent mechanism for providing information and incentives, individual actions will not reflect an accounting of the external effects of choice.[7]

These arguments have focused on the static externalities associated with the activities of economic agents. Once we broaden the definition of natural resources to include common property environmental resources and consider these resources as assets, then it must be recognized that their utilization patterns in any one period can result in externalities in that period or in future time periods.[8] A common property resource is

---

[6] Scitovsky [12], writing in the early 1950s, observed that: "The concept of external economies is one of the most elusive in economic literature" (p. 143). It was in this context that he argued that examples of such economies were "somewhat bucolic in nature, having to do with bees, orchards and woods," and that this was not an accident since it was not easy to find examples from industry.

[7] The conventional literature on static externalities calls for a system of effluent charges to provide these signals.

[8] Mohring and Boyd [13] introduced the distinction between the treatment of externalities by Pigou and Knight in terms of the comparison of a "direct interaction" versus an "asset utilization" perspective. The former seems to have dominated much of the economic literature on externalities, which has tended to limit the attention given to these types of intertemporal problems.

one which is equally accessible to all members of society. The allocation of these resources does not take place through market mechanisms, and so the market is not available to provide incentives for individual agents to limit their patterns of consumption or rate of utilization of the resource's services. In our introductory essay we sought to inquire how the presence and use patterns of such resources might affect evaluation of the adequacy of natural resources for economic well-being. If these resources are recognized as natural assets, should they be treated as renewable or exhaustible? Renewability in these cases would imply that the resource has natural regeneration or growth with time so that some mechanism permits the resource to provide, over defined levels of total use, the same quantity of constant quality services in each time period. The answers to these questions must arise out of the physical characteristics of the elements comprising the biosphere and not necessarily the analytical convenience (or lack of it) of the models which might result.

For example, the recent work of Kneese and Schulze [14] and Schulze and coauthors [15] has offered some suggestive empirical evidence indicating that mortality rates related to cancer may be associated with the extent of human intervention in the chemistry of the environment. These analyses candidly acknowledge the difficulties encountered in such econometric studies. The limitations are considerable, ranging from the poor quality of the input data (to the empirical study) to the long latency period generally associated with most carcinogens. Nonetheless, the evidence has been accumulating and can lead to a disconcerting conjecture that the effects of new chemical compounds, combustion processes, heavy use of nitrogenous fertilizers, and halocarbons may reduce certain common property resource services which are associated with human health and well-being.

While we can cite further examples, such as depletion of the ozone layer and its effects on the ultraviolet radiation reaching the earth, one of the central issues addressed here and in our introductory essay is whether such effects are exotic special cases or representative of a pervasive class of externalities.

We should note that our concerns, if correct, seem to call for an alternative institutional mechanism to facilitate the efficient allocation of these resources. One possibility would call for a rather important broadening in the scope of Meade's [16] indicative planning concepts referred to in note 9. He considered a comprehensive set of forward and contingency markets, an indicative plan developed by government as an informational service to individual citizens on the prospective paths of future market prices, and econometric modeling of markets to provide equivalent information.[9] However, a procedure which mimics forward and contingency markets only for those goods and services which exchange on current markets is incomplete. It ignores the role of the nonmarketed goods and services whose exchange, as we have observed, is not mediated through this institutional mechanism. Therefore, we cannot rely on procedures based on the attributes of existing markets to furnish information on marginal costs and valuations of alternative use profiles through time because there are direct physical interdependencies of economic activities and natural systems which are not reflected in market outcomes. Direct information from the engineering, earth, and life sciences is necessary to supplement market-generated information developed through the type of indicative planning called for by Meade. The most constructive form and structuring of this input is itself a research issue.

For the most part, economic evaluations of externalities have implicitly assumed the underlying physical medium serving as their receptacle to be a continuously renewable resource. Moreover, these analyses have also assumed that the rate of utilization of the services of these resources has been below their absorptive capacities, or the physical limit which allows the resource to regenerate its capacity. If these implicit assumptions were an accurate reflection of reality, then comparative static analysis of the implications of externalities would be sufficient to consider the full effects of alternative policy choices. However, once it is acknowledged that the receiving medium may be affected by the level of its use and that there may be cumulative and irreversible effects, then intertemporal analysis similar to that done for exhaustible resources is warranted.

To our knowledge, there are few studies of economic problems that combine direct evidence on the role of common property resources with conventional natural resources.[10] d'Arge and Kogiku [18] appear to be the first economists to consider these problems in an integrated fashion. They evaluated the implications of activities generating stock pollutants which also required the services of a depletable resource. Their model investigated the characteristics of a plan which maximized discounted

---

[9] Meade [16] observed that three approaches offer the means of providing the information consumers would need for efficient decisions—a full set of markets, his indicative planning process, or well-developed econometric models. He suggested that: "The essence of the matter then so far is to find a procedure which will give citizens a foresight of future market prices so that they can make their present plans in the knowledge of what future costs of inputs, selling prices of outputs, and so on will in fact be" (p. 11).

[10] One could also view Krutilla and Fisher's [17] analysis of the allocation problems associated with irreversible decisions for natural environments as addressing these problems.

per capita utility. Society's utility function was assumed in their model to be strongly separable in usable outputs and in the term of the planning horizon. They observed:

Issues emerging from environmental management arise not only from the optimal rate of waste generation in a closed medium but also with regard to the rate of extractive (or renewable) resource exploitation. *If extractive resources are finite in magnitude and can for all practical purposes be exhausted, then optimal environmental management involves a "conjunctive use" type allocation problem where one must consider rates of extraction and rates of waste generation.* Thus, the "pure" pollution problem and questions like these become relevant: which should we run out of first, air to breathe or fossil fuel to pollute the air we breathe? [18, p. 68, emphasis added]

While their model is quite restrictive in several dimensions, it does highlight one view of the indeterminacies in the problem. In short, they demonstrated that the treatment of common property environmental resources *can* affect one's appraisal of resource adequacy.

In related work, Cropper [9] has recently examined the implications of decisions where there is a small probability of large losses, a feature which is often used to characterize the examples we cited above. Her results are important because they provide evidence that the analytical specification of society's objective function and the treatment of uncertainty directly bears on the results we can expect from either optimal planned or decentralized behavior. More specifically, the Cropper model specifies society's planning problem in terms of maximizing its discounted expected utility. In the presence of pollutants which accumulate as a stock and have the potential of preventing further utility-generating activities, we find that the results of conventional optimal planning models must be substantially modified. That is, once we acknowledge that pollution can accumulate as a stock with correspondingly serious implications for sustaining life, then the conclusions of the earlier models which treat pollution as a static phenomenon must be modified:

When the effects of pollution are potentially catastrophic the unique, stable equilibrium which characterizes many pollution control models . . . no longer obtains and multiple equilibria, as well as a no equilibrium solution, are possible. Allowing the pollution stock to enter the utility function directly guarantees the existence of an equilibrium solution but does not rule out the possibility of multiple equilibria. [19, p. 13]

Thus it seems that the limited information we have on the implications of these types of problems for economic analysis of patterns of growth, properties of decentralized decision-making systems, and formulation of optimal centralized plans, all seems to suggest a need for substantial reorientation of our approach to dealing with these issues.

IV
Implications

This volume has raised a number of questions regarding the conventional views developed in *Scarcity and Growth*. We have not offered answers to these questions, but rather have attempted to identify the elements of a research program that is needed to evaluate them. Two of these issues deserve repeating. The first concerns the long-run supply of the physical materials, conventionally treated as synonymous with the full set of natural resources. We have argued, with the support of the literature cited in Brobst's paper (chapter 5), that there are a number of competing hypotheses concerning the long-run availability of materials, particularly our mineral resources. Without a more clear-cut reading of the nature of this supply response, it is difficult to judge whether natural resources will ultimately be a limitational input. Moreover, we must inquire in the same spirit whether the private markets involving these resources are sufficiently free of imperfections and institutional influences to transmit accurately the marginal values and costs of these resources. Beginning with the Internal Revenue Codes of 1916 to the present, public intervention through tax policy affecting the extractive sector has been pervasive. Yet, we have not evaluated the direct and indirect effects of these institutional changes on market transactions and their prices. It may be that in this case, one should not rely on unadjusted market prices as Barnett and Morse did for a part of their empirical analysis.

The second general concern is the consistency between the formulation of economic models and the constraints on man's activities imposed by physical laws. In modeling production processes and specifying the role of the physical environment, the economist's penchant for simplification and partial analysis has often led to a type of "tunnel vision," a failure to fully appreciate the static *and* intertemporal implications of his production and consumption decisions. Physical laws will constrain the constituent elements in production activities. They will limit substitution possibilities in response to increasing scarcity of materials. Moreover, they can place direct limits on the absorptive capacity of environmental systems.

Both of these problems share a recognition of the potential for interactions between the economic system and other noneconomic considerations in our interpretation of the realistic scope of future economic activities. That is, in the first case we must recognize the role of institutional constraints on the social interactions of markets and in the second the interaction between man's production and consumption activities and the physical environment. Ultimately this view is an extension of the concepts of conjunctive management advocated by d'Arge and Kogiku in their discussion of the implications of their model.

As we suggested earlier, the market cannot generate all of the data necessary for the formulation of prudent natural resource policies. Meade's [16] indicative planning is not the complete answer, for it attempts to mimic the function of existing markets. It is necessary to enlist the aid of natural scientists in obtaining information on the nature of interdependencies between the results of market activities and the biosphere's life support processes.

Failure to treat the uses of natural resources conjunctively can lead to economic activities which usurp one or more common property resources without providing any mechanisms for a response by the economic agents involved. Accordingly, a research program addressing these issues must develop analyses of physical, environmental, and institutional constraints on economic behavior that are relevant to the concerns of policy makers who must reconcile the needs of mankind with the earth's supply of resources and society's ability to utilize them.

References

1. E. A. Wrigley, "The Supply of Raw Materials in the Industrial Revolution," *The Economic History Review,* 2nd. Ser., vol. XV, no. 1 (1962) pp. 1–16.
2. W. S. Jevons, *The Coal Question* (London and Cambridge, 1865) p. viii.
3. H. J. Barnett and C. Morse, *Scarcity and Growth: The Economics of Natural Resource Availability* (Baltimore, Johns Hopkins University Press for Resources for the Future, 1963).
4. R. V. Eagly, *The Structure of Classical Economic Theory* (New York, Oxford University Press, 1974).
5. J. M. Buchanan, "The Relevance of Pareto Optimality," *Journal of Conflict Resolution* vol. 6 (December 1962) pp. 341–354.
6. A. Randall, "Property Institutions and Economic Behavior," *Journal of Economic Issues* vol. 12 (March 1978) pp. 1–21.
7. E. J. Mishan, "Pareto Optimality and the Law," *Oxford Economic Papers* vol. 19 (November 1967) pp. 247–280.
8. W. D. Nordhaus, "The Allocation of Energy Resources," *Brookings Papers on Economic Activity* no. 3 (Washington, D.C., Brookings Institution, 1973).
9. A. V. Kneese and C. L. Schultze, *Pollution, Prices, and Public Policy* (Washington, D.C., Brookings Institution, 1975).
10. A. M. Freeman, III, "Air and Water Pollution Policy," in P. Portney, ed., *Current Issues in U.S. Environmental Policy* (Baltimore, Johns Hopkins University Press for Resources for the Future, 1978).
11. V. G. Rosenblum, "The Continuing Role of the Courts in Allocating

Common Property Resources," in E. T. Haefele, ed., *The Governance of Common Property Resources* (Baltimore, Johns Hopkins University Press for Resources for the Future, 1974).

12. T. Scitovsky, "Two Concepts of External Economies," *Journal of Political Economy* vol. 62 (1954) pp. 143–151.

13. H. Mohring and J. H. Boyd, "Analyzing 'Externalities': 'Direct Interaction' vs. 'Asset Utilization' Frameworks," *Economica* vol. 38 (November 1971) pp. 347–361.

14. A. V. Kneese and W. D. Schulze, "Environment, Health and Economics— The Case of Cancer," *American Economic Review, Proceedings* vol. 67 (February 1977) pp. 326–332.

15. W. Schulze, A. Kneese, S. Ben-David, and B. Ives, "Cancer and the Environment: What Cost the Risk," unpublished paper, University of New Mexico, undated.

16. J. E. Meade, *The Theory of Indicative Planning* (Manchester, England, Manchester University Press, 1970).

17. J. V. Krutilla and A. C. Fisher, *The Economics of Natural Environments* (Baltimore, Johns Hopkins University Press for Resources for the Future, 1975).

18. R. C. d'Arge and K. C. Kogiku, "Economic Growth and the Environment," *Review of Economic Studies* vol. 40 (January 1973) pp. 61–78.

19. M. L. Cropper, "Regulating Activities with Catastrophic Environmental Effects," *Journal of Environmental Economics and Management* vol. 3 (June 1976) pp. 1–15.

Index

Library of Congress Cataloging in Publication Data

Main entry under title:
Scarcity and growth reconsidered.

   Includes index.
   1. Natural resources—United States—Congresses.
I. Smith, Vincent Kerry, 1945–   II. Resources
for the Future.

HC103.7.S25   333   78-27236
ISBN 0-8018-2232-7
ISBN 0-8018-2233-5 pbk.